W9-CZX-001

LIFTING THE YOKE:

LOCAL SOLUTIONS TO AMERICA'S FARM AND FOOD CRISIS

Note: ISBN 978-0-915731-07-7
Printer: Villanti & Sons Printers, Inc.
Milton, Vermont
Date: January, 2010
Second Edition
Publisher: Whetstone Books
Price: $25.00

To order the *Lifting the Yoke - Local Solutions to America's Farm and Food Crisis*

Please email Ron Krupp, woodchuck37@hotmail.com

Phone: 802-658-9974 • Website: liftingtheyoke.com

But ... we should first learn the winds and the nature of the sky,
the customary cultivation and the ways of the place.
What each region nears and rejects,
Here corn shoots up, and there grapes do,
Elsewhere young trees grow strong and the wild grasses.
Virgil, The Georgics, Book I, 29 B.C.

Photo by Marilyn Maddison

FOREWORD

A few years ago, just before it became fashionable, I decided to spend a year feeding my family solely from the food grown in our Vermont valley. I hesitated at first, worried about bland and changeless dinners; but Otter Creek, our local brewery, had just started brewing beer made with wheat from the valley, so I decided to give it a shot.

It turns out it was one of the best eating years of our life -- not just because the food was delicious but because the food meant something. We knew where it had come from, and by whose hands; we made dozens of new friends that year as we sought out cider and beef and bread. (And root vegetables. Lots of those.) It turns out we're not unique -- a recent study found that shoppers at farmers markets had ten times as many conversations on average as shoppers at supermarkets.

In other words, the local food revolution that Ron Krupp describes so beautifully here -- made so real that you can almost taste it -- is also a social revolution, though a calm and gentle one. The process of rebuilding local food networks will be one of the key tasks in rebuilding working communities generally. After decades of relying on cheap fossil fuel, we need to start relying on neighbors again. This book shows how -- in practical terms, and in political terms too. Because our leadership will need to spur this process.

Vermont, for instance, could be far further down this road already with real help from both Montpelier and Washington. We don't need ethanol. We need carrots, and cheese, and wheat. And beer. And Ron Krupp.

-- Bill McKibben Ripton, Vermont

PREFACE

THOUGHTS ON A COLD DAY IN THE GREEN MOUNTAINS WINTER 2009

I never planned to write this book. My goal was to write another gardening book as a sequel to *The Woodchuck's Guide to Gardening*, published in October, 2000. But I got sidetracked when a multitude of burning issues came forth like shooting stars. The more I studied the politics of food and farming, the more alarmed I became. It was as if wild beasts were loose in the fields laying waste to the family farm and sucking out the vitality of our rural communities.

It became clear how the mass food market is controlled by a handful of global corporations, including Monsanto, Cargill, Archer Daniels Midland (ADM), Nestle, Philip Morris, McDonald's, and Wal-Mart, in cahoots with the Federal government. I call them the Corporate/ Agricultural/Industrial Machine or CAIM; they're also referred to as "industrial agriculture," "factory farming" and "agribusiness."

- CAIM can be described as an oligopoly, in which a small number of corporations control the vast global food market.

- Their lobbyists influence legislation in the halls of Congress. A similar scenario exists with energy, insurance, investment companies and the pharmaceutical industry. CAIM could not exist without the support of the global financial network - the same institutions that helped to create the current economic meltdown.

- CAIM and its food apparatus include the production, processing, marketing, and distribution of most of the food on our dinner plates. It spreads itself like peanut butter on everything we eat. This is especially true of fast-food restaurants, which the average American frequents twice a week.

- CAIM has increased its market share of our food dollar year after year with cheap processed food resulting in a nation of overweight, unhealthy people, especially among the poor. Fast, processed food is cheap, abundant and high in calories. It contributes significantly to the obesity epidemic in adults and children as well as to heart disease, cancer, and stroke.

- Rather than eating healthy whole foods, we're fed Twinkies and Happy Meals. CAIM breaks food into its parts and re-processes it into unhealthy substitutes, which make us ill and fat. Because of our current eating habits, our children's life spans may be shorter than that of their parents.

QUESTIONS

In order to provide alternatives and solutions to CAIM, we first need to ask the right questions.

Farmers and Farmland: Why are local family farms becoming an endangered species while factory farms are growing in size and number? Why do U.S. farmers have to produce more food to stay in business if they already produce a surplus? Why have we lost so much farmland?

Government Policies: Why have farmers been paid low prices for their farm products for the past 50 years? Why has the federal government supported a "cheap food" policy through massive farm subsidies paid with federal tax dollars? Why, for years, did the Agricultural Extension Service tell family farmers to "get big or get out?" What are they telling farmers today?

Agribusiness: Why has agribusiness become so powerful? What can be done to counteract our dependency on global food corporations? Even organic food has gone global. You can now buy organic food from China.

Food Fragility: How uncertain is our current food supply? How many days of surplus food would be available if the trucks stopped rolling down the highways? As an example, Massachusetts has three days of surplus food available. Twenty percent of trucking in the state is devoted to transporting food. The Bay State is wholly dependent on the trucking industry, as is the rest of the country.

Food Insecurity, Hunger and Obesity: Why, in this "land of plenty," do so many people go to bed hungry? Why don't schools provide healthy foods to our kids? What is the connection between obesity, poor health, processed junk food, and agribusiness? If local farm products are sold at premium prices, can low-income people afford to buy them?

Poor Health: Why do we eat food that has so little nutritional value and vitality? When did the nature of food begin to change in the U.S. from healthy, whole foods to processed foods, shipped thousands of miles across the country? What policies were behind this change and what does the future hold?

Consumers: Most people don't know who grows their food, how it's grown or where it comes from. The result is a disconnect between the consumer and healthy food. How do we reconnect the public to farmers' markets and other local food initiatives?

WHEREVER THERE IS DARKNESS, THERE IS LIGHT

My passions run deep when I read and observe how farming is losing its soul to agribusiness. And it's all happening so fast. What we need are alternatives to the corporate global food system, especially in light of the current worldwide "recession." Some economists believe we're already in a "depression." Local food and farming initiatives would give people employment, put money back into our rural communities and provide a sustainable way of living for years to come.

One thing is clear. It will take a concerted effort to create local, renewable food models. What's needed is a concentration of farmers, regional producers, food processing centers, local markets, distribution networks, and infrastructures like slaughterhouses, mills and creameries. Veterinarians, truckers, feed store managers, and farm machinery dealers are also a critical part of the mix as are land-use policies that provide opportunities for farmers to stay on the land plus training for new farmers.

Farmers need to organize and to empower themselves through political action such as collective bargaining. Wheat farmers in North Dakota took a courageous step by stopping the importation of genetically modified spring wheat seeds for the entire state. For too long, farmers, especially dairy farmers, have been placed at the bottom of the manure heap, sometimes by their own doing, allowing middlemen to take most of the cash from the milk can.

Consumer groups need to stand fast with farmers for more fairness in the marketplace. They also need to be educated about farm and food issues and to begin to take control of their food dollars. As an example, the buy-local movement is the rage these days. Customers at restaurants are demanding that local food be served.

The newest word in Webster's dictionary is "localvore." Some consumers in Vermont, and throughout the country, have formed local-food groups called "localvores," in which there is a commitment to supporting local farmers and processors within 100 miles of their homes. But this movement to eat local needs to carry over to the general population, not just to the few. The reality is that most people don't know how to change their food habits and lifestyles. Local farm and food initiatives are not widely accessible to the greater population, though this is beginning to change.

THE GREEN MOUNTAINS

Most of the solutions described in Lifting the Yoke take place in Vermont where I have lived and worked for 43 years. Within each solution, there is a challenge, an opportunity, and a story to tell. Vermont is in the midst of a renaissance of farm-to-school programs, farmers' markets, community supported initiatives and other forms of direct sales from farmers to consumers.

In October of 2008, the Vermont Agency of Agriculture sponsored an important marketing event in Randolph. It was a rare mix of 40 buyers and 60 sellers. The buyers included restaurants, schools, food distribution companies, food co-ops, supermarket chains like Hannaford, and state institutions like prisons and hospitals. The sellers included local farm and food processors. Even Wal-Mart showed up to meet with Vermont food producers and farmers to explore marketing and distribution opportunities. What a world!

Even though Vermont is a small state of 624,000 people -- 1/500th of the nation's population -- it has a large rural population for its size and enough farmland and farms to provide more food for its people. The Green Mountain State serves as a model for other regions of the country since it has, per capita, the largest small farm initiative in the country and the greatest per capita purchasing of local food from direct market outlets. This includes farmers' markets, farm stands and Community Supported Agriculture (CSA) operations. In 1993, there were 78 certified organic growers; today the number stands at 530.

Eric Schlosser, author of *Fast Food Nation: The Dark Side of the American Meal* (2001), said at a gathering in Burlington, Vermont on June 28th, 2008, that Vermont is "just totally irrelevant" by national standards. But it is precisely because of its size and scale and "the sensibility that is taking hold here" that Vermont has the potential to be in the forefront of a movement away from corporate domination of food production and distribution, and toward a greater reliance on locally produced food.

With all the positive news, there are considerable challenges ahead. Vermont produces less than it consumes in almost every category, except dairy; the supplies of local meat, poultry, eggs, grains, beans, fruits and vegetables are all less than amounts consumed. Research from the Vermont Sustainable Agricultural Council shows that the state could potentially produce 38 percent of its food needs. However, by U.S. standards, Vermont's crop diversity is low. Thirty-one states have more potential than Vermont to feed themselves, with Minnesota ranking #1 at 88 percent. Vermont leads all New England states except Maine.

Vermont, like much of the Northeast and other parts of the country, is dependent on outside food sources. I've often heard the figure of 90-95 percent dependency used. One thing is for sure -- a change towards twenty-five percent greater food self-sufficiency would bring millions of dollars into the regional farm economy, support local market initiatives, keep the land open for farming, and provide the glue that holds our rural communities together.

Vermonters will continue to buy oranges from Florida, rice from Louisiana and wheat from the Midwest. And Vermont farmers and processors can only provide a portion of the food needs of the urban areas of the country. But Vermont, and other rural communities throughout the country, can cut the margins of food dependency on outside sources, become more self-reliant and export value-added food products.

There are other benefits. Building a robust local food and farm system can have a dramatic impact on "food miles traveled" thereby reducing fossil fuel consumption and greenhouse gas emissions which will reduce global warming. My mantra is "Go Local or Go Loco." So let's get started.

P.S. You will note the sub-title "Side Notes" throughout the book. These are my own social, political, and economic views on the various topics in the text. I believe in local solutions when they are both practical and sustainable.

CONTENTS

The book is divided into **three** parts. The **first** part describes the Food Crisis and Farm Bill of 2008 and then analyzes how agriculture began to lose its soul in the 1950s. The main body of the text examines the structure of the corporate global food system, including the takeover of organic food by agribusiness.

The **second** section makes the connection between the increase in obesity, the loss of nutrition in children and adults from processed food and how it's all related to the global food supply. Hunger and lack of food security are also addressed, as well as successful farm-to-school food programs.

The **third** part holds out the promise of local change through such alternatives as farmers' markets, natural food co-ops, training and education of new farmers, agritourism, the development of value-added food products and needed infrastructures such as slaughterhouses and processing plan.

PART III. SUSTAINABLE MARKETS & REGIONAL SOLUTIONS

INDUSTRIAL FARM

CALIFORNIA TOMATO HARVEST

LOCAL VERMONT DAIRY FARMER

PART 1

THE GLOBALIZATION OF FOOD AND FARMING: DEVOURING THE ALBATROSS

Second Photo Courtesy of *Fatal Harvest, The Tragedy of Industrial Agriculture*
Third Photo Courtesy of Vern Grubinger, University of Vermont Extension Service

PART I

THE GLOBALIZATION OF FOOD AND FARMING: DEVOURING THE ALBATROSS

A. THE FOOD CRISIS OF 2008

Life has become rather stressful at the dinner table these days. Grocery bills are rising through the roof. Food banks are running short of donations and food shortages are causing sporadic riots in countries around the world. Over a dozen people were killed in Yemen during riots over the doubling price of food. Malnutrition and famine are increasing in parts of Africa and South Asia.

Obesity: At the same time, it's estimated that roughly one in four adults are overweight, and many of them are obese. North Americans spend $1 billion a year to lose weight, while hundreds of millions of people in poor nations can't afford to buy enough food to put on a little weight. (The world's population is 6.7 billion and growing by 78 million people a year, with projections of an additional 2.5 billion people by 2050.) Indian officials say that if both middle-class Americans and Indians slimmed down, many people in poor countries would have enough food on their plates.

Waste: While all this is going on, the U.S. wastes 27 percent of available food, in supermarkets, restaurants, and in people's homes. That works out to a pound of food a day for every American.

Grocery stores discard products because of spoilage and cosmetic blemishes. Restaurants throw away what they don't use and most of us throw out everything from bananas that have turned brown to other leftovers.

In 1997, the United States Department of Agriculture (USDA) estimated that 96.4 billion pounds of the 356 billion pounds of edible food was never eaten. A more recent study by the Environmental Protection Agency (EPA) said that 12 percent of landfill waste comes from food. And just think about all that methane produced from rotting food that goes up into the atmosphere in the form of greenhouse gas. Most of that could be converted to energy. The USDA estimates that recovering just 5 percent of the wasted food could feed four million people a day; recovering 25 percent would feed 20 million.

* Go to wastedfood.com for more information.

Population: Some would argue that the current world food crisis is the result of too many people on the planet. The fact is, there is enough food to feed the world's entire population. It's a problem of who controls the food supply and its distribution.

Market in Bhutan. Photo Courtesy of Lilianna Bright Susskind

Developing Countries: The worldwide food crisis worsened in developing countries when their governments stopped supporting small farmers with help in purchasing seeds and fertilizer, storing grain, providing loans and distribution networks. The dismantling of the agricultural support system has made these countries more dependent on imports. This change was the result of trade policies brought on by the International Monetary Fund and the World Bank. More on this later.

U.S. FOOD FACTS AND PERCENTAGES

For the past three years food prices have soared. The cost of basic staples such as eggs, milk, bread and meat rose sharply. Milk went up 26 percent and eggs a whopping 40 percent. At the same time, food reserves are at a 30-year low.

Source: Bureau of Labor Statistics (BLS)

Overall food costs rose 5.8 percent in 2007 and increased another 4 percent in 2008. BLS estimates that food inflation in the U.S. will continue to drive prices up as high as 7.5 percent over the next 5 years. The Boston Globe reported in 2007 that the grocery bill of a family of three in New Hampshire rose from $125 per week to $200 over the course of the winter.

People in the U.S. are accustomed to inexpensive food but that may be a thing of the past. What most people don't realize is that U.S. households still spend a smaller portion of their income on food than any other developed country. Japanese grocery shoppers spend 26 percent of their income on food; in India, it's 51 percent. Over a billion people live on less than one dollar a day and most of this is spent on food.

In 2006, the average American family spent 10 percent of its income on food, except for those consumers who purchased organic and high-end niche items. Today, the average family spends 13 percent.

CAUSES FOR THE FOOD CRISIS

The three main reasons for higher food prices are speculation by food traders on Wall Street, higher energy costs, and profit-making by global food corporations. Other reasons will be discussed in the next three pages.

Commodity Farm Prices, Genetically Modified Seeds and Subsidies: From 2006 to early 2008, world grain prices on rice, wheat, corn and soybeans – the prime ingredients in what we eat – doubled. In 2006, the average price for a bushel of corn was $3. By July, 2008, it had increased to $8. Soybeans were $6 a bushel in 2006. They increased to $11 a bushel in 2008.

Eighty nine percent of soybeans and 61 percent of corn grown in the U.S. comes from genetically modified (GM) seeds. (22 percent of silage corn grown in Vermont comes from GM seeds.) The global biotech corporation, Monsanto, owns and controls the production of GM seeds.

According to the USDA, cereals and bakery products rose 9 percent in 2007. A 100-pound bag of wheat sold to bakers increased 157 percent. U.S. wheat stocks are at their lowest point in 60 years, partially because of plant diseases and an increase in acreage devoted to corn. In 2005, a bushel of wheat was selling for $3.35. In 2008 it went up to $10.

Wheat has increased in price since 2007 due in part to fewer acres being planted. Wheat's genetic complexity compared to corn and soybeans has yielded fewer hybrid varieties that might expand its planting range and therefore attract investments. Wheat growers do not receive the large subsidies that corn and soybean farmers receive.

Farm subsidies on corn and soybeans provide farmers the extra income they need in order to make a small profit per acre of land. In other words, it's not the value of the crop that's so important, it's the subsidies. And the more acreage farmers put into corn, the more subsidies they receive. Subsidies keep many farm towns alive even though rural areas are losing families as more land is gobbled by mega-farms for growing corn and soybeans.

* The new documentary, King Corn, lays it all out in language that folks can understand. Check it out, as well as ewg.org. EWG stands for Environmental Working Group. See more on Farm Subsidies in the next chapter on the Farm Bill.

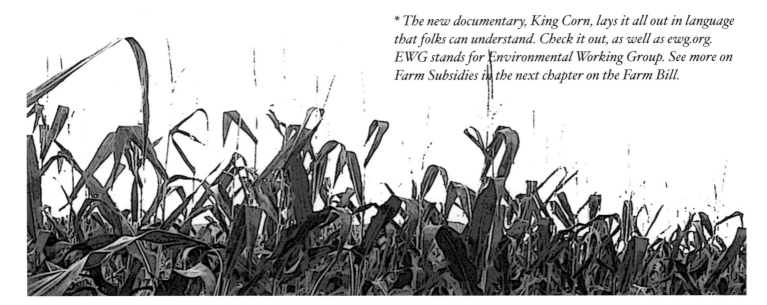

Chicago Board of Trade Futures Market (CBOT)

The purpose of CBOT is to help stabilize food prices using tools that manage risk, pursue profit potential, minimize price swings and maintain stability in a modern economy. The goal is to ensure a consistent supply of grains, soybeans, and processed foods and to make trade smoother and more predictable. The vast majority of planted acreage in the U.S. consists of five essential crops: soybeans, corn, wheat, rice and oats. Futures contracts on each of these commodities are traded at the CBOT by sellers and buyers.

CBOT helped to formalize grain trading by developing standard agreements called futures contracts. Buyers and sellers participate within the CBOT system. Futures agreements began in Chicago in 1848, with the appearance of the railroads. Chicago, being centrally located, emerged as a hub between Midwestern farmers and producers and the east coast population centers. The modern commodity markets have their roots on the trading of agricultural products. Wheat, corn, cattle, and pigs were widely traded in the 19th century. Other foodstuffs such as soybeans were more recently added to the trading list.

Much has changed in the last ten years. Hedge funds and other sources of hot money are pouring billions of dollars into the food commodity market in order to escape sliding stock markets.

Investment funds now control 50 to 60 percent of the wheat traded on the world's biggest commodity markets. It has been calculated that the amount of speculative money in food commodity futures -- markets where the investors do not buy or sell a physical commodity like rice or wheat, but merely bet on price movements, ballooned --from $5 billion in 2000 to $175 billion in 2007. 🌿

Hedge Funds

Another culprit in the increasing price of food comes from companies like General Mills -- the name behind such brands as Cheerios, Nature Valley and Yoplait. General Mills has been placing big bets in the grain market. It's called hedging. If they place their bets early, they can turn a profit from Futures trading. General Mills made $151 million in the last quarter, raising per share earnings by 27 cents. It did this by locking in 66 percent of its purchasing of grain in 2008.

Most companies like General Mills, Kellogg's, and Kraft don't talk about their hedge fund activities. We don't know, for example, whether those Corn Flakes you buy were manufactured with $2.30 a bushel corn in 2007 or $5.30 a bushel corn in 2008. Did you know that cost of corn in Corn Flakes is, on average, about 14 cents or 3 percent of the total price? 🌿

OTHER FACTORS
IN THE RISING COST OF FOOD

The Raging Midwest Floodwaters: The heavy rains in June, 2008 swallowed up crops in the Midwest and sent corn and soybean prices soaring. It wasn't long before the effects of the disaster were seen on your grocery shelves. The floods engulfed an estimated 2 million or more acres of corn and soybean fields in Iowa, Indiana, and Illinois.

Farmers were worried that excessive rain in the corn belt would damage crops, hurt yields, and add to food inflation. It costs farmers $50 to replant an acre of corn. That may not seem like much unless you're replanting hundreds of acres. As of June, 2008, 20 percent of the corn crop in Iowa was lost due to flooding.

Higher Feed Costs: Beef, pork, poultry, and even milk, cheese, and eggs went up in price due to higher feed costs. Livestock owners went out of business or were forced to slaughter more cattle, hogs, turkeys, and chickens to cope with the rocketing costs of corn-based animal feed.

Kansas producer Rod Brennerman figured it costs him $30 more to feed a single hog than the previous year because of record-high prices for corn and soybeans, the main ingredients in animal feed. Before the increase in grain costs, corn farmers were enjoying record profits for the first time in years by selling the grain for feed and use in ethanol production, cereals, and as a sweetener in soda and candy.

Organic Food: As prices of organic foods rise, conventional fruits and vegetables are suddenly looking better. Some middle-class folks who bought organic can't afford the high price of organic food anymore. The health-food craze mushroomed during this decade, growing 150 percent since 2001 to reach $19 billion in sales in 2007.

Today, a $6 gallon of organic milk doesn't look as appealing when a gallon of conventional milk at Kroger goes for about $4.00.

In a recent poll, only 27 percent of shoppers thought organics were worth the money. After years of increasing annual sales, consumers are cutting down on organic food. Folks simply can't afford those $6 a pint organic strawberries in February when gas costs $3 a gallon. The rising cost of organic grain -- about twice that of conventional grain -- makes it hard to justify feeding those organic chickens in the coop behind your house.

Fertilizer: Increasing food costs are directly related to high chemical fertilizer costs, which are the result of higher fuel costs. It takes large amounts of natural gas to produce fertilizer. Link Leaven of Ventura County, California now pays $600 for a ton of fertilizer, twice what he paid six months ago, at his lemon and avocado farm. Midwestern growers of corn and grain have been able to absorb the cost hikes as their crops fetched higher prices.

IS ETHANOL TO BLAME
FOR THE FOOD CRISIS?

Four reasons for the surge in ethanol production from corn are the increase in fuel prices at the pump, demand for greater energy security, concern over relying on oil imports from politically volatile regions, and growing concerns about the increase in carbon dioxide from fossil fuels -- the principal greenhouse gas linked to global warming. Corn is used in most animal feed and is a key ingredient in other products such as a sweetener in soft drinks. As more corn is grown for ethanol production, corn prices have risen causing a ripple effect on the agricultural commodity market that in turn has resulted in higher food prices.

Because of the rising demand for ethanol American farmers are growing more corn than at any time since World War II.

See more on the corn-based ethanol debate in Lifting The Yoke. com, Part 1.

By the summer of 2008, energy costs went down and ethanol production declined. In early 2009 energy prices began to rise again.

The International Monetary Fund (IMF) stated in the summer of 2008 that the increased demand for biofuels like ethanol contributed 15 to 30 percent to food price increases. In some cases biofuel production is competing directly with food crops. What's needed are biofuels that can make fuel out of plants like switch grass, not from food crops like corn.

Speculation: The manipulation of food prices by speculators, traders, and hoarders is the main reason for higher food prices.

Global agribusiness firms like Cargill and ADM are also raking in the dough. The profits of the largest grain dealer, Cargill, rose 36 percent from 2006 to 2007 and 77 percent in the last quarter of 2007. Profits at Archer Daniels Midland (ADM), "Supermarket to the World," increased 67 percent. Some call this an opportunity for greater market share; others call it greed. It's one of the main reasons for higher food costs.

Brewster Kneen's *Cargill and Its Transnational Strategies*

What's happening with food is also taking place with petroleum supplies. Global energy companies are raking in huge profits and investments firms are speculating in the "free market." Matt Cota of the Vermont Fuel Oil Association said, "The giant hedge funds and investment banks like Goldman Sachs keep finding ways to screw Main Street." Cota asked the following question on a recent "60 Minutes" show. "Why, in May of 2008, when there was plenty of supply and little demand, did gasoline prices skyrocket?"

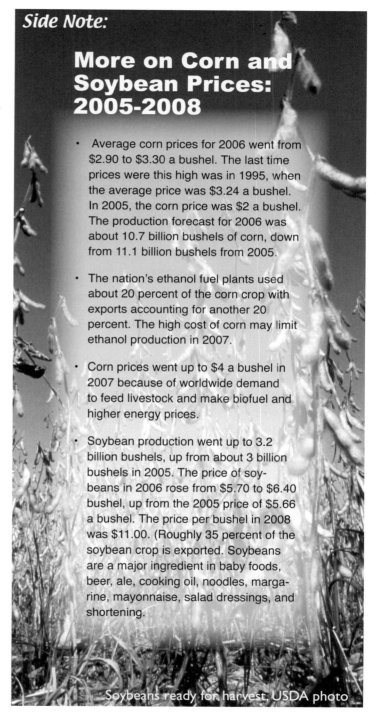

Side Note:

More on Corn and Soybean Prices: 2005-2008

- Average corn prices for 2006 went from $2.90 to $3.30 a bushel. The last time prices were this high was in 1995, when the average price was $3.24 a bushel. In 2005, the corn price was $2 a bushel. The production forecast for 2006 was about 10.7 billion bushels of corn, down from 11.1 billion bushels from 2005.

- The nation's ethanol fuel plants used about 20 percent of the corn crop with exports accounting for another 20 percent. The high cost of corn may limit ethanol production in 2007.

- Corn prices went up to $4 a bushel in 2007 because of worldwide demand to feed livestock and make biofuel and higher energy prices.

- Soybean production went up to 3.2 billion bushels, up from about 3 billion bushels in 2005. The price of soybeans in 2006 rose from $5.70 to $6.40 bushel, up from the 2005 price of $5.66 a bushel. The price per bushel in 2008 was $11.00. (Roughly 35 percent of the soybean crop is exported. Soybeans are a major ingredient in baby foods, beer, ale, cooking oil, noodles, margarine, mayonnaise, salad dressings, and shortening.

Soybeans ready for harvest, USDA photo

ADDITIONAL GRAIN, SOYBEAN AND GENETICALLY MODIFIED SEED FACTS

- China is the world's top-grain producing country. The U.S. comes in second, with India third and Russia fourth.

- The U.S. is the world's largest grain exporter.

- Thirty-seven percent of grain is fed to animals. Almost all rice is used for human consumption.

- Corn covers more land in the U.S. than any other crop.

- Soybeans are the fastest growing crop in the world. Only one-tenth is eaten by humans. One-third goes to cooking oil, and the rest goes for animal feed. A large percentage of these seeds are genetically modified.

- Genetically modified crops are the fastest growing food technology in the world.

- Monsanto is the largest producer of genetically modified seeds on the globe. Their first quarter earnings in 2008 more than doubled in Latin America because of the sale of genetically modified soybean seeds.

Rice - USDA

SUPPLY AND DEMAND

Prices on grains, meats and dairy products fluctuate month to month and year to year depending on supply and demand. As prices decrease, consumers buy more. When prices increase, as they have done recently, consumers will purchase less.

IS THE CURRENT SITUATION IN 2009 HEALTHY FOR U.S. FARMERS?

Farming in the U.S. is complicated and volatile. You'd think that American farmers were encouraged by the higher prices they received in 2007 and early 2008. For example, there has been a higher demand for animal feed grains and dairy products from China and India where people are adopting diets richer in milk and meat.

In response to greater demand and higher prices, farmers borrowed money to buy more farmland, purchase chemicals and seeds and upgrade their equipment. However, with higher farm profits came soaring land values and increasing farm debt. According to the USDA, total farm debt increased 30 percent from 2003-2008 by $52.8 billion. The increase in food prices motivated investors to put more capital into buying commodities like wheat, corn, and other grains, as well as investing in farmland.

Vermont Dairy Farmer
Photo Courtesy of Vern Grubinger,
University of Vermont Extension
Service

Farming is a risky business especially in today's economic climate. Consumers are spending less on food items such as dairy products.

*See next page on Volatility in Milk Prices.

Examples of Volatility: In 2006 Vermont dairy farmers received $12 for 100 pounds of milk. In 2007, it went up to $17. In January, 2009, the price spiraled down to $12 for 100 pounds of milk. It costs farmers $16 per hundred pounds of milk to break even. This is an example of volatility and why farmers need more stable milk prices.

And what happens when grain production increases worldwide and there is not the global demand that there was in 2007 and 2008 from American farmers. Or how about geo-political events like the Soviet grain embargo after the invasion of Afghanistan in 1979. At the time, farm productivity was high, government subsidies soared, and the oversupply drove commodity prices and land values down dramatically. Many rural farm banks went out of business, along with thousands of farmers.

The Politics of the Ethanol Debate: Top international scientists have recommended halting the use of corn ethanol, saying it would cut corn prices by 20 percent. The scientists are part of CGIAR, a global network that fights hunger. Rattan Lai, an Ohio University soil scientist, said, "We need to feed the stomach before we feed our cars."

The World Bank study estimated that corn prices rose by over 60 percent from 2005-2007, largely because of ethanol. The International Food Policy Research Institute concluded that the rise in food prices from 2000-2007 was due to increased production of biofuels like ethanol.

Former President Bush stated that the U.S. should increase ethanol use because of national energy, security matters and high gas prices. Bush said, "It's in our national interest that our farmers grow energy, as opposed to us purchasing energy from parts of the world that are unstable or may not like us."

In the spring of 2008, grocers and farmers faced off over subsidies for ethanol. On one side was the American Farm Bureau and other farm groups that defended ethanol production and on the other side were trade groups, such as the Grocery Manufacturers of America, which believe that the increased production of ethanol had driven up the prices of corn and other grains which, in turn, boosted prices for bread, meat, and dairy products.

Side Notes:

For years, family farmers barely made a living on what they received for their farm products. You can't turn on the national news without mention of high food prices. Farmers are sometimes blamed for the current food crisis. Why are they placed on the chopping block? Even though they're receiving higher prices, the cost for fuel, fertilizer, feed, and chemicals has skyrocketed. Do consumers blame a manufacturer when the cost of an electronic gadget goes up because fuel costs and shipping and material costs jump up? Do consumers understand that the global food giants and the speculators are making excessive profits? It's not the farmers that are making out like bandits, it's the processors and other middle men in the food chain. 🐾

DOMESTIC HUNGER

Hunger in the U.S. existed well before the Food Crisis of 2008 set in, but now the food lines are getting longer. Even when the unemployment rate was below 5 percent, the economic system didn't provide the income to cover people's basic needs: housing, energy (heat, transportation, utilities), health care, and food. One of the main reasons for this was the growing gap between the rich and the poor. What will happen if the Recession of 2008 turns into the Depression of 2009?

Some 28 million Americans received food stamps in March of 2008, up 1.5 million from a year earlier. Food stamps provide an average of one dollar per meal.

Ironically, hunger has taken on a new set of clothes. When Robert Kennedy, the Attorney General of the United States, went to the Mississippi Delta in the 1960s to publicize the pervasiveness of poverty, he found thin, malnourished people living in shacks. If Kennedy were alive today, he would see many obese families.

The term used today in the U.S. for people who don't have enough food on the table is **"food insecurity,"** and some poor families are experiencing **"food insecurity plus hunger."** Maura Daly, a lobbyist for America's Second Harvest, the Nation's Food Bank Network, said rising food and energy costs plus record home foreclosures have created a "perfect storm" for needy families. She says food banks are seeing a 20 percent increase in the number of people turning to them for help.

When Crystal Rockwell loads up her shopping cart these days at the Chittenden County Food Shelf in Burlington, Vermont with cereal and SpaghettiOs, she notices more people doing the same thing. A lot of these folks are people she has never seen before. The number of people at the Food Shelf increased by more than 2,000 since 2006. According to Rob Meeham, the new director of the Food Shelf, "The people who I'm seeing are the traditional middle class. They can't believe they're here. "

More and more people in Vermont and across the nation are using food stamps. (One in ten Vermonters went on food stamps in 2009) The average Vermont household receives $187 a month, but that doesn't buy much food these days. The working poor are also being crushed by increases in fuel and housing prices.

Coffee Line during the Great Depression,
Public Domain photo

WORLD HUNGER

The World Food Crisis of 2008 created protests and riots around the world over the surging cost of many "basic" foods. From Haiti to Cameroon to Bangladesh and even Austria, people took to the streets in anger over high food prices. In fear of political turmoil, world leaders have called for food aid, as well as more funds and technology to boost agricultural production.

As stated earlier, the price of wheat went up 130 percent over last year and rice doubled in price in Asia in the first three months of 2008 alone.

Cereal exporting countries closed their borders to protect their own domestic markets. Liberia banned all food exports in May 2008, saying profiteers had been taking advantage of its cheap rice prices by trucking the grain, already in short supply, to neighboring countries where they resold it at higher prices.

Rice Merchant and Farmer in India.
Photo Courtesy of Monica Marshall

According to Grain, an international non-governmental organization, three decades of "neoliberal" globalization policies have made the world hunger situation go from bad to worse. The developed nations and international lending agencies have allowed food to be transformed from something that nourishes people and provides them with secure livelihoods into a commodity for speculation and bargaining on world markets.

Trade Liberalization and Structural Adjustment:

These two neoliberal policies have been imposed on poor countries by the World Bank and International Monetary Fund (IMF) since the 1970s. They were reinforced by the World Trade Organization (WTO) in the mid-1990s and more recently by a barrage of free trade and investment agreements. The result has been the dismantling of tariffs and other tools that developing countries created to protect local agricultural products.

Developing countries have been forced by international loan agreements to open their markets to global agribusiness, but they can't compete with the cheap food coming from rich countries whose commodity foods like corn and soybeans are subsidized. The poor countries divert their fertile lands, which were once used for local food crops to the production of high-value crops like strawberries for Western supermarkets. Today, roughly 70 percent of all developing countries are net importers of food.

Grains of rice

TWO EXAMPLES OF EXPLOITATION: HAITI AND THE PHILIPPINES

Haiti: A few decades ago Haiti was self-sufficient in rice. But conditions on foreign loans, particularly a 1994 loan package by the IMF, forced it to open up (liberalize) its market. Cheap subsidized rice flooded in from the U.S., and local production was wiped out.

ADDED NOTES ON THE INSTABILITY OF PLANET EARTH

The Global Food Crisis of 2008 has contributed to worldwide economic unrest and threatened the political stability of the developing nations -- prone to food insecurity. Some say the crisis has become more dangerous than terrorism. It's a ticking time bomb ready to explode.

The irony in all of this is that farmers across the world produced a record 2.3 billion tons of grain in 2007, up 4 percent from 2006. Since 1961, the world's cereal crop output tripled, while the world's population doubled. The fact is that there is enough food in the world to feed the population. The problem is that it doesn't get to all of those who need it. Less than half of the world grain production is directly eaten by people; most goes into animal feed and, increasingly, biofuels.

Source: For more information on the Food Crisis around the globe and World Hunger, check out: www. grain.org. Grain is one of my favorite websites

The Global agro-chemical companies like Cargill's Mosaic Corporation control much of the world's potash and phosphate supply. Their profits more than doubled in 2007. Syngenta was once the world's top pesticide manufacturer and third-largest seed company. Their profits rose 28 percent in the first quarter of 2008. Syngenta was bought out by Monsanto a couple of years ago. Monsanto controls the production of genetically engineered (GE) seeds. Their goal is to control all seed production around the globe.

 * A bit of good news is that the Ecuadoran government has taken the unprecedented step of declaring their land free of genetically engineered (GE) seeds and crops in order to preserve biodiversity.

Haiti, Continued ...

Haiti is the poorest country in the Americas. The price for rice has risen more than 50 percent since 2007 - making it hard for Haitians to afford this basic staple, which they call "Miami Rice."

At the same time that the Haitian people are starving, the country is shelling out millions in debt repayment to the tune of $1 million each week. The irony is that the debt repayments go to wealthy banks that were supposedly established to fight poverty.

Haiti's current debt stands at $1.3 billion, 40 percent of which was run up by the Duvalier dictators, who between 1957 and 1986 stole part of these loans for themselves. A group called Jubilee USA Network is calling for immediate debt cancellation for Haiti and all poor countries.

The Philippines: Why would a self-sustaining rice-consuming country become largely dependent on imports? Unlike corn, less than 10 percent of rice is traded on the open market. Yet in 2008, the price of rice nearly tripled, from $380 a ton in January to more than $1,000 a ton in April. This inflation has been caused by wholesale cartels which buy and sell rice.

In 1986 when dictator Ferdinand Marcos ran the country, he provided farmers with subsidized fertilizer and seeds, provided credit and built up the rural farm infrastructure. There was a surplus of rice in government warehouses. When the democratically elected Corizon Aquino came into power a few years later, the country chose to make payments of their $26 billion dollar debt a priority. The results of debt repayment schedule were disastrous. Irrigation stagnated, rice yields went down, infrastructure collapsed and rice began to be imported.

The experience of Haiti and the Philippines parallels other countries subjected to the harsh policies of the IMF and WTO. A study of fourteen developing countries by the UN's Food and Agricultural Organization found that the levels of food imports in 1995-1998 exceeded those in 1990-1994. Former U.S. Secretary of Agriculture

Farmers Working in Rice Paddy. Photo Courtesy of Wikipedia

John Block said in 1986, "The idea that developing countries should feed themselves is an anachronism from a bygone era. They could better ensure their food security by relying on U.S. agricultural products, which are available in most cases at lower cost." Block left out the fact the lower cost of U.S. products was the result of massive farm subsidies.

Developing countries are being integrated into a global food system dominated by genetic engineering firms like Monsanto, grain-trading corporations like Cargill and Archer Daniels Midland, and transnational food retailers such as British-owned Tesco and French-owned Carrefour, the second largest retail group in the world in terms of revenue, after Wal-Mart. Africanist Deborah Bryceson calls this phenomenon "de-peasantization":

the phasing out of peasant farms and the phasing in and accumulation of capital by the global food giants.
Source: Two Examples of Exploitation came from an article by Walden Bello, Manufacturing A Food Crisis, The Nation, June 2, 2008.

* Deadly Embrace is an informative and well-made video on the effects of neo-liberal policies of structural adjustment on the people of Nicaragua. For a copy of the video, write to: Ash Eames, Buffalo Mountain Road, Wentworth, NH 03282.

*The Zero Hunger Program
In 2007 Nicaragua provided close to 33,000 poor families with seeds, fertilizer, etc. This helped small farmers become more self-sufficient and enabled them to sell their surplus food crops.

B. THE 2008 $300 BILLION FARM BILL

The Farm Bill of 2008 has great implications on the health of our nation. Every five years Congress re-authorizes a new farm and food bill. The program covers food assistance, conservation, agricultural trade, credit, rural development, research and farm subsidies on crops such as corn, soybeans, sugar and rice. The Farm Bill of 2008 combines these different programs into one farm bill.

The Compromise: In the fall of 2007, there was a huge debate in Congress over the 673 page Farm Bill, officially named The Food, Conservation and Energy Act of 2008. Rarely has a past farm bill galvanized such activism, mainstream media attention or range of urban and rural stakeholders. On June 18, 2008, the bill passed, overcoming its final hurdle by overriding the veto of former President Bush.

On one side were the strong farm states with their powerful lobbies pushing for a continuation and increase of farm subsidies for corn, soybeans, rice, sugar and wheat. These commodity crops received about $35 billion while the bill's support for specialty crops was only $1.3 billion over ten years. On the other side of the debate were advocates for the environment, the poor, and the preservation of the family farm.

Michael Pollan, author of *The Omnivore's Dilemma* and *In Defense of Food*, said, "We need to reform North America's food system by providing more healthy, sustainable solutions. We are in the midst of a national epidemic of obesity, diabetes and heart disease -- at the same time that our government is subsidizing the production of unhealthy food by supporting farmers who grow corn for sugar and soybeans for oil."

In a similar vein, Eric Schlosser, author of *Fast Food Nation*, said, "We need agricultural policies at the national level that end the subsidies for unhealthy food and that make good foods much less expensive. Low-income families shouldn't have to worry about whether they can afford to eat well. We have an overabundance of food in this country -- and a system that encourages the mass consumption of the wrong foods."

Powerful members of Congress from farm states agreed to food programs for the needy as long as there was an increase in farm subsidies. The subsidy program was the sticking point in negotiations that dragged on for over a year. The outcome was a compromise. Two-thirds of the Farm Bill paid for domestic nutrition programs with increases in food stamps and emergency food aid for the needy. The nutrition reforms do much to support a strong and diverse agricultural economy -- something absolutely necessary in reducing hunger in America.

Michael Pollan doesn't believe the Farm Bill of 2008 addressed the destructive effects of processed food on our nation's health, which is directly connected to farm subsidies of corn and soybeans.

Gus Schumacher, former Massachusetts Commissioner of Agriculture, said that despite its flaws, the bill made an unprecedented commitment to support locally produced food and expand access to these healthy products for all.

Overall, the Farm Bill provides a safety food net for the poor who are struggling with rising food costs, supports soil and water conservation programs, makes loans available to rural communities to improve waste and water infrastructure, and provides money for farm-based renewable energy projects. It includes more spending on conservation, the obesity epidemic, organic research and conversion to organics, a new program to put more local fruits and vegetables in the schools, and more support for farmers' markets.

THE FARM BILL AND PROBLEMS WITH SUBSIDIES

Subsidies have been around since the Great Depression of 1929 -- to prop up low farm commodity prices and help farmers compete globally. Between 1995 and 2003, U.S. farmers received $131 billion in federal subsidies, with the largest share -- 28 percent -- steered to Midwest corn growers. Other groups that receive large benefits include cotton, soybean, wheat, sugar, and rice growers. In 2003, about one-third of U.S. farmers received a total of $16.4 billion in federal subsidies.

Critics say the subsidies benefit mostly large agribusiness operations rather than small family farms. USDA figures indicate that 8 percent of producers collect 78 percent of the subsidies. These farmers say that such payments are critical to their businesses as production costs outstrip commodity prices.

For many years, two-thirds of the nation's farmers received little or no benefit from farm programs because they produced "non-subsidy" foods, such as fruits, vegetables, meat and hay. The Farm Bill of 2008 provided for the first time support for fruit and vegetable growers as well as those farmers converting to organics.

A single cotton plantation in Louisiana collected $2.9 million in crop subsidies in 2005. That's exactly the amount the government spent on its primary research program to support the entire national organic industry in 2004.
In 2005, the Agriculture Economic Research Service of the USDA showed a correlation between rural counties receiving the most subsidies and those counties that suffered the most rapid population decline.

Direct Payments: Over the past five years, one-third of the $300 billion spent on subsidies has been devoted to direct payments to large commodity growers and investors in the Midwest and west. Farmers can receive a payment from the government whether they plant a major commodity crop or not. In the last ten years, individuals and groups (non-farmers) have invested in farm real estate, knowing that they will receive payments on the land that's again -- either planted or not. There are no caps on how much they can receive. This is a smart investment. There are rules on how much these individuals and groups of investors are allowed to profit under the federal tax code of the Internal Revenue Service but a savvy accountant can work wonders with all kinds of income tax deductions. Legislators from farm states receive campaign contributions from their constituents, many of whom profit from the Direct Payment Program.

Donald R. Matthews put his sprawling new residence in the heart of rice country in El Campo, Texas. Matthews is not a farmer but an asphalt contractor who receives $1,300 in annual "direct payments" because his land was once used to grow rice. Matthews is not alone. The subsidy program paid $1.3 billion in subsidies for rice and other commodities in every year since 2000 to people who don't farm. Houston surgeon Jimmy Frank Howell has received a total of $490,709. These programs benefit millionaire landowners, foreign speculators, and absentee landlords and farmers. Some call it "corporate welfare."
The Direct Payment Program is one of four major subsidy programs. The other programs provide loans to farmers.

Rice grower Chris Isbell (left) and ARS' (Agricultural Research Service Agent) Bob Dilday check a field of Akita Komachi rice. Photo Courtesy of USDA.

The Farm Bill of 2008 made small cuts to the direct farm commodity payments, which are distributed to some farmers no matter how much they grow. It eliminated some federal payments to individuals with more than $750,000 in annual income or married farmers who make more than $1.5 million. The legislation made individuals who earn more than $500,000 or couples who earn more than $1 million in non-farm income ineligible for subsidies. Previously, there were no limits on farm-based income.

OVER-PRODUCTION: THE OTHER PROBLEM

Subsidies are not connected in any way to farm prices, whether they are high or low. They encourage over-production rather than help farmers get fair prices for their commodities. The federal government guarantees growers a set price regardless of how much they grow or how much the market will pay. What's even more insane is that the current Farm Bill would expand subsidies for corn, soybeans, wheat, cotton, and rice, and continue government payments to some wealthy farmers and non-farmers.

Many groups are advocating for reform of the commodity programs. They believe that public monies should not be linked to production, a practice that distorts the marketplace. Instead, tax dollars should be invested in ways that stabilize the family farm, and don't harm poor farmers in other countries.

Food Security and Nutrition Programs: Lawmakers moved more dollars from crop subsidy programs to food stamps and other programs that serve the needy. About 75 percent of the $300 billion Farm Bill of 2008 was devoted to nutrition programs, most of which went to food stamps, the largest single recipient at $70 billion. That compares to 55 percent six years ago.

Another positive step was the setting up of farmers' markets to accept food stamps through the use of Electronic Benefits Transfer (EBT) plastic cards. EBT is a way to receive and use food stamps. Food Stamp benefits are deposited in one's EBT account, much like a bank account.

The Farm Bill does not fund nutrition programs such as the School Breakfast and Lunch Program, the Child and Adult Care Food Program, the Summer Food Service Program, and the Women, Infants and Children's program called WIC. All of these are essential in ensuring that children have access to nourishing food all year long. Separate legislation in 2009 will be voted on to fund these programs.

Go on the web to the Economic Research Service of the USDA for more information on Farm Subsidies.

CONSERVATION PROGRAMS

The Farm Security and Rural Investment Act of 2002 included legislation for conservation funding and for focusing on environmental issues. It focuses both on the working landscape (farms) and the natural landscape. The conservation programs includes the stewardship and care of wildlife habitat, the protection of soils from erosion, the protection of grasslands, rivers and streams, wetlands and other environmentally sensitive areas including farmland.

For example, manure runoff is a major source of pollution in our rivers and lakes. By providing farmers with money to fence-off livestock from the rivers and streams, less erosion and nutrient run-off from fertilizer and manure will takes place.

The Conservation Program in the 2008 Farm Bill receives $5 billion a year for the next 5 years. In 2002, $2 billion was allocated. There are basically three conservation programs along with a number of smaller initiatives.

Farming near Klingerstown, Pennsylvania. Photo Courtesy of USDA, by Scott Bauer

THE BIG THREE

1. The Conservation Reserve Program (CRP) keeps land out of production. About $2 billion is spent each year, the largest amount of any conservation program. The amount of acreage in the program may soon change because farmers are putting land back into production due to high commodity prices for corn, wheat and soybeans.

The net effect of the Conservation Reserve Program is to limit the pressure to plow fragile native grasslands in the west, which destroys the habitat while contributing to climate change by releasing carbon stored in the soil.

2. Environmental Quality Incentives Program (EQIP) was reauthorized in the amount of $1 billion in 2008. EQIP is a voluntary incentive-based program which helps agricultural and forest producers solve natural resource problems through improved air quality, healthy soils and abundant wildlife. For example, EQIP offers financial and technical assistance to help fix a manure lagoon system. Some other examples are reduction of non-point source pollution, reduction of groundwater contamination, reduction of soil erosion, and other pollutants.

3. Conservation Stewardship Program (CSP) - The CSP program has steadily grown over the years as more acreage is put into the program. One billion dollars was set aside for CSP. Its mission is to encourage farmers and landowners to advance the stewardship of the land for future generations by preserving the plants, animals and natural communities through management of land and water resources. In 2002, it was called the **Conservation Security Program.** A conservation management plan is necessary in order to apply for funding. One farm may focus on wildlife management; another on protecting the water shed.

Money for the program goes to working farms for conservation purposes to control wind and soil erosion, restore wetlands, bring back wildlife habitat, manage manure runoff, provide riparian protection for streams and rivers, set up rotational grazing and filter strips, and develop organic production.

Ezekial Goodband of Scott Farm,
Photo Courtesy of Hunger Mountain Food Co-op

CONSERVATION SECURITY PROGRAM - (FROM THE FARM BILL OF 2002)

Ten farms in Vermont received $103,000 each year for five years in the last Farm Bill to continue their conservation practices and share their knowledge with other farmers. Ezekial Goodband of Scott Farm Orchards in Windham County, Vermont, received a grant from the Conservation Security Program of 2002. Operating Scott Farm with environmentally sound practices, is something Goodband does simply because it is the best way to farm. He set up buffer zones near the streams in the orchard, conserved energy on the refrigeration system for keeping apples cool after harvest, and upgraded his weather forecasting equipment for more accurate tracking of insects and fungal diseases.

It's difficult and often more expensive to implement conservation programs, but Goodband says it is the only way he would ever run his 570 acres of land. According to Drew Adams, a district conservationist who works in the USDA Brattleboro, Vermont office, "This is the first program of which I am aware that rewards people for doing the right thing."

Farmland Conservation Program (FCP): Its primary focus is to conserve productive farmland vital to the rural economy of each state through a mechanism called the purchase of "development rights."

The Vermont Land Trust (VLT) works to conserve farmland in Vermont. VLT, a non-profit, has helped landowners to permanently protect 639 farms totaling 150,000 acres. Overall, VLT has protected 470,000 acres -- almost 8 percent of Vermont privately-owned land through the purchase of "Development Rights."

Each state and or non-profit must provide matching funds to the federal monies for the Farmland Conservation Program. Four thousand donors, 71 percent who live in Vermont, contributed more than $880,000 in funds in 2007. More than 92 percent of VLT's total budget is expended directly for land protection. VLT does not own land but occasionally acquires land and resells it, subject to conservation restrictions.

* For more information on conservation programs, contact The Sustainable Agriculture Coalition. Another informative website is the: Community Food Security Coalition (CFSC) 110 Maryland Ave. NE Suite 307 Washington, DC 20002 (202)-543-8602 www.foodsecurity.org

THE NORTHEAST

The Northeast is a strong agricultural region despite the fact that it is densely populated. While Northeast farmers receive only about 3 percent of farm subsidies, they generate about $15 billion in revenue, and include about 170,000 farms, 15,000 dairy farms, and provide 13 percent of the nation's timber. The region leads the nation in the number of organic farms, community supported agricultural (CSA) farms, and farmers' markets.

One-third of Northeast farm sales come from specialty crops like vegetables, melons, berries, nuts, fruits, potatoes, greenhouse and nursery crops. These are not considered commodity crops and have not received any government support up to 2008.

Most of the specialty crops in the Northeast depend on local and regional markets. Increased funding and marketing assistance through the 2008 Farm Bill will help the regions producers.

THE DAIRY PROVISION:
MILK INCOME LOSS CONTACT (MILC)

Support for the Northeast's dairy industry is another priority as dairy farming represents about one third of the region's agricultural sales.

Milk prices are set by the federal government. They fluctuate from year to year and from season to season. These changes in milk pricing make it hard for dairy farmers to plan ahead. Because of low milk prices, and the higher cost of production in the Northeast, many dairy farmers have called it quits. In 1980, there were 5,000 dairy farms in Vermont. Today there are less than 1,100.

The government has responded to low milk prices with the MILC program. The 2008 Farm Bill provides a $410 million expansion of the $1.2 billion MILC program over the next five years. The cap on milk production covered by the federal subsidy went from 120 to 165 cows. That increase would cover nearly all of Vermont's approximately 1,100 dairy farms.

Second, the bill would raise the payment rate from 34 to 45 percent. When milk prices drop below $16.94 per hundred pounds of milk, dairy producers are given a subsidy based on the difference between the market rate and $16.94. Finally, the bill would, for the first time, include the grain cost of feeding dairy cows as a factor in triggering program payments. Rising feed costs, fueled by higher energy costs, are hurting dairy farmers. The MILC program's new "feed cost adjustor" would be based on the three commodities used in feeding cows: corn, alfalfa, and soybeans.

Go to the LiftingTheYoke.com, Part 1, for 2008 Farm Bill Projects, plus, How Does the 2008 Farm Bill Impact Vermont?

C. A SHORT HISTORY OF HOW AGRICULTURE LOST ITS SOUL

Farming has gone through major structural changes in the past 60 years. In order to understand these changes, let's go back in time.

AGRICULTURE BEGAN

independently about 12,000 years ago in three different regions of the world: the Middle East (the Tigris/Euphrates river valleys or present-day Iraq), Southeast Asia, and Central America. People began to save and plant seeds, domesticate animals, and create permanent communities within these geographical settings.

From that time until the late nineteenth century, food cultivated from the land came almost entirely from local sources and harvests were variable. In good years, there was plenty of food for storage during the long winter months and for seasonal festivals. In bad years, famine and starvation took the lives of many folks. This pattern was the norm in most pre-industrial societies.

THE AGRARIAN PAST

At the time of Thomas Jefferson, 95 percent of the population farmed the land. Jefferson espoused "the agrarian ethic," in which there was equal distribution of land, meaning that it was best for the country when farms were similar in size to one another. This fostered democracy.

In the latter half of the 19th century and first half of the 20th century, farming communities were the main fabric of North American culture, and farmers were the thread that held the cloth together. They learned about living through the rhythm of daily life, were self-reliant, used common sense and helped their neighbors.

UVM Baily-Howe Collections

This is what Thomas Jefferson meant when he spoke about the link between farming and morality.

Much earlier in the 19th century, new farm technologies such as John Deere's self-scouring steel plow (1837) paralleled the settlement and development of the Midwest. Deere was born in Rutland, Vermont in 1804. He was raised by his mother in Middlebury, Vermont, where he worked as a blacksmith. They moved to Illinois where he continued with blacksmithing and found that cast-iron plows didn't work well in the tough prairie soils. Deere came to the conclusion that a plow made out of highly polished steel and the right-shaped moldboard would handle the heavy soils of the prairie. The rest is history.

Later on came other equipment, like the McCormick-Deering automated binder, combines, silos, and grain elevators for storage.

At the time of World War I, the face of farming underwent a radical change. The manufacture of ammunition and explosives in 1914 led to the production of chemical fertilizers. In 1909 the chemist Fritz Haber came up with a solution to the shortage of fixed nitrogen when he discovered how to manufacture vast quantities of nitrogen-rich anhydrous ammonia. The first commercial application of this new chemistry, the Haber-Bosch process, was used to make explosives during the two world wars.

Sarin, or nerve gas, developed in 1938, just before World War II, was modified to make chemical pesticides, insecticides, and herbicides.

DURING AND AFTER WORLD WAR II.

The farming landscape went through major changes during and after the war. Vast quantities of fossil fuels were used in the production of pesticides and artificial fertilizer to grow nitrogen-hungry corn. Today, corn is America's no. 1 cash crop, accounting for over 25 percent of our cropland.

The demand for agricultural goods remained high for a short period of time after the war. Due in part to the Marshall plan, the U.S. was committed to feeding Europe. One question that loomed large in the country was, "What will happen down on the farm when the boys come marching home."

Other Changes - Transportation and Technology: Before the war, railroad boxcars were filled with ice for refrigerating fruits and vegetables, milk, and meat. Long-distance shipping at the time was both impractical and expensive. The Transcontinental Railroad of the mid-nineteenth century was revolutionary but it was not until the advent of the Interstate Highway System in the 1950s that radical change took place in the transportation of food across the country. Refrigerated long-haul trucks began to transport fruits and vegetables across the country using low-cost fuel.

The development of new food processing techniques and refrigeration provided greater availability and variety of foods for the urban consumer. In the 1950s, factory farming began to take over our food plates. Farmers reaped remarkable gains due to technology. The average harvested acre of farmland yielded 200 percent more wheat than it had 70 years ago. In two decades, chickens grew 25 percent larger due to improved breeding and feed. The average cow produced 60 percent more milk due to breeding, balanced nutrition, hybrid seeds, and synthetic hormones. Overall farm production in the U.S. during World War II increased by one-third.

Me and Mom...

Side Notes:

During the 1940s and early 50s, people's food baskets weren't as diverse as they are today. Urban dwellers looked forward to traveling out to the country to local fruit and vegetable stands. Most of the produce consumed was grown on nearby farms. When I was a youngster in the mid-1940s, my mother would take me on a short bus ride to the Haymarket on Market Street in Louisville to buy fresh fish and produce.

My good friend Ash Eames of Newburyport, Massachusetts, remembers how local farmers along the coast shipped their produce short distances to Boston by rail. He also recalls the Fens in Bean Town, with all the backyard vegetable gardens, close to Fenway Park, the home of the Boston Red Sox. They began as "Victory Gardens" during World War II.

DARK CLOUDS

By the 1950s, dark clouds began to appear on the agricultural horizon. Low farm prices, an increase in hunger, a decrease in the number of farmers, an increase in the use of agricultural chemicals -- all contributed to structural and social shifts in rural America.

Life on the farm changed radically as production exceeded demand. Because of declining market prices many farmers were forced to expand production, but that only increased surpluses and drove prices down. Thousands of family farms went out of business as farm commodity prices went below the cost of production.

Increased production was aided by greater mechanization, hybrid seeds, and agro-chemicals. This proved to be a curse for some farmers. The over-production of corn and other agricultural commodities like wheat and soybeans became a problem. As yields rose, the market was flooded and prices collapsed.

Parity: Parity was a statistical model used during the 1930s to try to find out if farm income was keeping up with farm costs. From 1910-1914, the prices that farmers got for their crops and livestock were roughly in balance with the prices they had to pay for goods and services they used in the production of crops, livestock and family living. The concept was written into law in the 1933 Agricultural Adjustment Act, where it became the goal of the U.S. government to get prices close to parity. The Department of Agriculture paid farmers not to plant some crops and cull livestock herds. Less supply and a steady demand would raise prices.

From 1943-1953, the parity system for the pricing of farm products continued as farmers received a fair price for their efforts and investments. Back then, the nation's agricultural landscape was made up of small family farms, but times were changing rapidly and factory farms were starting to make their way onto the scene.

In the late 1950s and into the 1960s, the prices that farmers paid for production inputs (fertilizer, feed grain, seed) and living expenses continued to go up. Today, it takes a lot more wheat to buy a tractor than it did in 1914, but today's farmers also grow wheat more efficiently because of technological advances.

Market in Bhutan, Lilianna Susskind

Developing Countries: Since the 1950s, U.S. farm policy has not provided parity (fairness) in terms of the prices paid to small farmers relative to the real costs of production. This not only affects family farms in the U.S., but also farmers in third-world countries. I'll explain.

Dexter Randall, a Vermont dairy farmer from North Troy and a former legislator in the Vermont House of Representatives, went on a 2006 Oxfam farm tour to Mali, a West African country.

Joined by American farmers from Virginia, Kansas, Texas, Illinois, and Vermont, they met with working farmers in Mali, as well as government officials from the U.S. Randall found that U.S. agricultural policy, especially the effect it has on developing countries, was "shameful." He said that farmers in Mali aren't asking for handouts, but a fair price. For example, take the problem caused by the billions of dollars in cotton subsidies to large U.S. cotton growers: $5 billion for a crop worth $4 billion. This subsidy-driven surplus of cotton enters the world market and lowers the price, threatening the livelihoods of small farmers all over the globe.

Mali cotton farmers can't compete with low U.S. subsidized cotton prices and are forced to move to the cities, creating severe social and economic problems. This same phenomenon is happening with U.S. subsidized corn exported to Mexico, forcing Mexican farmers off the land into the cities and/or to immigrate to the U.S.

The 2008 Farm Bill increased subsidy payments to U.S. farmers. This encourages the overproduction of corn, cotton, and rice. This in effect devastates farmers in developing countries who can't compete with low farm commodity prices in the U.S. Randall said that what we need are programs that provide fewer government farm subsidies for products like corn, sugar and cotton and more support for sustainable-organic farming. Source: Randall spoke on Vermont Public Radio in July, 2006.

Fewer Farmers: Less than two percent of people in the U.S. farm the land today. In 1790, farmers made up 90 percent of the labor force. In 1840, it was 69 percent and in 1890, 43 percent. In 1910 it was 31 percent and by 1940, the percentage had gone down to 18 percent. In the 1920s, there were 920,000 black farmers; by 1998 that number had declined by 98 percent, reflecting the two percent farm labor force in the U.S. The promise of "forty acres and a mule" after the Civil War has long been gone and for some was never true.

The Chemical Treadmill: More dark clouds appeared on the agricultural landscape in the 1960s and 1970s from the overuse of chemicals. With the rise of chemical pesticides and herbicides, the weeds in corn crops no longer had to be controlled with cultivator equipment. In the beginning the chemical sprays were effective and made life easier for the farmer, but after years of use, farmers found themselves trapped on the pesticide treadmill where they had to spray more and more.

The chemical salesmen continued to knock at the farmers' doors, describing all the benefits of pesticides and herbicides. The problem was that the bugs and weeds became more resistant to the sprays.

Other problems arose over time as large fields were planted with only one crop -- i.e., corn or soybeans -- year after year. Such monocultures encouraged an increase in the number of harmful insects and diseases.

The History of the War on Drugs: As the American population grew, demands on crop output increased. Chemical companies declared war on bugs with sprays, dusts, and granules, as early as the late 1800s. They waged a huge media campaign, which can be compared to today's blitzkrieg from the pharmaceutical industry.

Will Allen's new book, *The War On Bugs*, from Chelsea Green Publishers, reveals how advertisers, editors, scientists, government agencies, and even Dr. Seuss, colluded to convince farmers to use deadly chemicals, and hormones; today, they use genetically modified organisms (GMOs). Allen examines the historical connection between advertising and agriculture and how toxic chemicals were marketed and sold to farmers -- as safe, effective, and necessary.

In 1984, a gas leak at Union Carbide's pesticide plant in Byopal, India killed thousands of people. The pesticide was Sevin, a common chemical sold in farm and garden stores in this country.

Spraying Chemical Pesticides on Soybeans, USDA

Factory Farm Row Cropping, USDA

Corporate Catfish Operation, USDA

THE DANGER OF GENETIC UNIFORMITY

Most of the major food commodities like corn, soybeans, rice, cotton and canola are grown with genetically modified (GM) seeds, of which there are few varieties. That's why it's so critical to understand that "genetic uniformity" can lead to increased vulnerability to insects and diseases, resulting in agricultural catastrophes such as the potato blight.

History tells us that in 1845 and lasting for six years, the Irish potato famine killed over a million men, women and children and caused another million to flee the country. Lumpers was the main potato variety used in Ireland. When the same potato blight (fungus) hit Peru, they suffered fewer consequences due to the hundreds of potato varieties. Today, there are only four main varieties of potatoes grown in the world; thousands of varieties have become extinct.

CAIM: In the last 60 years, the U.S. has gone from small, diversified farms to large specialized factory units. What I call the Corporate-Agricultural-Industrial-Machine (CAIM) and what others call "industrial agriculture" now controls the production, processing, marketing and distribution of your food basket. Supermarket food is transported long distances, and many new processed food items have been introduced.

These changes have eroded the local agricultural infrastructure -- the creameries, slaughterhouses, granaries, mills, and processing plants that were once part of the rural landscape. In addition, the steady decline in the number of local farm-related businesses, such as farm machinery dealers, and seed and fertilizer plants, has radically transformed the fabric of our rural communities.

* See more on CAIM on page 36.

For More Information on the Early History of Farming in the U.S., see LiftingTheYoke.com, Part 1, The History of Plunder at Home and Abroad; the American Revolution, the Constitution and Shays Rebellion.

3 Agricultural Periods in U.S. History

Expansion Period (1600-1920)

There were increases in food production and more land was put into production. Technology played a minor role.

Mechanization Period (1920-1970)

There were technological advances in farm machinery, synthetic fertilizers and pesticides, irrigation, and new hybrid seeds. Farm productivity increased. Most of these gains were the result of cheap, abundant fossil fuels.

Saturation Period (1970-Present)

Increasing amounts of pesticides have produced negligible crop yields. The result is that greater amounts of pesticides and herbicides have been applied to counter pest and plant disease resistance.

Source: These historical periods were described in a lecture at the E.F. Schumacher Society in Stockbridge, Massachusetts by Richard Heinberg in October 2006.

Vermont in the 50s: Sixty years ago in Vermont, you would have seen a working landscape filled with thousands of small dairy farms, local creameries, and members of extended families out haying in the fields and stacking bales in the barn. One of the favorite drinks back then for heat exhaustion when haying was called "Haymaker's Switchel," made from apple cider vinegar and honey. Now and then, you can taste switchel at farm fairs.

Today, the farmer can produce those square hay bales by him or herself with a good-sized tractor, a mower/conditioner, hay-tedder, hay-rake, kicker baler and an open hay wagon. It used to be that the whole family took part in making hay. Today, it can be a rather lonely profession. In 1955. a farmer got 40 to 50 cents for a dozen eggs and could buy a new car for less than $2,000 and send his kids to college. In the last sixty years that's all changed. Farmers don't receive much for their work and consumers have become accustomed to artificially low food prices.

All in all, the farming culture has gone through major social transformations. We will never again see a working landscape in the country's rural communities. The only way to view that way of life today is through photographs and stories; now and then you'll see a family out haying the land on a summer's eve. There is still a land ethic for the family farmer but their numbers have diminished significantly, and they continue to be under great economic pressure.

The Grange: Another change is the decline in the number of farm groups such as the Grange. This organization represents a farming culture that once flourished throughout the country, but its political clout and numbers have diminished significantly in the last 35 years. The Grange reflects what was good about America and its rural past; its lobbying was largely responsible for the birth of the Extension Service, Rural Free Delivery, and the Farm Credit System. Its primary legislative objective today is to represent the views of rural residents and the agricultural community. (The word "grange" comes from a Latin word for grain, and is related to a "grainery," or, more generically, a farm.)

Side Notes:

On a hot, muggy summer night in July, 2005, I had the good fortune of going to a delicious potluck supper at the Wooster and Capital City Grange in the rural hinterlands of Central Vermont. And in the fall of 2006, I joined the Capital City Grange in Montpelier. I enjoy the gatherings on Saturday evenings, the Grange ceremony and its connection to farming, the sing-alongs accompanied by a piano player, the educational component with speakers on subjects such as hunger, and new farm initiatives. And, of course, a potluck supper and the dance later in the evening. ✌

Source: Check out the website of the Vermont State Grange.

Vermont State Logo

The Grange came into being in 1867 from the vision of Oliver Hudson Kelley, a Minnesota farmer and activist. Kelley and some of his friends organized the National Grange, officially known as the Order of Patrons of Husbandry. Kelley had long held that farmers, because of their independence, needed a national organization that would represent them much as unions were beginning to do for industrial workers.

Farmers were at the mercy of merchants for both farm supplies and the marketing of their crops. Railroads and warehouse companies were taking advantage of farmers by charging exorbitant rates for transporting goods to market. In response, farm groups like the Grange decided to organize. Many struggles were fought against the companies. In the 1880s, the Grange went into the production of farm machinery but they were defeated by the large machinery companies and railroads.

Early in its history, Grange leaders realized that social interaction was important to rural residents, especially during the long winter months. For nearly 130 years, Grange halls have existed as community centers where residents gather for meetings and socializing.

The 4-H Club, Future Farmers of America, Scouting and Camp Fire groups have thrived in part because of Grange involvement. The National Grange has a membership of 300,000 in 37 states and the District of Columbia. Many farm families and rural folk are familiar with Grange halls. In the 1950s, there were close to 20,000 members in Vermont. However, as farming has declined, so has the number of members.

We need to rebuild our communities and forge new connections between rural families. The Grange is a perfect mechanism for this activity. Although the Grange is no longer as politically active as it once was, it could be renewed if more people got involved, especially the young.

Side Notes:

When I bought a small farm in Saxton's River, Vermont in the early 1970s for $32,000, the man who once farmed the land, Ernie Dowe, a "Granger," had long been gone. The fields were overgrown and the barns and sheds in disrepair. I remember walking into the gray, weathered house for the first time. Someone spoke to me as clear as day even though there was no one in the room. I'm sure it was Ernie Dowe. I told him he could go on from being a ghost on earth to heaven as all would be peaceful again on the farm. I worked hard, repaired the outbuildings and the farmhouse, plowed and replanted the fields and it wasn't long before the sounds of animals were coming from the barn. I never heard from Ernie again.

It's hard to imagine Ernie Dowe living today, with his three milk cows and 2 acres of strawberries and raspberries. I'm told he could be seen working in the fields in skimpy shorts and taking the milk, cream, and berries with his horse-drawn wagon down the gravel road into the village of Saxton's River. A lot has changed since Ernie's time when there was a working landscape. There aren't any Ernie's left today, or very few. I'm not trying to romanticize the past as the work was hard and the material rewards were few. However, some would argue that the quality of life was much better then. We now live in a radically different world. Our modern standard of living would no longer support the Ernie Dowes of the world. 🌿

The Farm Bureau

Another national farm organization is the Farm Bureau. There are over 5100 members in 14 counties in Vermont. The Farm Bureau is the largest grass-roots general farming organization in Vermont. It began in Broome County, New York in 1911 and in Vermont in 1915. The Farm Bureau spread across the country and now is the largest agricultural advocacy organization in the U.S. with five million members.

Vermont Farm Bureau
2083 East Main Street
Richmond, VT 05477
(802)-434-5646

Membership provides discounts on tires, batteries, baler twine, chains, veterinary supplies and other farm products along with low cost long-distance service, computer hardware, and insurance. The bureau has taken conservative positions on political farm issues for many years even though it is beginning to be more flexible and diverse in its activities. The Farm Bureau has begun to rid itself of the "old school" way of thinking and include sustainable/organic agriculture in the mix of solutions. For more information go on the web to the Vermont Farm Bureau.

Photo and Logo Courtesy of
The Vermont Farm Bureau

On a Personal Note:

Harold "Gersch" Krupp, in the 1950s

The same corporate forces that control the energy and pharmaceutical industries work in similar ways as the corporate giants in the fields of agriculture. What's happening in the global food economy is also taking place in "downtown USA."

Just look at the loss of local hardware stores, drug stores, and even gun shops. In the future, I don't see a lot of little guys surviving like Bob Letorneau, owner of Bob's Gun Shop in Georgia, Vermont, who said he couldn't compete against the "big guns" at the malls or Wal-Mart. Bob can provide better knowledge, service and experience than the chains, but even with this advantage, he probably won't survive unless he can develop a specialized, niche market. I'm not sure what that market is; perhaps special guns to kill moose in the North Country. When you add in internet buying and catalog sales, it's hard to compete with the "big boys" of the world.

My father, Harold "Gersch" Krupp, ran a local drug & liquor store, ice cream parlor and apothecary in the 1940s and 1950s - called Krupp Drugs and Liquors in Louisville, Kentucky, two blocks from the Greyhound Bus Station. Many of the soldiers at the army base, Fort Knox, some thirty miles away, would pick up their 1/2 pints of liquor at my dad's store before getting on the bus.

The Louisville Lip, Cassius Clay, also known as Muhammad Ali, used to come into my dad's store for ice cream after working out at the gym down the street at Memorial Auditorium. Krupp Drugs and Liquors was a real community store where people gathered for more than beer, liquor, hot dogs and ice cream. If my father were alive today, he'd be working in a drug store chain. My grandfather on my mother's side, Julius Fine, ran a community grocery store at the corner of 18th and Chestnut. Today, he might be working at Wal-Mart in the grocery section, making $8 an hour -- unless he was downsized due to the Economic Crisis of 2009.

EXTENSION

THE LAND GRANTS AND THE AGRICULTURAL EXTENSION SERVICE

Agricultural research had its institutional beginning in the land-grant colleges provided for by the Morrill Act of 1862 and the Hatch Act of 1887. In 1862, Vermont Senator Justin Morrill authored the Morrill Land Grant Act which established colleges of agriculture throughout the U.S. In 1865, the Vermont legislature passed a bill creating the University of Vermont and State Agricultural College. The federal 1887 Hatch Act provided funds annually for each state to support an agricultural research experiment station under the direction of the land grant college.

The Agricultural Extension Service, instituted by the Smith-Lever Act of 1914, provided a means of bringing new knowledge to the farmer's door through knowledgeable agricultural professionals called Extension Agents. Agricultural research supported by government funds provided a steady stream of innovations that turned into a flood of technological advances on the farm in the 20th century. Extension services are run out of state university systems and are part of the Land Grant College and University system.

(The United States Department of Agriculture [USDA] does research as well as providing regulatory services along with the Environmental Protection Agency [EPA], and the Food and Drug Administration [FDA].)

Research, USDA

County Agriculture Extension agents helped farmers with technical issues such as the appropriate application of chemical fertilizers and pesticides, how to increase milk production in dairy cows, better manure management, and the control of apple diseases. They also told farmers that to compete they had to add acreage, plow up more land, use larger equipment and increase production by using chemical fertilizers and pesticides. The result was greater production but with large surpluses, which flooded the market.

This movement towards modernization was a boon to some farmers, but many small farm families were forced off the land as they could not afford the increased costs of land, machinery, and fertilizer. One might hear comments from agricultural leaders telling farmers, "You don't need to make a profit, as your land will appreciate in value," and, "One day, you can sell the farm and live comfortably."

A typical farm in the 1950s and 1960s might include a Case 19 tractor costing about $5,000 along with hydraulics and a two-bottom plow with a set of corn cultivators. Today, a larger tractor might easily cost $35,000 or higher without the attachments.

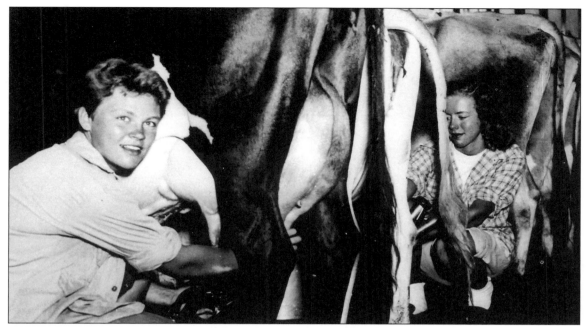

Vermont Milk-Maids From Earlier Times, UVM Baily-Howe Collections

Vermont dairy farmers received about the same amount for 100 pounds of milk in 2004 as they did in 1970; plus, all the input costs went up, including fuel, feed and the cost of the tractor. Yes, milk production per cow rose significantly, but not enough to make up the difference in overall expenses.

It wasn't only the Extension Service that pushed farmers into increasing production by adding acreage and buying expensive machinery. Farm credit and lending agencies often told farmers that they needed to add more cows to the herd to make a profit or build a silo for storing more corn silage. Farm machinery salespeople sold farmers on the newest farm technology. And farmers went along with the mantra of getting bigger and adding new machinery.

The Extension Service has not continued to push the "get bigger or get out" rationale the way it had in the past, especially during the presidency of Richard Nixon, when Earl Butz was the Secretary of Agriculture.

They now recognizes there is a place not only for the small family farm, but also for sustainable, organic agriculture.

The Extension Service has continued to provide the latest in technology to farmers. Three of the major advances are balanced feed rations, higher producing hybrid seeds, and better animal breeding to increase milk production. Other advances include no-till methods for growing corn, the use of drip irrigation to save water in fruit and vegetable production, and more effective use of pesticides through Integrated Pest Management (IPM).

However, funding for the Extension Service agents has been cut by the land grant schools and the federal government. There used to be an Extension agent in each county in Vermont, but that hasn't been true for some time. In January 2009, the State of Vermont cut 25 percent of funding to the University of Vermont Extension Service because of the current economic crisis.

I remember Ray Pestle,
the Vermont agricultural extension agent who served Windham County for thirty-one years.

Ray Pestle spent the years from 1945-2006 traveling the back roads of the county, meeting with farmers in their fields and sharing what he learned with anyone he happened to meet. He was a knowledgeable servant of the farmer, both small and large. While farming changed through the years, Pestle kept ahead of the new trends, getting dirty and asking questions and learning everywhere he went.

When Ray started working with local farmers, dairy farming and apple growing were still strong in Windham County. Organic farming was not in vogue in those days. Large amounts of chemicals were being used on orchards and corn fields.

I first met Ray one hot summer day in 1969, when he visited Hill and Dale Farm in Putney. This was an organic beef, apple and vegetable operation, a rare occurrence in the late 1960s. I was working at Hill & Dale Farm with my friend, Robert King, both of us apprenticing under Erling Anderson, a biodynamic farmer from Sweden. We had been squashing potato bugs close to the farm pond and had gone skinny-dipping, due to the heat and remnants of the larvae. While we were in the pond, Ray came up in his classic green uniform and asked

to speak to Erling, who was a rather proper person. Robert and I kept prodding Erling to get out of the water and talk to Ray, who was getting a quite chuckle out of the affair.

Over the years, Ray Pestle often came to my small farm in Saxton's River, Vermont, where I grew 3 acres of organic vegetables and berries. I believe we learned from each other. At the time, Ray was not as oriented to organics as he was to conventional farming practices.

After he retired from the extension service, Pestle continued as an agricultural consultant until early September 2006 when he died at the age of 85. At the time, Ray Pestle was honored by farmers and friends.

"The reason our sweet corn had no worms is Ray Pestle," said Jack Manix, a vegetable grower from Dummerston. Pestle helped him and his family at the Walker Farm for some 30 years, and continued as a paid consultant until a few months before he died. Manix said, "He taught me and my wife and kids. We have the education he left, and it just keeps getting passed down. That's the main thing."

Vern Grubinger was hired in 1990 as the University of Vermont vegetable and berry

specialist. He is doing much of what Pestle did, but on a statewide basis. When they met, Ray Pestle offered to drive Grubinger around the county to meet farmers.

Grubinger said Pestle wanted to learn about new methods, such as Integrated Pest Management, where garden pests are monitored so that less pesticide use is necessary. He said, "Ray wasn't trapped into any dogma about how people should farm. When new ideas came along, he was right there. He embraced peoples' interests. His knowledge was deep, but he was always practical. He had a perspective you only get from a life lived serving agriculture. There are not many people like him. We lost an icon."

In 1976, the state of Vermont stopped paying for county agricultural agents, but Pestle continued to work as a consultant. There were still statewide dairy and fruit specialists. Many services of the Extension Service were taken over by private farm enterprises and non-profit educational organizations, such as the Northeast Organic Farming Association (NOFA) of Vermont.

The Seven Deadly Myths of Industrial Agriculture

Andrew Kimbrell is the editor of *Fatal Harvest: The Tragedy of Industrial Agriculture (IA)*. Industrial Agriculture is very similar to CAIM, with more emphasis being placed on farming. It is like CAIM's sister-in-arms. In *Fatal Harvest*, Kimbrell describes the Seven Deadly Myths: Industrial Agriculture will feed the world. IA is safe, healthy and nutritious, cheap, efficient, offers more choice, benefits the environment, and its problems will be solved by biotechnology.

1. **HUNGER:** World hunger is not created by lack of food but by poverty, landlessness and lack of democracy, which deny people access to food. Industrial Agriculture (IA) actually increases hunger by raising the cost of farming and by pushing millions of farmers off the land. IA is primarily there to make high export profits and to produce luxury crops.

2. **SAFETY AND NUTRITION:** IA contaminates our foods with pesticides and other harmful chemicals. We're witnessing an explosion in health risks and a significant decrease in the nutritional value of food. Foodborne illnesses are at an all time high as is obesity.

3. **COST:** When you add in the cost of IA in terms of loss of health and the destruction to the environment, the real cost of food s high even though we've had a "cheap food" policy in the U.S. for the past 50 years. See below for an explanation of "cheap food" under Lack of Parity on page .

4. **EFFICIENCY:** Small farms produce more agricultural output per unit of area than large, mega-farms, which require more mechanical and chemical resources.

To the corporations, our modern system of food processing and distribution is state-of-the-art efficiency. However, when you add in the subsidies for gasoline and roads, the loss of farmland, the effects of air pollution, and the ecological problems caused by industrial farms that supply the mammoth distribution centers, the "efficiency" factor begins to wane.

And along with all that "efficiency" is the loss of thousands of family farms resulting in communities unable to feed themselves.

Production surpluses have been a boon to everyone but the farmer and the taxpayer. Then who does benefit? The food processors, integrated livestock producers, supermarkets and fast food restaurant chains.

5. **CHOICES**: Thousands of crop varieties of fruits and vegetables have been lost due to Industrial Agriculture.

6. **ENVIRONMENT:** IA is the single greatest threat to the earth's biodiversity. Factory farming is responsible for high energy use, soil-eroding monocropping, heavy toxic pesticide and herbicide applications, the planting of genetically modified crops and other farming practices that increase production but harm the environment.

The water stakes are raised every day as our aquifers are being drained by massive farming projects. Seventy percent of the water used in the U.S. goes for irrigation purposes but this may be changing soon due to water shortages.

7. **BIOTECHNOLOGY:** New biotech crops will not solve the world's food problems, but will concentrate the world's food supply in the hands of a few large corporations. Biotechnology will destroy biodiversity and food security, and drive small farms off the land.

For a fuller description of the Seven Deadly Myths, read Fatal Harvest. To use a term from the 1960s, it will "blow your mind." Fatal Harvest is a large book with page-wide photographs and more than 40 essays by leading agricultural thinkers including Wendell Berry, Wes Jackson, Vandana Shiva, and Gary Nabhan. The Fatal Harvest: The Tragedy of Industrial Agriculture, edited by Andrew Kimbrell, Island Press, Center for Food Safety, 660 Pennsylvania Avenue, SE Washington, DC 20003, (202)-547-9359

Factory Farms vs. Family Farms -- The Pictures Say It All

Factory Farming - Poultry

Factory Farming - Pork

Factory Farming - Beef & Milk

* Photos Courtesy of
Farmsanctuary.org

Small Farming - Pork

Photo from Farmsanctuary.org

Small Farming - Poultry

Photo from USDA

Small Farming - Beef and Milk

D. THE FORCES THAT CONTROL YOUR FOOD BASKET

THE CORPORATE AGRICULTURAL INDUSTRIAL MACHINE (CAIM)

By far, the biggest player in your food basket is the Corporate-Agricultural-Industrial Machine. CAIM is involved at every level of the food chain: from producing agro-chemicals, such as fertilizer and pesticides; to selling seeds: to purchasing raw materials like corn; to processing them into corn chips; and retailing them to consumers at supermarkets and fast-food restaurants.

How food decisions are made and who makes them impacts are lives every day with every mouthful. Not only where and what Americans eat, but how much they eat is influenced by CAIM. CAIM's mantra is similar to what Julius Caesar said when he invaded eastern Turkey at the Battle of Zela: I came. I saw, I conquered - Veni, vidi, vici.

Legislation: A handful of mega-corporations employ an army of lawyers and food lobbyists with strong connections to the U.S. Congress whose sole purpose is to influence legislation and the Farm Bill, which comes up for reauthorization every 5 years. After a term or two in the U.S. Congress, former representatives may become lobbyists for an agribusiness firm.

They know how to influence legislation and are familiar with Washington politics and the good "old-boys" network.

According to the Center for Responsive Politics, the major agribusiness corporations spent $119 million on lobbying activities in 1998. This dwarfs the $6.8 million spent by environmental groups. In 2007, agribusiness political campaign contributions totaled $107 million.

A parallel situation exists in the defense establishment, where retired generals move from the military into the defense industry as lobbyists. Add to this the fact that many individuals change jobs back and forth between agribusiness and the USDA. This game is called the "Washington Shuffle." There's a lot of politics mixed in with food. It's like putting together a big pot of stew. Instead of beef, potatoes, onions, and carrots, the main ingredients are:

- one part agribusiness CEOs
- one part lawyers
- one part lobbyists
- one part legislators, governors and presidents

ECONOMICS 101
Supply & Demand:

It's is helpful to know something about supply and demand economics. When prices fall, it makes sense for farmers to cut back on production. This lowers the supply and drives up prices, a basic law of economics. The problem is that farmers do just the opposite; they produce more food to keep their total income from falling. This lowers prices even further. If U.S. farmers were paid a fair price for their farm commodities in the first place, they wouldn't be compelled to over-produce nor would they need subsidies to prop up the prices paid to them.

If we acted like the Canadians and practiced "supply-side economics," in which dairy farmers produced only as much as needed, we wouldn't have this problem. This supply-side system takes control and discipline on the part of the government and the farmer. 🌿

PRICES AND ADVERTISING

Corporate suppliers, manufacturers, purchasers, marketers, and sellers dictate the price and availability of food products. The majority of food consumed in the U.S. passes through a factory or processing plant before reaching our tables. The $450 billion food industry packs supermarkets with 45,000 different food items in cans, boxes, pouches and packages, most of which are produced by ten multi-nationals. Most of this is processed food, the foundation of the typical American diet. Millions of dollars (30 percent of the CAIM budget) goes to advertising to make sure the consumer buys their products, much of which is targeted to children and such products as sugar-laden cereals.

THE QUESTIONS

CAIM hasn't been around that long -- only sixty years. Since then, CAIM has proceeded to take over the entire food system. The question is, will they open up more markets and continue to control our food supply? Will health and nutrition continue to take a back seat to unhealthy, processed foods? Just look at the increase in foodborne diseases such as E. coli in hamburgers, spinach and tomatoes. It's very difficult to trace these diseases because the food system is so large, centralized. and unmanageable. Will the farm workers who harvest the vegetables and fruits and process the food in the factories continue to be paid low wages and receive almost no health benefits?

THE FARM AND FOOD OLIGOPOLY

CAIM's growing corporate network has consolidated power in the hands of a few. It's called an "oligopoly." The CAIM agricultural/food oligopoly is similar in nature to the energy oligopoly (Exxon-Mobil, Shell, Texaco) or the pharmaceutical industry.

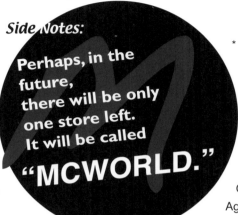

Side Notes:

Perhaps, in the future, there will be only one store left. It will be called "MCWORLD."

* An oligopoly relates to a specific market or industry which is dominated by a small number of sellers. The actions of any one of the sellers will materially affect the price, therefore having a measurable impact on its competitors.

Check out: www.oligopolywatch.com

* For more information on Corporate Power, See LiftingTheYoke.com, Part 1 - The Nature and Power of Corporations: the history of corporations, the rise of global corporate dominance, the lowered standard of living in the U.S., and two solutions for controlling the power of corporations.

* See a more comprehensive description of CAIM in PART I. - "The Structure of Modern Agriculture 101," on Page 62.

Please Note - The Supreme Court ruled in January 2010 that corporations can now spend as much on political campaigns as they wish.

RESEARCH

CAIM's influence is all-pervasive in the U.S. Congress. Your tax dollars pay for research into the genetic engineering of corn and soybeans. This money benefits companies like Monsanto - the largest biotech corporation in the world.

Research funds flow from the government into our land-grant universities and back to agribusiness and pharmaceutical companies. Take, for example, the National Institute of Health, which does research on new drugs. Global pharmaceutical companies like Eli Lilly then produce these new drugs that end up in the pharmacies and eventually in your home.

CAIM AND GLOBAL ECONOMIC POLITICS

CAIM has been implicated in illegal actions in the Third World, including the violent overthrow of governments. According to killercoke.org, Coke's worldwide abuses include the following:

- reported complicity in the murder, torture and death threats against unionists in Columbia.
- union-busting policies in Nicaragua, Turkey, and Indonesia.
- illegal child labor practices in sugarcane fields.
- pollution of water resources in India and Mexico.

Coke beverages include: Dasani, Fanta, Minute Maid, Nestea, Odwalla, Powerade, Sprite, and Tab. *Source: The Nation. "It's the Real Thing: The Drink That Represses," by Michael Blanding, May 1, 2006.*

The United Fruit Company has played a role in influencing the U.S. government to overthrow Latin American democracies in the last 50 years, including Chile, Guatemala, and Nicaragua.

Banana company Chiquita Brands International of Cincinnati, Ohio has been implicated in providing $2 million to para-military forces in Columbia. On March 15, 2007, Chiquita paid a $25 million fine for involving terrorists in a banana farming region in Columbia.

The para-military group killed or massacred thousands of people. Chiquita is being sued by families of people killed by the guerrillas.

The Bible and the New Deal

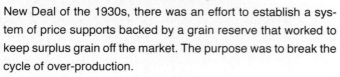

In the Old Testament, there's talk about the lean times as well as the fat years. The Bible advises the creation of grain reserves to smooth out the swings in the market. (Joseph knows that there will be seven years of good crops and then seven years of famine -- so he tells folks to put some crops aside.) During the New Deal of the 1930s, there was an effort to establish a system of price supports backed by a grain reserve that worked to keep surplus grain off the market. The purpose was to break the cycle of over-production.

Here's how it worked. The government set and supported a target price (based on the actual cost of production) for storable commodities like corn. When the market price dropped below the target, the farmer was given an option. Rather than sell his corn at the low price, he could take out a loan, using his corn as collateral, for the full value of the crop. The farmer stored the corn until the market improved, at which point he used the money to repay the loan. If the market didn't improve, the farmer could discharge his debt by handing over his corn to the government. This was placed in a grain reserve, managed by the USDA.

The government would sell the corn when prices went up during times of poor harvest. This kept the cost of food more or less steady. It wasn't a perfect system, but it did keep cheap grain from flooding the market. And it did not cost the government a lot since most of the loans were repaid. What was left over in surplus could be sold by the USDA. This system is no longer in place. 🌿

Source: This historical information came from an article by Michael Pollan, "The (Agri)Cultural Contradictions of Obesity." New York Times, 12 October, 2003.

The para-military force, known as AUC, is responsible for some of the worst massacres in Columbia's civil conflict and for a sizable percentage of the country's cocaine exports. Prosecutors said Chiquita made the payments in exchange for protection of their workers. Leftist rebels (FARC) and far-right para-militaries have fought over Columbia's banana-growing region, though the victims are most often noncombatants. U.S. global companies Dole and Del Monte also made payoffs to AUC.

Steven Kinser's book, *Overthrow: America's Century of Regime Change*, outlines the history of how the U.S., through covert actions has overthrown many democratically elected regimes, including Iran, Haiti, and Guatemala. In some cases, this was tied to the wishes of the United Fruit Company.

The CEO of Nabisco once defined the goal of economic globalization to be the creation of "a world of homogenous consumption" in which people everywhere would eat the same food in a centrally managed economy.

OTHER FORCES:
LACK OF PARITY, GOVERNMENT SUBSIDIES, CHEAP WATER, LABOR AND ENERGY

LACK OF PARITY

In order to understand why we have a "cheap food" policy in this country, we need to go back to the early 1940's, to the passage of the Steagall Amendment. The amendment, attached to the Defence Act of World War II, passed Congress in 1942. It provided for 100 percent parity for farm raw materials, including hogs, eggs, chickens, turkeys, milk, butterfat, peas, beans, flaxseed, peanuts for oil, cotton, potatoes, and sweet potatoes. From 1942-1943, the amendment ensured great stability of farm prices, kept farmers on the land, and provided great prosperity for the nation.

HOW DOES CAIM BREAK DOWN

- **Suppliers of Chemicals and Seeds:** Bayer, Monsanto, Dow, DuPont and Syngenta. The supply system includes fertilizer, pesticides, seeds, and other inputs. Some of the new inputs in the last few years include bovine growth hormones and genetically modified seeds controlled by large agro-chemical-biotech companies like Monsanto. Monsanto produced Agent Orange and DDT, but has recently moved away from chemicals to become the major player in the biotechnology industry with genetically modified seeds.

- **Purchasers and Processors of Raw Products Produced by Farmers:** Cargill, ConAgra, Smithfield, Tyson/IBP. Archer Daniels Midland (ADM) of Decatur, Illinois. ADM is also known as the "Supermarket to the World." It is the world's largest corn and food processor.

- **Food Manufacturers:** Coca-Cola, Mars, Nestle, PepsiCo, Philip Morris, Unilever (current owners of Ben & Jerry's).

- **Supermarkets:** Stop and Shop, Hannaford, Albertsons, Kroger, and Wal-Mart In North Platte, Nebraska, Wal-Mart has a series of airplane hangar-sized food warehouses, 860,000 square feet to be exact, filled with mammoth refrigerators, ripening rooms, and packing sheds, and those Banquet TV dinners. These giant warehouses weren't around 55 years ago.

- **Fast Food Chains:** McDonald's, Kentucky Fried Chicken, Burger King.

FAT CATS

In the early 1950s, President Dwight Eisenhower pushed for lower prices for farmers. In 1952, the Steagall Amendment was allowed to expire, and parity for farmers began to slide. There was a song being heard around the country that went something like, "one pound of butter for 2 pounds of gold." Rumors were circulating that urbanites were being abused by farmers. The urban lobby was exerting pressure on the U.S. Congress to lower food prices and, surprisingly, Senator George Aiken, a moderate Republican from Vermont, was behind this movement of ending full parity for farmers.

The Committee for Economic Development (CED), made up of corporate presidents and academics from the land grant universities, was behind much of this activity. Dale Hathaway, an agricultural economist from Michigan was one of the leaders who helped set in motion a national "cheap food" policy. Hathaway's economic plan made food cheaper at the expense of farmers. The idea was based on the assumption that with modern technology farmers could produce more per acre, which would mean that food could be cheaper. In this scenario, thousands of farmers would be moved off the land and into the cities as they would not be needed anymore.

A spokesperson for CED said, "Removal of excess resources [farmers] needs to be utilized in other sectors of the economy, to generate greater returns on investments." And, "If the farm labor were to be, five years hence, no more than two-thirds as large as its present size, of approximately 5.5 millions, the program would involve moving off the farm about two million of the present labor force ... "

The CED plan was called "The Adaptive Approach." Again, the role of government was to get farmers to produce more per acre through modern technology while lowering the price paid to farmers, making food cheaper for the urban population.

The corporate presidents and academics from the land grant universities, who made up the CED, also wanted to increase corporate investment in agriculture, lower the price supports on farm products, increase foreign trade, provide cheaper raw materials for domestic food and fiber processors. At the same time, the American shopper would begin to rely more and more on low-priced packaged and processed foods.

Source: Information on Parity, the Steagall Amendment and CED was taken from a presentation by Eddie Albert at the 81st Annual Convention of the National Farmers Union held in San Diego, California, March 1, 1983.

* If you want to read more about the Steagall Amendment and Parity, check out Charles Walter's book, Unforgiven. (Acres USA) Copyright 1971, 2003 Revision. Walters is the founder and publisher of Acres USA, the most informative sustainable farm magazine in the country.

Modern day irrigated fields and industrial feedlots.

Farmsanctuary.org

The Indian Tragedy

The Hindu, a leading English-language newspaper in India, reported that in Vidharbha, a cotton-growing area in the state of Maharashtra, 540 ruined cotton farmers committed suicide between June 2005 and May 2006. Throughout the country, Indian farmers committed suicide at a rate of 48 a day between 2002 and 2006 -- more than 17,500 a year. At least 160,000 farmers have taken their lives since 1997. This is astounding.

The epidemic dates to the 1990s, and is generally attributed to slashed subsidies, tougher global competition such as cheap imports of cotton from the U.S., drought, predatory money lenders, and expensive genetically modified seeds. It is India's cotton belt that has been hit hardest by the suicides.

A decade ago, the Indian government began cutting farm subsidies as it liberalized the economy. The farmers' costs rose as the tariffs that had protected their products were lowered. Banking reforms forced farmers to be more dependent on private moneylenders with short payback times and high interest rates. Many of the moneylenders now own farmland.

Farmers and analysts say another blow was the introduction of genetically modified (GM) cotton seeds, notably Monsanto's "Bt" seeds, which are resistant to boll worms. The GM seeds are more productive but three times more expensive plus large amounts of chemical fertilizer and pesticides are needed to grow the cotton.

Source: Sam Dolnick, "Suicides Spike Among Indian Farmers." Associated Press, 12 May. 2008.

MORE NOTES ON GOVERNMENT FARM SUBSIDIES

Farm subsidies have been a major factor in our "cheap food policy" these past sixty years.

They prop up low farm prices, help farmers compete globally and lower the cost of food to the consumer. The subsidies fall into three categories: commodities (farm products), conservation, and disaster relief. Commodities by far receive the largest proportion of funds.

The idea behind the farm commodity program is to provide a safety net and pay farmers prices based on the production of six main crops: corn, soybeans, sugar wheat, cotton and rice. Smaller subsidies went for peanuts, barley, and oats.

For the past 35 years, low farm commodity prices on corn, wheat, soybeans, sugar, cotton, and rice have been subsidized by the federal government with billions of tax dollars. During 2005, the USDA provided farm commodity subsidies totaling in excess of $21.1 billion, with 10 percent of farmers collecting 72 percent of the funds and two-thirds receiving nothing. Because of low farm commodity prices, many farmers couldn't survive without subsidies.

Thousands of farmers apply for crop subsidies but are turned away. Many of those that receive the funds are doctors, lawyers and other investors. The top recipient in 2005 was the Arkansas cooperative Riceland Foods Inc., which brought in more than $15 million. Iowa corn farmers and investors received the most subsidies, chalking up more than $2.2 billion.

* Source: Farm Subsidy Database, Environmental Working Group.

Soy Seedling, USDA

THE CONNECTION BETWEEN AGRIBUSINESS AND SUBSIDIES

Two of the major global food giants, Cargill and ADM, purchase subsidized commodities like corn and soybeans and process them into sugars and fats that go into those popular cokes, fries and burgers. These are the cheapest calories on your supermarket shelves and fast food joints as compared to fresh fruits, vegetables and whole foods.

Cargill and ADM are able to purchase corn, sugar, soybeans, meats, and oils at low prices from factory farms that receive massive farm subsidies, and then process and market them to the masses for large profits. These foods fill our plates from fast-food joints to sit-down restaurants to take-home meals from the supermarket. They're loaded with sugars, fillers, artificial flavors, and "bad" fats, like hydrogenated oils.

These processed foods are high in calories and cause obesity and many diet-related illnesses like diabetes. The two main ingredients in fast and processed foods are corn and soybeans. Most of a McDonald's meal and the processed food in your supermarket comes from corn and soybeans. The corn provides the added sugars and oil. The soybeans the added fat. Both provide feed for animals. High fructose corn syrup is the main sweetener in soft drinks.

Cornfield in Johnson, Vermont, Courtesy M. Vallette

Soy and Corn

SUBSIDIES AND THE LOSS OF MAIZE

One might ask why a country like Mexico, where corn has been domesticated for thousands of years, would become dependent on imports from Uncle Sam. Mexico has now become a corn-importing country because of "free market" policies promoted by the IMF, World Bank and NAFTA. This all began in the 1980s with the debt crisis in Mexico. The deal worked out was that farm tariffs would be eliminated along with the dismantling of Mexican government support for farmers.

One of the so-called successes of the North American Free Trade Agreement (NAFTA) was the opening of Mexico to American farmers, who sold millions of bushels of cheap, subsidized corn to Mexico. NAFTA passed in 1994. This resulted in the price of Mexican corn falling by half.

According to a 2003 Carnegie Endowment report, imports of U.S. agricultural products threw at least 1.3 million farmers out of work. Thousands of small Mexican farmers were forced off their land and into the slums of Mexico City. Others migrated across the border to pick our crops. Mexican farms were often sold to large, industrial farms in Mexico, sometimes owned by Americans, who export fruits, vegetables and meat to the U.S. None of this makes any sense unless you're a U.S. corporation that profits from the sale of cheap subsidized corn to Mexico.

The Sacred Grain: Cheap American corn imported into Mexico also threatened the original corn, Zea maize, and the millions of people who depended on this sacred, indigenous plant. Mexican farmers who had grown maize for thousands of years have been responsible for maintaining the genetic diversity of the species. They have grown hundreds of varieties of open-pollinated varieties called "landraces." The genetic diversity of corn has been evolving for 10,000 years. (Landrace refers to domesticated animals and plants adapted to the natural and cultural environment in which they live or originated.)

The genetic importance of maize is inestimable. In 1970, the U.S. corn crop was decimated by a blight. Over $1 billion worth of corn was lost. Yields were reduced as much as 50 percent. New hybrids were eventually developed by using indigenous open-pollinated varieties of corn from Mexico.

The problem is that U.S. farmers raise only a few identical hybrids. The cheap U.S. corn that is driving these Mexican farmers off the land threatens to dry up the pool of genetic diversity on which the future of the corn species depends.

The whole scenario is changing as U.S. corn exports to Mexico are going down significantly due to ethanol production. Less corn was sold to Mexico in 2007. Thousands of people staged demonstrations in Mexico City to protest the 60 percent increase in the price of tortillas. The diversion of corn for ethanol was one reason for the increase in corn prices in Mexico, though speculation by transnational middlemen played a large role as well.

THE CENTRAL AMERICAN FREE TRADE AGREEMENT (CAFTA) 2005

CAFTA is the newest trade deal between the United States and Central American countries and the Dominican Republic. It will eliminate tariffs on more than 80 percent of U.S. exports of consumer and industrial supplies, phasing out the rest over the next ten years. Robert Zoelick, U.S. Trade Representative, and corporate backers such as the U.S. National Association of Wheat Growers, claim the agreement will open up new markets to U.S. manufacturers and create workers' rights protections that will enforce and improve labor laws and environmental standards.

Public Citizen, the U.S. advocacy group, says CAFTA serves to "push ahead the corporate globalization model that has caused the `race to the bottom' in labor and environmental standards and promotes privatization and deregulation of key public services," i.e., water and phone services.

Public Citizen claims that independent farmers in the U.S., Canada, and Mexico have been hit particularly hard by NAFTA. Thousands of farmers have lost their farms with their land shifting into the hands of key agribusiness corporations like Tyson Foods and Cargill.

COTTON AND SUGAR: TWO PRODUCTS OF UNFAIR SUBSIDIES AND LABOR

Cotton Growers Around the World: In 2004, large cotton growers in the U.S. received $4.5 billion in federal farm subsidies; almost as much as the entire crop which was worth $5.9 billion. The subsidy enabled U.S. growers to plant more cotton, export three-quarters of their harvest, and control about 40 percent of world trade. This helped to destabilize the cotton farm economies of two African countries -- Mozambique and Mali. The World Trade Organization (WTO) found the United States in violation of trade rules in the spring of 2006. The ten largest U.S. cotton growers, including Kelly Enterprises and J.G. Boswell, used their political clout through lobbying efforts to keep the subsidies in place.

BIG SUGAR

This is the story of sugar: Sweet, white, and deadly. To begin with, the federal government limits sugar imports, offers loans to growers, and guarantees them 22 cents per pound even though the world price is well below that number. People in the U.S. pay three times as much for sugar as their neighbors to the north, the Canadians. This is called "corporate welfare."

The U.S. Congress awards on average $1.4 billion in subsidies to the sugar industry each year. The 17 largest sugarcane producers receive 58 percent of those subsidies. One company in Florida, Flo-Sun, receives about $65 million a year, according to the U.S. General Accounting Office (GAO). During the reauthorization of the federal farm bill in 1995, Congress tried to phase out a wide variety of farm subsidies. However, after a multi-million-dollar lobbying and advertising effort by the sugar industry, the measure failed by five votes.

U.S. Sugar Corporation and Flo-Sun grow more than 65 percent of the sugarcane in Florida. U.S. Sugar Corporation farms cover 194,000 acres in three Florida counties and produce 700,000 tons of raw sugar annually. Flo-Sun, owned by the Fanjul family, (wealthy exiled Cubans), is the parent company of Florida Crystals Refinery, Inc., which operates more than 400,000 acres of sugar farms in Florida and the Dominican Republic. Its corporate offices are in downtown Palm Beach -- about as far away from the traditional family farm as you can get.

Sugarcane Harvesting Photos Courtesy World Bank.

U.S. Sugar and Flo-Sun also own and operate sugarcane refineries, allowing them to control the entire production process: from planting to harvesting to refining to wholesaling. During the 1990s, the sugarcane lobby spent $26 million on political campaigns across the country.

The Environment: Sugar subsidies fueled the expansion of the sugarcane industry in Florida. In the 1940s, the Army Corps of Engineers drained 500,000 acres of ecologically sensitive land in an area which was once a part of the northern Everglades. The land was converted into farmland, much of it for sugarcane production. Before the Corps of Engineers changed the ecology of the land, the water table was two feet above ground level. This was an ideal habitat for a wide variety of swamp-dwelling plants and animals.

The Army Corps spent $60 million in South and Central Florida draining the water table for sugar cane production. The sugar cane fields required large amounts of chemical fertilizers, especially phosphorous, which leached back into the water supply and is partly responsible for polluting drinking water in South Florida as well as the pollution of the Everglades.

History: As late as the 1920s, U.S. sugar production was limited to Louisiana and Hawaii. The U.S. imported most of its sugar from Cuba, the largest producer in the world, as Florida was not suited for growing sugar, a dryland crop that needs fertile soil and a system of controlled watering.

Working Conditions: Working conditions on the Fanjul family sugar plantations in the Dominican Republic (DR) are appalling. Haitian cane cutters are the main work force in the DR. Workers at Central Romano, a Fanjul-owned plantation, at times go hungry, working 12-hour days and earning $2 for picking about 2,000 pounds of cane a day. Cutting sugarcane with a machete is both hard and dangerous work.

Sugarcane Harvester, Courtesy World Bank

The Fanjul family denies any allegations of unfair labor practices. The cane cutters live under terrible conditions on plantation camps where they must buy all their food and other necessities from the company store. They aren't even allowed gardens for growing vegetables.

The dark history of "Big Sugar" began in the 18th century on West Indian sugar plantations. It was there that the British brought slaves from Africa and treated them as indentured servants. Today, we still have slave masters and the sugar cartels, like the Fanjul family.* See more on Corn, Obesity and CAIM in Part 2, Page 94.

The Business of Sugar is Connected: From the cane fields, to the corporate board rooms, to lobbyists and the halls of Congress. The Fanjul family maintains strong ties to whomever is in the White House.

Source: The information on Sugar Supports came from a book edited by Andrew Kimbrell, Fatal Harvest. 2002. Other information came from a CBC Canadian documentary, "Big Sugar," aired on television, May 18, 2006.

* In June, 2008, it was announced that U.S. Sugar, the nation's largest sugar producer and third-largest citrus producer in Florida was selling all its holdings to the government for $1.75 billion. This is the nation's largest ecological restoration project -- reconnecting 187,000 acres stretching from the Everglades to the headwaters of Lake Okeechobee. It will take five years for the transition to take place. In 2009, it was announced that the land deal was being scaled-down because of the nations economic crisis. Stay in touch on this issue.

U.S. Sugar produces 10 percent of the sugar in the U.S. It was once the nation's largest privately held agricultural company.

CHEAP WATER

It's not only crop subsidies that have provided "cheap food" in the U.S. for many years. Federal water subsidies have also furnished western farms with cheap irrigation water at charges well below cost. Otherwise, the hot climate in these areas would make it difficult to grow crops. Most of us are supplied with fresh vegetables and fruits grown in the Southwest and West all year round.

Side Notes:

While this is a great project from an environmental perspective, one needs to raise the question of why such a large corporation which poisoned the land and water for so many years should be paid such an exorbitant amount of money?
What is their responsibility?

For over 50 years, western farmers have received large water subsidies (cheap water) to grow much of the food that feeds us through the year.

California's Central Valley, which produces the bulk of the nation's fruits and vegetables, receives no rainfall during the summer months, basically relying on irrigation. The problem is that the snowpack in the Sierras, which supplies water for irrigation, is declining, as are the aquifers.

The Ogallala Aquifer spans 173,000 square miles and provides drinking water and irrigation to one of the most productive regions in the world. Currently, 200,000 pumps are operating on the aquifer 24 hours a day, seven days a week. The U.S. Geological Survey has determined that parts of the aquifer are being drawn down 14 times faster than nature can replenish it. The aquifer is beginning to run low.

In Ulysses, Kansas, the water table has dropped 25 feet in the last decade. Some farmers there have switched from corn to cotton, which needs less water. After nearly a century of state policy that doled out water rights to farmers, Kansas has virtually banned any new use of water along the state's western edge. Former Governor Kathleen Sebelius has proposed paying farmers to stop watering their crops. According to hydrologists, once the water is used, it won't replenish itself.

Source: Garance Burke. "Great Plains Aquifer is Starting to Run Low." Associated Press, 12 Feb. 2006.
is Starting to Run Low." Associated Press, 12 Feb. 2006.

A Story About Water: Here is a story about how a farmer decided it was better for him to stop farming and start selling water. Ron Aschermann, whose family has farmed in southeastern Colorado since 1911, can barely eke out a living raising melons, cucumbers, and tomatoes on his 300-acre farm. Quitting the business would earn him more than $1.2 million. Aschermann and other farmers on the high plains in southeastern Colorado are now selling water to Denver suburbs rather than growing melons.

The same thing is happening across the West as the nation's fastest growing region shifts more water from farms to thirsty cities. California recently approved a 75-year shift of water from desert farms to San Diego, the biggest transfer in U.S. history.

John Pierre Menvielle, a third generation farmer from Heberm California, has been raising crops in the valley for 32 years. Now it's easier for him to go to the mailbox and pick up a water check than to put in a long week on the farm.

The 450,000 farms in the West currently use as much as 95 percent of the nation's water resources. The business of the future may be water brokering, not farming. One day, we could have a limited supply of fruits and vegetables due to the lack of water.

To learn more about the commercialization of public water supplies, see Blue Gold: The Battle Against Theft of the World's Water by Maude Barlow, a Canadian water-rights activist. Barlow predicts that water will be as valuable as oil once was.

The question for many communities is whether groundwater should be held in the "public trust." In other words, water supplies cannot be owned by one person or a corporation but belong to everyone. Currently in the U.S. about 50 percent of the water comes from underground aquifers. Barlow says that the use of groundwater has increased dramatically in recent years because of the pollution of surface waters that are now undrinkable.

Water Facts: USDA

- About 70 percent of fresh water in the country is used for agriculture and livestock production.

- 16 percent of all cropland is irrigated, largely in the western states. That acreage generates about $60 billion or about half the value of U.S. crops.

- Irrigation accounts for the largest demand on freshwater supplies in the U.S. It lays the cornerstone of modern agriculture in the western U.S.

- Irrigation west of the Mississippi has caused streams to dry up, lowered reservoirs and threatened the land's long-term viability.

- California's Central Valley, which produces the bulk of the nation's fruits and vegetables receives almost no rainfall during the summer months, basically relying on irrigation. The snowpack in the Sierras is declining as are the aquifers.

Cotton Irrigation, Wikipedia

48

The Global Water Policy Project estimates that 10 percent of the food supply is produced by growers who over pump groundwater; it calls irrigation a "hidden subsidy" for farmers. Sandra Postel of Global Water Policy said, "If you're pumping more water than is being recharged, you're in a deficit situation in regards to water." She went on to say, "You're producing food today in a manner that's not sustainable because you're using some of tomorrow's water to meet today's food demand."

Source: On the Web: Global Water Policy Project www.global-waterpolicy.org

Several states have taken steps to curtail irrigation. Colorado shut down about 400 wells in the summer of 2006. Farm states such as Kansas and Nebraska have also been developing plans to stem over pumping. Kansas is paying farmers to stop irrigating and retiring water rights on wells that draw on underground sources such as the massive Ogallala Aquifer, which has shown signs of depletion. Some western farmers are beginning to use less water by shortening the growing seasons and applying drip irrigation instead of large overhead sprinkler systems.

Biofuels, Water Shortages and the Developing World: The increase in corn production to produce ethanol is causing serious concern because it could produce greater water shortages around the world. This is happening in countries which plan to produce more biofuels such as China and India. Water is needed for food crops - not for ethanol crops - to feed the growing population in the developing world.

The demand for biofuels (ethanol) could place poor countries that depend on staple food crops like rice to feed their populations at a disadvantage. Setting aside more land for biofuels could also raise prices for everything from eggs to beef, as feed would become more expensive.

The International Water Management Institute (IWMI) said China and India are counting on increased corn and sugar production, which use large amounts of water, for their biofuel programs. An earlier study by the institute warned that increased production of these crops for ethanol could also threaten water supplies in the United States.

To meet their biofuels target, China would need to produce 26 percent more corn (maize). The study said China needs to focus on crops that use less water, such as sweet sorghum for ethanol. India has announced plans to plant 7.7 million acres of Jatropha on plantations by 2009. (Jatropha seeds are crushed into oil and mixed with fuel to produce biodiesel. Other seeds oils are vegetable, corn, rapeseed, and palm oil.)

Source: Michael Casey. "Study: Foreign Biofuel Plans Could Cause Water Shortages." Associated Press, October 2007.

Other Problems: We face not just a warmer climate, but more droughts, floods and stronger storms -- all disruptive to farming. Almost the entire spinach crop comes from a single valley in California. Imagine what a freak storm could do.

Micro-Drip Irrigation is Used to Distribute Water Directly to the Plant Root Zone.
Courtesy Nova Scotia Agriculture and Fisheries.

Erosion Caused from Poor Land Conservation Practices,
Photo Courtesy USDA

A Quick Primer on Water

O f all the water on our planet, 97 percent is undrinkable because of its salt content. Of the remainder, more than two-thirds is in the form of glaciers and ice caps. Only a minute share of the Earth's water, less than "one-hundredth" of 1 percent, is both fresh and renewed each year. It circulates annually in the seas, air, and land, in an endless cycle driven by the sun. After it rains or snows, much of this water evaporates into the atmosphere. Only a third of the total water supply runs back to the sea via rivers, streams, and underground aquifers.

A portion of the runoff is available for irrigating crops, powering turbines, supporting industry and providing water for human consumption. Freshwater is more than a strategic resource such as oil; it is fundamental for life support and is not replaceable by any other substance. It is estimated that by 2025 some 3 billion people will live in places where it will be difficult to get enough freshwater to satisfy their industrial, food and household needs.

CHEAP LABOR

In 2008, farm workers in Florida won a major battle when their wages increased for the first time in thirty years. Workers in Florida tried for years to organize into a union but to no avail. Eric Schlosser, the award winning investigative journalist and author of *Fast Food Nation*, asked Senator Bernie Sanders of Vermont to meet with the farm workers in Florida. Sanders was shocked at the working conditions and low pay. He held hearings in the Senate and -- along with legislators -- was able to put pressure on the food industry in Florida to raise wages.

Some would ask the question, what does Vermont have to do with Florida? Vermont imports a good share of its food -- a lot coming from Florida and California. Why shouldn't people in the Green Mountains be concerned about where and how their food is grown and the working conditions of the people who harvest and process the food? Aren't we our brothers' keepers?

Grapes: It's not only the farm workers in Florida we need to concerned about. Most of us would not be willing to work in 100 degree conditions, picking grapes on our knees for 8 hours a day.

Add in all the poisonous pesticides and fertilizers and you have a whole bundle of health care problems, including heat-induced illnesses, headaches, dizziness, nausea, blindness, and, in some cases, death. Giumarra Vineyards in California, America's largest and most powerful table grape company, denies basic health care to the United Farm workers (UFW) who pick the grapes.

John Giumarra, vice-president of Giumarra Vineyards, told a local newspaper reporter that the women "did not have pesticide-related injuries and showed symptoms of urinary-tract infections." People who pick grapes for a living generally aren't well-educated. But they aren't stupid either. They know that breathing difficulties, dizziness, nausea and unconsciousness are not symptoms of vaginal infections.

Mexican Farm Workers on Vermont Dairy Farm. Photo by Caleb Kenna, ***Golden Cage Exhibit***, Vermont Folklife Center, Middlebury, Vermont

Worker Labels:

A movement is beginning for a new kind of labeling that would guarantee that food is produced in ways that benefits workers as well as the environment. The Organic Consumers Association organizes buyers over the Internet and is working to get "sweat-free food" ordinances in major cities. The Oregon-based Food Alliance offers farmers certification in training workers and establishing procedures to resolve conflicts.

The National Organic Standards Board is leading a coalition that is developing a social justice label to be used alongside organic certification. A label would be placed on the food signifying that the food was grown by workers who were provided with decent working conditions, healthcare, and the right to organize.

Jim Cochran, the owner of Swanton Berry Farm was the first and only California grower to negotiate a union contract. The farm workers are paid $8 to $12 an hour and receive medical, and dental care, pensions, and paid vacations. Cochran processes, packs, and distributes the berries and leases the land from a non-profit land trust. His brand is popular locally at farmers' markets and natural food stores. 🌿

☙ United Farm Workers®

The United Farm Workers is striving to win health and disability benefits for the farm workers. For more information, go to the United Farm Workers website .

As you can see, there is another "force" to be reckoned with: the people who labor for low wages in the fields and food factories of the nation. Workers come from the U.S. and others immigrate from Mexico and Central America. Many of them are in the U.S. illegally. About 10 percent of American families have at least one member who is here illegally. The prospect of shutting down this cheap-labor option by lowering the number of illegal immigrants does not sit well with growers or corporate America.

Americans are used to those big, not-so-juicy or sweet strawberries in spring and boxes of lettuce (lechuga) throughout the year. What would a head of romaine cost if the farm workers were paid a fair wage? It would certainly cost more, but not that much more.

According to Eric Schlosser, it's estimated that the average middle-class family in the U.S. would pay $50 more a year in food costs for fruits and vegetables if farm workers were paid double their current wage.

And what are we going to do anyway -- deport 12 million illegal immigrants along with their 3 million U.S. born children? The new immigrants from south of the border do all the hard work of picking vegetables, cleaning hotel rooms, and working in the slaughterhouses. They are performing the tasks that others won't do. On the other hand, the growers and the meat-packing industry that employ many of them provide the low wages that people in this country can't afford to live on. There is only one thing that keeps many illegal immigrants in the U.S. and that's jobs.

California grows and harvests about half the nation's fruits, nuts, and vegetables -- a massive undertaking, which employs 225,000 workers year-round. That number doubles during the peak summer season.

More than half are immigrants who cross the Mexican border illegally and travel from field to field picking some 400 crops that ripen at different times.

For decades, California has relied on low-paid workers from south of the border. In recent years, growers in California and other western states have watched as tighter border enforcement and competition from the booming construction industry has threatened their labor supply. When the building bubble bursts as it did in 2007/08, will laborers go back to low-paying, back-breaking jobs in the fields? Some growers are doubtful, as the number of migrant farm workers went down in 2007-08. Seasonal migration has been marked by worker shortages, and some fruits have been left to rot in the fields.

During World War II, the U.S. Bracero farm worker program came into being as an emergency manpower act and remained in place until 1964 when it was terminated. The "guest worker" program has been in effect for a number of years. This program basically benefits growers and corporate agriculture. After all, who's gonna pick those tomatoes and work in the mega-slaughterhouses in the Midwest and South?

There is currently an immigration bill in Congress -- which is still pending -- having been stalled for years. The outcome will determine, to a large degree, how undocumented immigrants will be treated in the future. The current guest-worker program needs fixing ASAP.

One change that has taken place in the last couple of years in California and the western states is that farmers are suffering from lack of farm-laborers to harvest fruits and vegetables. It has gotten so bad that some farmers have moved their operations to Mexico.

Mexican workers send more than $16 billion per year to family members back home, making labor, after oil production, Mexico's second-most profitable enterprise. It has become an essential foundation, along with labor from other Central American countries, of American construction, hospitality and agricultural businesses.

Close to 46,000 acres of produce has gone south of the border and Mexican government supports this change in ownership by U.S. farmers.

Many immigrants work on land that once comprised one-third of the United States. This land belonged to Mexico prior to the treaty of Guadalupe Hidalgo in 1848.

MIGRANT FARM LABOR IN THE NORTHEAST

It is difficult for Northeast farmers to secure local labor because of competition from other employment sectors. Farm work is typically low-paying. According to CATA (El Comite de Apovo a Los Trabajadores), a New Jersey based migrant farm-worker program, the average per capita income of farm-workers is between $7,000 and $8,000. Most workers are young, male, unmarried Hispanics, not well educated and non-U.S. citizens. An average wage picking fruits and vegetables is $260 a week. Most of this money is sent home to Mexico and Central America.

Mexican Farm Workers on Vermont Dairy Farms.

Photos by Caleb Kenna, ***Golden Cage Exhibit***, Vermont Folklife Center, Middlebury, Vermont

The Green Mountains:

Photo by Caleb Kenna. *Golden Cage Exhibit*, Vermont Folklife Center

Most of the apple picking today in Vermont is done by Jamaicans and pick-your-own operations. When I worked at Green Mountain Apple Orchard in Putney in the 1970s, we had three crews: Jamaicans, blacks from Mississippi, and local, white, hippie-counterculture types like me. Today, the blacks and whites are mostly gone. A number of the larger vegetable farms and apple orchards still hire farm workers mostly from Jamaica. Organic farms are smaller and generally use family and local labor.

There has been a major change on Vermont dairy farms in the use of migrant farm laborers in the last six years. Some Mexican workers who once picked oranges in Florida and peaches in Georgia as the harvest season moved along, have now found work on dairy farms in Vermont and Northeast. Workers in Mexico typically work 10 to 12 hours a day and make $8 a day -- wages they can make in one hour on a dairy farm in Vermont.

Some dairy farmers in Vermont have gone out of business because they can't find reliable help. The wives of farmers may have to work off the farm in order to bring in added income and provide health insurance

One of the main reasons immigrant labor is necessary is because milk prices have been low for a number of years and farmers can't afford to pay a livable fair wage. State officials say that one-third of Vermont's dairy industry employs about 2,000 Mexican workers, who are willing to do work that many Vermonters will not do or can't afford to do.

If farmers were paid a fair price for their milk; if the hourly wage was $12 and there was universal health care, there would be more local labor. The reality is that without the immigrant work force, many dairy farms would have gone under.

According to a Vermont Farm Bureau survey, roughly half of all the milk produced in the State is result of Mexican labor.

(In most industries, the costs are passed onto the consumer; however, that isn't true with dairy farms because they don't set the price for their milk. The Federal Milk Market administrator sets the price through the Federal Milk Marketing Order. The Amish don't have this problem as they have large families that stay on the farm.)

The Mexican farmworkers are more involved in milking and animal care, than tractor and field work. They are paid about $8 an hour and given housing -- often a trailer -- along with heat, utilities and health care. In most cases, the farm workers pay a broker, who sets up the original contract with the farmer.

Workers in Mexico typically work 10 to 12 hours a day and make $8 a day -- wages they can make in one hour on a dairy farm.

Photo by Caleb Kenna.
Golden Cage Exhibit,
Vermont Folklife Center

Most of the Mexicans are healthy men between the ages of 20 and 40, and are here alone to work temporarily as they have families back in Mexico. Farmers try to provide transportation to the supermarket, post office and doctor's offices. And, there is the language barrier to deal with.

In Addison County in the Champlain Valley, the second-largest dairy county in Vermont, a group of concerned citizens in Middlebury supports the immigrant farm workers by helping them get to local health clinics and providing other needed social services. However, most of the farm workers choose not to meet as a group in public from fear of being deported.

The dairy farmers in Addison County who hire the workers have become interconnected, yet language barriers and cultural differences complicate everyday interactions. To facilitate greater public awareness of the issues facing both farmers and workers, photographer Caleb Kenna and former ESL English as a Second Language teacher Chris Urban, decided to join forces with the Vermont Folklife Center in Middlebury and offer a multimedia exhibit to provide a more human perspective on the situation.

The name of the project is called "The Golden Cage," after the Spanish song "La Jolly de Oro."

Thousands of miles away in Mexico, the typical home has a dirt floor and an open fire for cooking; water is hauled in from a communal pipe, and electricity is sporadic. The migrant workers send most of their money home to provide better housing, indoor plumbing, and electricity for their families. The main disadvantage for the migrant laborers is the isolation of living in a cold, rural environment far away from their families. Only a few bring their wives and children with them.

* **Under the Cloak of Darkness** is a new 46-minute film directed by Bjorn Jackson. The film explores the hidden world of Mexican migrant workers in Addison County and their role in the struggling dairy industry through the commentaries of migrant workers, farmers, politicians, and community organizers.

A recent report by the Vermont Health Department reflects the unmet health-care needs of the laborers even though Vermont farmers will tell you they pay the bills for Mexicans seeking medical help.

It's pretty clear the workers aren't fond of Vermont winters. They love their families and their country.

According to Peter Conlon, a dairy labor support specialist who lives in Cornwall, the key is to provide a sound guest-worker program that would allow the immigrant laborers the ability to return to Vermont and at other times be able to be with their families in Mexico.

* Franklin County, north of Addison County, is the largest dairy county in Vermont. Because of its proximity to the Canadian border, border guards have picked up and deported a number of dairy migrant workers from Mexico. There is not the social service network in Franklin County that supports the farm workers as there is in Addison County. This only adds to the isolation and stress of the farm workers.

☞

Photo by Caleb Kenna.
Golden Cage Exhibit,
Vermont Folklife Center

Side Notes:

Charlie White, his wife Elaine, and their son Elijah milk 185 Holsteins in Corinth. Their hired man, Jose Zacharias, age 29, and his wife, Rosa, had worked for the Whites for the past 18 months until June of 2006, when federal agents swooped down and arrested the couple, leaving their two small children behind.

Jose Zacharias is one among many Mexican immigrants who came to work on a Vermont farm. Most operate underground and rarely leave the farm. Zacharias made the mistake of registering a car in Vermont. The problem is that Federal authorities are looking for people who have been deported or have criminal records. Jose Zacharias had been deported before.

Elaine White said she didn't believe Jose Zacharias had done anything wrong as he had trouble working in Mexico because of the poor wages. Why wouldn't he try and find work to make his life better? We need a legal worker program for farm workers from Mexico to provide labor for Vermont's dairy farmers.

Vermont state officials and local police are aware that most of the foreign workers are illegal and subject to being deported if caught by federal agents. In general, they aren't active in catching and deporting the Mexican farm workers, but that could change. Ironically, a $12,000 federal Rural Business Enterprise Grant is currently providing the cost for a dairy farmer's Spanish language class to help them communicate with their Mexican farm workers.

"They're just here to earn something that they could never provide for their family, you know, and their goal, every one of 'em that I talk to, their goal is to give their family an education, give 'em a chance. It's the same goals that every American moved to this country with..." -- Vermont Dairy Farmer

Senator Patrick Leahy, a Democrat from Vermont, wants to legalize the undocumented workers.

He said, "Finding help on the farm is becoming increasingly difficult on hundreds of Vermont farms." Leahy said the hiring of illegal workers to do the jobs most Vermonters no longer want to do is helping preserve dairy farming, but puts the workers and the farmers in a difficult position.

Leahy is working on a bill whereby 1.5 million illegal immigrants working on farms in the U.S. would be allowed to apply for a "blue card," permitting them to stay in the country. They would not have to return to their country of origin before applying for the card.

To qualify for the card, they would pay an application fee of $500 and show they had worked for at least 150 days in the past 2 years, have paid taxes and have no serious criminal record. The new law would allow the worker to extend a "blue card" for up to 3 years, at which time the worker could apply for a "green card," awarding them permanent residency status. The provision also requires employers to prove they cannot find local people to do the work. The bill has not yet passed.

While 60 percent of the dairy farm laborers in Vermont are Mexicans, the other 40 percent are white Vermont farm workers. You don't hear much about them. They're a hidden migrant population who have been working on Vermont farms for generations. Many of these migrant farm families move from one farm to another. Their children are among the neediest and least visible of Vermont's population groups. Because of their transience and isolation, it is easy for school children of migrant farm families to fall out of step both academically and socially.

The Vermont Migrant Education Program (VMEP) provides support services to young people (age 21 and under) of families that relocate in order to obtain seasonal or temporary employment in agriculture. The free services provide books, tutoring, homework support, summer programs, and referrals to local resources. The program is supported by the federal government and is under the direction of the University of Vermont Extension Service.

Some of the children involved with VMEP attend Camp Exclamation Point!, a non-profit charitable organization that provides a week of free residential summer camp on Lake Fairlee each year to over 100 children. The camp was founded in 1991 and is supported by donations, VMEP, and many volunteers. I volunteered for two summers many years ago and found it a meaningful way to spend an August vacation.

Photos Courtesy of Camp Exclamation Point.

Cheap labor
Two Modern Day Versions of "The Jungle":
SMITHFIELD & GRIMMWAY

Smithfield

In the last few years, the meat-packing industry has launched an aggressive campaign against the unions representing packing-house workers, closing plants, slashing wages and reopening plants with cheap labor and forcing immigrants to work in harsh conditions. Many believe that we have the domestic labor force if workers were paid fair wages and worked in safe and healthy workplaces.

It has been more that 100 years since Upton Sinclair's book *The Jungle* exposed the greed and exploitation of the U.S. meat-packing industry. The book portrayed the dangerous, low-wage jobs of the immigrants and how there was widespread contamination of meat. New laws were passed under President Theodore Roosevelt to protect workers and set health standards on slaughtering meat.

Meanwhile, Smithfield Meatpacking, the largest hog slaughtering operation in the world has violated a wide variety of labor laws and created an atmosphere of fear and intimidation to prevent workers from joining the United Food and Commercial Workers (UFCW) union.

Smithfield is located in Tar Heel, a poor town in North Carolina that has strong racial divisions that carry over to the plant. In 2000, Charles LaDuff, a New York Times reporter, worked undercover in the plant and described Smithfield as a segregated workplace where whites had the best jobs, African-Americans did the heavy lifting on the "kill floor," and Mexicans were given the worst jobs.

Smithfield threatened to close the plant if workers voted to join the union, harassed workers who joined the union, fired some of them and paid others to spy on the union workers. Smithfield asked workers to lie during testimony to the National Labor Relations Board and refused to hand over company videotapes that the government had subpoenaed. Union members were beaten and arrested by security officers. The chief of security at Smithfield also served as the local deputy sheriff and carried handcuffs and a gun on the job in the factory.

During George Bush's presidency, the meat packing industry became more powerful. Food and worker safety standards were weakened. The former chief of staff at the USDA was the chief lobbyist for the National Cattlemen's Beef Association. As of fall of 2006, Smithfield hadn't been fined or indicted for its many violations.

Wages: By the 1930s, the meat-packing industry had been unionized and by the 1950s, meatpacking workers had one of the highest-paid manufacturing jobs in the U.S. In 1970 the typical meatpacking worker earned about 20 percent more than the typical factory worker. Today, they earn 20 percent less. Big companies bought out smaller companies; slaughterhouses moved away from urban areas where unions were strong; imported workers from Mexico had their wages cut by 50 percent. Today, meatpacking workers have one of the poorest paid manufacturing jobs and one of the most dangerous. In 2001, they had the nations highest rate of serious injury.

Source: The information on Smithfield was taken from an article by Eric Schlosser, "Hog Hell." The Nation 11 Sept. 2006.

Grimmway's

HARD LABOR AT GRIMMWAY'S

The workers in the Grimmway Plant in Arvin, California are no different than others who process vegetables. And the packing sheds at Grimway's look like the other same drab, windowless buildings. In this case, the workers are processing organic baby carrots that are so much the rage in your evening salads.

Employees wade through pools of water several inches deep on the plant's rubber floor as the machines make deafening sounds. At the grading tables the workers in masks and hairnets separate the good carrots from the bad. Supervisors stand by to time bathroom breaks.

Beatriz Gonzales stands for eight hours a day, wearing rubber gloves and down ski pants to keep her warm, as she throws the defective carrots in a bin. She has developed swelling and arthritis in her arms and hands. Gonzales makes $7.30 an hour. When she began four years earlier, she made $6.75. Gonzales studied law in Mexico but left for the U.S. because she needed a job.

Now she says she has neither money nor an education.

There are 2,000 organic farms in California. Gonzalez's employer, Grimmway, is a leader in organic foods. They made $450 million in 2005 and sell 40 percent of the world's carrots, more than any other grower. One would have thought the workers on the organic farms would be treated bet-

> **One would have thought the workers on the organic farms would be treated better but that is not the case.**

ter but that is not the case. They are just as invisible as the other farm workers.

The migrants from the border who work in the fields or in the processing plants generally earn the minimum wage or a little more, with no health benefits. A 1999 study of 150 organic farms found that more than half of the workers were paid minimum wage. Only 10 percent were paid more. And another study found that organic farmers agreed in theory that labor standards and health benefits were important but disagreed with adding them to requirements for organic certification.

Fieldwork on organic farms is especially hard because of the weeding by hand and other back-breaking work. As a result, many organic laborers develop serious bone and muscle problems, strains, fractures and lacerations that are not as common on conventional, chemical farms. On conventional farms, one worker can spray pesticides at a cost of $30 per acre whereas organic labor costs are as much as $1,000 per acre due to all the handwork.

Most of the organic farm workers live in the same towns as the other farm workers who work on conventional farms. These places have high rates of poverty and poor quality food in the local markets. Most organic farm workers can't afford to buy the food they grow.

Source: The information for Hard Labor at Grimmway's came from an article by Felicia Mello. "Hard Labor." The Nation, 11 Sept. 2006.

CHEAP ENERGY

The foundation of our food supply depends almost entirely on petroleum products. The end of "cheap oil" is already radically changing the way we grow, process, store, and transport food. It takes a lot of energy to grow all the fruits and vegetables, corn, wheat and other grains needed to feed the nation.

This is especially true with the advent of "industrial agriculture," which uses massive amounts of energy to produce the chemical herbicides, pesticides and fertilizers needed to grow the plants and to process, refrigerate and transport all that food to market. Seventeen percent of the energy used in the U.S. goes to food production. Since the mid-1940s, we have been fed "cheap food" via "cheap oil."

Today, most food is moved thousands of miles by truck to central warehouses, and then transported again to regional locations and, finally, to supermarkets. It takes diesel to fuel the trucks, oil to pave the roads, and electricity to keep food refrigerated from the field to your kitchen table. And burning all those fossil fuels creates more global warming from carbon dioxide pollution.

Alan Baer, president of the non-profit international energy agency, Solar Quest, studied the connection between agriculture and fossil fuels. Baer forecasted models related to future energy supplies for the United Nations. He says it takes 10 kilocalories (kcal) of energy to produce 1 kcal of food and this has been gradually increasing over the past several decades. From 1945 to 1994, agricultural energy consumption increased four-fold, while crop yields only increased three-fold. Today, that translates to over 400 gallons of oil needed to feed every American each year.

It's clear that there are not enough energy reserves for industrial agriculture to continue as it exists today. Minor disruptions in energy supplies will continue to send shock waves through the food system. Baer believes that oil reserves are a thing of the past.

ENERGY COSTS "DOWN ON THE FARM"

After the energy crisis of the 1970s, researchers studied the role of energy in the entire food system. A 1989 study by David Pimental at Cornell University showed that the food system in the U.S. uses 17 percent of the total energy supply in the form of fossil fuels in the U.S.

Other studies go as high as 20 percent. Agriculture uses energy in the form of gas, diesel, propane, electricity, and oil. Tractors, irrigation pumps, heating systems, cold storage, refrigeration, ventilation, and lighting all consume energy for the production of our food supply. Shipping is an additional energy cost, as most crops are transported an average of 1,500 miles before reaching the consumer. Another energy cost lies in the production of synthetic fertilizers and pesticides, whose manufacture requires high temperatures and large amounts of fuel. One of the largest inputs on dairy and cattle farms is feed, which mostly comes from corn -- the grain that takes the largest amount of chemical fertilizer to grow.

According to the United States Department of Agriculture, energy use on the farm typically breaks down as follows:

Production - 17 percent
Processing & Transportation - 35 percent
Sales (Wholesale and Retail) - 2.6 percent
Restaurants - 17 percent
Home preparation - 25.9 percent

Energy & Transportation Costs:

A 2001 study by the Leopold Center in Iowa found that the conventional food system uses 4-17 times more fuel than the local Iowa based food system. The same conventional system releases 5 times more carbon dioxide from the burning of this fuel than the local system.

- Another study of Iowa's food system and "food miles traveled" estimated that growing and transporting 10 percent more food within Iowa would result in an annual fuel saving of 294,000 gallons and a yearly carbon emission reduction of 7-7.9 million pounds.

- The average plate of food in the US travels 1,500-2,000 miles from source to table, according to Cynthia Barstow in The Eco-Foods Guide (New Society Publishers, 2002). The average semi-tractor gets 5.6 mpg. Compare this 1,500 figure to 45 miles for a local farmer or a farmers market in a regional site. That's quite an energy savings. Going local produces less pollution and less greenhouse gas. Also, local foods are often bought and consumed fresh, thus using less packaging, processing and refrigeration. Fresh peas, for example, require 40 percent less energy to be expended than a frozen bag of peas.

- Much of the transportation of food is unnecessary. In 1998, Britain imported 175,000 metric tons of bread -- and it wasn't that they didn't have the ingredients to make the bread on their own. That same year, the UK exported 150,000 metric tons of bread. Excessive transport benefits only a few large-scale agribusinesses and brokers, which take advantage of government subsidies and exchange rate swings in search of higher profits.

- It is estimated that 6-12 cents of every dollar spent on food consumed in the home represents transportation costs.

* See LiftingTheYoke.com, part 1 for Energy Farm Alternatives in Vermont.

CALORIE USE

It requires 78 calories of fossil fuel to provide one calorie of protein from beef; it requires two calories of fossil fuel to provide one calorie of protein from soybeans.

E. THE STRUCTURE OF MODERN AGRICULTURE 101

THE AMERICAN FARMER OF THE 21ST CENTURY

The first element in the structure of modern agriculture is the family farmer, who has been able to produce large quantities of food for your dinner table.

The role of government in the past 50 years has encouraged farmers to produce more food without increasing the price. The idea is that with technology, farmers can produce more per acre. This has resulted in the creation of industrial farms and the loss of thousands of family farms along with the vital knowledge and experience they possess.

As the number of farms has dropped during the past century, the age of the remaining farmers has steadily increased. The average age of American farmers is between 55 and 60. Farmers are not being replaced by their sons and daughters and other members of the younger generation because it's so difficult to make a decent living from farming.

Photo Courtesy of the Federation of Southern Cooperatives

In 2002, nearly a quarter of American farmers were 65 or older compared with about 8 percent in 1910 according to Agriculture Department census reports. At the same time, the number of farmers younger than 35 years dropped to less than 7 percent in 2002 compared with 19 percent in 1982. The high costs for land and equipment are limiting the number of young people wanting to farm.

RETAIL COSTS VS WHAT FARMERS RECEIVE

Wheat Flour, 5 pounds retail $1.59
farmer receives .... 25¢

Bread, one loaf retail $1.39
farmer receives .... 5¢

Milk, one gallon retail $2.85
farmer receives $1.00

Eggs, one dozen retail $1.15
farmer receives... 52¢

Lettuce, one head retail $1.29
farmer receives .... 9¢

One pound sirloin retail $4.39
farmer receives .... 68¢/steak
* Source: USDA

Side Notes:

Some Vermont dairy farmers say it was easier to farm in the 1950s, before operations got too big, complicated, costly and stressful. The relentless drive toward automation and technology in the name of "progress" has led many farmers to either leave farming altogether or enlarge their operations. In the last couple of years, a third alternative has emerged: Organic dairy farms, just mentioned at the left.

STAY LOCAL

Stay Local: For every dollar a consumer spends on food, family farmers now receive 10 cents or less, compared to as much as 70 cents just a few decades ago. However -- and this is the main point -- the amount is about 80 cents if the product is sold locally. For example, local farmers' markets vendors keep from 80 to 90 cents of every dollar spent by the consumer.

The Loss of the American Farmer, Continued ...

In 1801, when Thomas Jefferson became president, 95 percent of Americans were farmers. By the turn of the 20th century, it was 45 percent and at the beginning of the 21st century, it was fewer than 2 percent, many of whom are supported by off-farm income.

There are more people in U.S. prisons than on the farm. In 1993, the U.S. Census stopped counting the number of Americans who live on farms. Over the past two centuries, the nation moved from the rural landscape to the urban and suburban population centers. The desertion of the small family farm constitutes one of the largest migrations in our nation's history. Farmers have become politically and culturally isolated from most other Americans. The folks who talk nostalgically about how wonderful it would be to live in the country have no idea of life "down on the farm."

During the past 60 years, there have been other great changes in the "fields" of agriculture. The emphasis on farmers "getting big or getting out" is coming true. A new study in 2004 by the USDA states that as American farms continue to get larger, they are producing a greater share of the nation's farm goods. The problem is that as farmers' investments get larger, the prices they receive go down. Yes, they produce more, but at what cost? They go into greater debt resulting in many farms selling out.

Big Time Ag: Yes, we still have agriculture in the U.S., but its mostly of the large-scale variety. Family farmers are victims of the same impersonal, national and international economic policies that have forced closure of local banks, groceries, newspapers, hardware, and other small stores.

Farms and ranches with annual sales of more than $500,000 generated about 62 percent of farm goods in 2004, compared with 56.6 percent in 1997. Three percent of all farms produce 62 percent of agricultural production in the U.S.

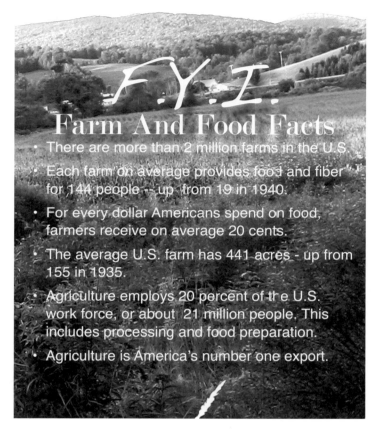

F.Y.I.
Farm And Food Facts

- There are more than 2 million farms in the U.S.
- Each farm on average provides food and fiber for 144 people -- up from 19 in 1940.
- For every dollar Americans spend on food, farmers receive on average 20 cents.
- The average U.S. farm has 441 acres - up from 155 in 1935.
- Agriculture employs 20 percent of the U.S. work force, or about 21 million people. This includes processing and food preparation.
- Agriculture is America's number one export.

Overall, the number of farms continues to shrink. In 2002, the last year an agricultural census was taken, there were 2.1 million farms in the U.S., a decrease of 87,000 from 1997.

So What is a Small Farm, Anyway? Over the years, the USDA has used a variety of measuring sticks to define just what a small farm is -- based on acreage, sales volume, or the ability of a farm to support a family. But extent of acreage doesn't necessarily correlate with sales volume. A fruit and berry farm with thirty acres can generate a lot of sales, whereas, a 200-acre dairy operation with 100 milkers may generate just enough income to support a small family farm. On average, this kind of farm employs two family members.

The USDA defines small farms as those with gross sales of less than $250,000. For many years, the average farm income has been on par with that of the average U.S. household, but not without the addition of off-farm income.

Is Big Beautiful? In 1962, the Committee for Economic Development, a conservative "think tank," produced a document entitled "An Adaptive Approach to Agriculture." The document argued that American agriculture was inefficient because there were too many farms. It proposed the removal of two million farmers from the land by reducing government price supports.

In 1981, Bob Bergland, the Secretary of Agriculture under President Carter, issued a report called "A Time to Choose," in which he warned "that unless present policies and programs are changed so that they counter, instead of reinforcing or accelerating the trends towards ever-larger farming operations, the result will be a few large farms controlling food production ..."

In 1998, the USDA National Commission on Small Farms issued "A Time to Act," in direct reference to the 1981 document, "A Time to Choose." The commission stated, "Looking back now nearly two decades later, it is evident that this warning was not heeded. Instead, policy choices made since then perpetuated the structural bias toward greater concentration of assets and wealth in fewer and larger farms and fewer and larger agribusiness firms."

CONTRACTS

Today, many farmers have "contracts" with food companies in which they are told not only how much to grow, but how to grow it. Those farmers have little control over their farming practices.

Bob Bergland, USDA

In a sense, they are like modern-day sharecroppers, except they own the land. However, these contracts form a system of vertical integration in which the giant food companies control the production, processing and marketing of food from field to kitchen.

Here's How it Works: The chicken farmer provides the land, building, and the labor. The companies supply and retain ownership of the chickens. They provide the feed and medicines like antibiotics. Growers are paid for growing the heaviest birds on the feed supplied by ConAgra. The company determines how well growers achieve those goals and pays them accordingly. They use a complicated formula that ranks each grower against the other.

Since the farmers don't own the chickens, they can't sell them on the competitive market; the contracting company is their only potential source of payment. They are merely company employees without benefits.

Several lawsuits have confirmed growers' claims that chicken companies, including ConAgra, have for years engaged in dirty tricks to cheat the farmers, such as delivering unhealthy birds, and shortchanging growers on the quantity and quality of the feed.

However, poultry farmers are no legal match for the likes of ConAgra and Tyson Foods, two of the largest global food giants.

Contracts have been used in various sectors of agriculture for years. The poultry industry, however, was the first to perfect this type of production contract, which gives the companies complete control over what the farmers produce. Steve Elka, of the Campaign for Contract Agricultural Reform, says the one-sided contracts are attracting increasing interest from other quarters in agriculture such as the corn, wheat and soybean processors in the mid-west.

Farmsanctuary.org photo

Between 1991 and 1995, poultry growers made an average of $11,000 -$25,000 annually or about $3,000-$4,000 per chicken house, a meager return. These figures don't include labor and other costs the growers have to pay. The debt the farmers incurred when they purchased and upgraded the chicken houses only made them more dependent on the chicken companies. These numbers come from a study by Bill Heffernan, a rural sociologist at the University of Missouri.

Stats from another study: A typical U.S. poultry farmer, who produces 240,000 birds annually in a "factory system" under contract to one of the major poultry companies, nets only $12,000 per year, or 5 cents per bird.

Source: The Ecologist, June, 2000

Tom Greene, A Modern Day Sharecropper

Tom Greene agreed to grow chickens for the global giant ConAgra about 14 years ago. He and his wife, Ruth, had just bought a 90-acre farm, a place they had dreamed of for years.

Tom Green said that he, along with 38 other chicken farmers in Enterprize, Alabama objected when ConAgra demanded that they take out loans to invest in new expensive equipment. They also balked at signing a contract that would forfeit their right to sue the company in case of disagreement.

Greene said that he and his neighbors piled up large debts when they signed up with ConAgra. They put out about $125,000 per chicken house to build facilities according to the poultry company's specifications. Most corporate chicken giants encourage farmers to build four or more chicken houses; the initial investment represents close to half a million dollars.

That dream ended with a dispute with the corporate giant and the loss of their farm.

Source: Karen Charman, "Down on the Farm: Modern Day Sharecroppers" published on Tom Payne.com, 25 Jan. 2002.

GRAIN GROWER CONTRACTS: WHAT WILL THE FUTURE HOLD?

Bill Heffernan, a rural sociologist from the University of Missouri, says companies like Cargill, ConAgra, and Archer Daniels Midland are beginning to take control of the grain crop by owning the grain seed, providing the inputs of fertilizers and chemicals required to grow the grain and finally selling the crops.

Just as chicken growers don't own the birds, soybean and grain farmers won't have clear title to their crops. They won't know anything about the genetic background of the seeds, as well as the fertilizers and pesticides being spread on their land.

Fred Kirchenmann, director of the Leopold Center for Sustainable Agriculture at Iowa State University, says that unless there is a turn away from corporate control of farmers, only huge mega-farms operating under contracts will survive. Just look at how the poultry industry has gone from having many small, independent processors that competed for growers to one dominated by a handful of giant corporations, such as Tyson Foods, Perdue Farms, Pilgrim's Pride and ConAgra. Heffernam says these top four companies control 55 percent of the poultry market, with 30 percent belonging to Tyson.

SO AGAIN, WHY ARE FARMERS GOING OUT OF BUSINESS?

Studies show that the average income for an independent farmer has decreased 32 percent since the 1950s. For the past twenty five years, their input costs on grain and fertilizer and machinery cost have been rising. What hasn't risen is the prices farmers receive for their farm products. It's only in 2007 and 2008 - during the Food Crisis - that farmers began to put more cash in their pockets.

While farmers have been getting a smaller piece of the American pie, consumers have been spending less of their income on food. In 2006 it was 10 percent. In the 1950s, the figure was closer to 25 percent.

Back then, the standard of living was lower and folks didn't have as much discretionary spending. Because the cost of food has gone up in the last two years, folks now spend 13 percent of their income on food.
Source: USDA

* We spend more on gambling today in the U.S. than food.

SO WHO'S BRINGIN' HOME THE BACON?

Take the "humble pork chop." Between 1976 and 2002, the price a farmer received for hogs varied from 50 cents to one dollar a pound. The price a consumer paid for a pork chop, however, increased steadily during that period from $1.75 a pound to the 2002 price of $4.50 a pound. This price difference between what the farmer is paid and the consumer receives benefits the processors, marketers and supermarket chains.

Most of the income generated from agriculture does not go to the farmer but to everyone else in the food chain. For every dollar spent on food in 1995, 21 cents went to the farmer; the remaining 79 cents went to the processing, trucking, packaging, and retail costs of selling the product.

THE MARKETERS: THE MIDDLEMEN

The farmer's share of the "market basket" declined from a World War II high of 53 percent to 40 percent in 1970. At the same time, the total bill for marketing farm food products increased steadily from $44 billion in 1960 to $68 billion in 1970. Increases are still occurring, due to increased processing of food and the changing habits of consumers.

The bill for marketing farm food products has gone up every year since 1939 as the result of the persistent increases in labor, transportation and processing. The upward trend in labor costs was caused by an increase in the number of people employed in the processing and distribution of food.

Until recently, the real incomes of consumers were rising. They chose to spend more on greater convenience and additional services such as packaging, credit, and delivery.

Even with all the increases in marketing costs, there are still those who say that farmers need to get better at what they do if they want to make money. This is a myth! Efficiency to some is defined as larger size and lower cost of production and yet small farms are actually the most efficient part of the food chain.

Some farmers have chosen to move to large factory-like containment operations where all they look at are cows udders and computer printouts. But the bigger-is-better idea doesn't always work. Many farms have expanded too quickly, leading to disastrous results because of specialization, inefficiency and too much capital investment. An increase in revenue does not necessarily stay in their pockets as costs outpace income.

At the other end are what's called "hobby farms," where most of the family income comes from "off the farm." Middle-size farms are too small to compete with the large farms but too big to be mere hobbies. Dairy farms in the Northeast (NE) fall under this category.

DAIRYING AND THE FAMILY FARM

Northeast dairy farms range in size from 60-200 milking dairy cows. A few dairy farmers have herds of 1000 cows or more.

Because of low and fluctuating milk prices, one management choice a number of dairy farms are making is to lower the herd size. This cuts out high labor and health care costs. Another choice is to dry the animals off in the winter and pasture them out during the warm months. This fits in well with a small cheese making operation. Another choice is go organic. The average organic dairy herd in Vermont is around 70 milkers; a few are close to 200, and the numbers increase every year with greater demand and higher prices for organic milk.

When all is said and done, preserving family farms is vital to the national interest, as local farms protect the food supply. Family farms are the backbone of a rural economy as they support rural businesses. Tourism in Vermont depends, to a great degree on farming. When urban folks travel to the country, they gain a connection to nature and the farming landscape.

At stake for farmers is a way of life that dates back many generations. If farms go, their green fields may soon become second homes and/or housing developments. Local milk will be replaced by milk shipped by tanker truck from thousands of miles away.

FIVE VISIONS OF THE MODERN FARMER

I would like to describe five different visions of the American farmer from the family farmer to the corporate farmer. These stories focus on large midwestern and mega-large western farms. They are taken from the views of three authors, two documentarians, and a photographer. The first description brings home how the family farm has changed in the last 50 years.

THE FIRST VISION:
AN OVERVIEW OF THE TRANSFORMATION

Marty Strange writes in his book, *Family Farming: A New Economic Vision*, that Americans see the farmer as stern, self-disciplined, and hard working. The farmer is also portrayed working out in the fields with bucolic images of fresh air, animals chewing green grass and lots of sunshine. These two pictures -- one pragmatic and one romantic -- don't really tell us much about what's going on.

Strange says that although no part of our cultural life is more widely thought of as true "Americana" than the family farm, with praise for its virtues and pity for its problems, most Americans simply don't know what's happening "down on the farm." Politicians always defend it, yet the family farm is an eroding institution.

Since Strange wrote his book in 1988, the conditions under which most farmers work have worsened. More and more farmers are going broke, rural communities are dying, the cost of government agricultural programs are rising, and the use of poisonous farm chemicals is increasing.

Strange writes of the long-term transformation in agriculture from small-scale family farms to industrial, corporate farms. In many cases, the new landowners are corporations and investors, not farmers. They have wielded the political power by changing farm policy to meet the demands of corporate farming, not the family farm.

Also there is the specialization of mono-crops -- acre upon acre of corn or soybeans. There are huge investments in infrastructures like large feedlots and mega-watering systems. Implicit in these trends is the separation of farmers and farm workers from the land. This is especially true in the Midwest and California.

In the midwestern states such as Iowa and Indiana, over 80 percent of the landscape is sown to genetically modified corn and soybeans. So much for biological diversity! These mono cultures depend on the regular application of agro-chemical cocktails, which leak into the surrounding environment, poisoning the drinking water and making our waterways uninhabitable for wildlife.

Strange describes how large scale-mechanization decreased the value of crops and drastically increased the amount a grower must produce to survive; corporatization made crops even less profitable, allowing a few large corporations to control prices. When the land could not keep up with increased demands, the stage was set for the greater use of synthetic fertilizers and pesticides. The chemical salesman's mantra is, "Your land isn't strong enough to support you. These chemicals will make up the difference." The result is that agriculture has became a business of pure extraction and nature an impediment to progress.

* Anhydrous ammonia is used more than any other nitrogen fertilizer in the country, especially on corn. It provides four times the output compared with the fertilizer our grandfathers used on their farms. This is one of the reasons we have so much corn production in the U.S. It is classified as a hazardous substance. It must be handled carefully and farmers need to wear protective gear when applying it. Anhydrous ammonia is used and stored under high pressures, which require specially designed and well-maintained equipment.

This view of the modern American farmer is quite different from what the American horticulturist Liberty Hyde said in 1913, "Learn from the land;" or what Alexander Pope said in 1731, "Let nature never be forgot." More recently Wendell Berry, in an essay, "A Practical Harmony," cataloged authors over a period of two hundred years advising agriculturists to work in response to their land's unique qualities. He asked questions about the future; what will happen to the land? Who will own the land, how will it be paid for, and who will decide its purpose?

Strange writes about the new technologies being used on the modern farm. First, the genetic engineering of plant species, in which the farmer has less control over the type of seeds planted in the fields. Second, the large machinery that has dramatically increased the amount of land farmers can manage, as well as the volume of food they can produce, which in turn, has driven food commodity prices down and increased competition for land. This works against small land ownership and the family farm. The trends are clear. Get big or get out. Over half of the food in America is produced by 4 percent of the farmers.

Corporate Super-Factory Farms, An Oxymoron of Sorts: The newer corporate super-farms are larger and more complex --technologically, financially and managerially. They operate on thinner margins than the family farm.

Making mistakes places them in a highly vulnerable position, whereas independent family farmers can weather a setback or two.

Marty Strange describes the loss of topsoil in America's heartland. In the last 100 years, farmers have destroyed half the topsoil in the Midwest, more than all the communal cultures of the Native Americans destroyed in a millennium. Strange says we have been richly endowed with topsoil but have wasted it.

Source: Marty Strange, Family Farming: New Economic Vision. Lincoln and San Francisco: University of Nebraska Press and the Institute for Food and Development Policy, 1988.

THE SECOND VISION: THE AGRO-INDUSTRIAL CORNUCOPIA IN CALIFORNIA

Marty Strange focused on the loss of the family farm and the transformation of farming in the U.S., whereas Richard Walker in *The Conquest of Bread* (New York New Press) sketches out the breadth and width of the corporate farm. Walker tells us that one-third of what Americans eat is grown in California. That's not just because of the fertile valleys and good weather, but also because of the banks that finance the giant farms, the biological engineering of crops, the world's largest water storage and distribution system and the thousands of migrant farm workers who pick the crops.

Feeding dairy cows, and row cropping. Photos Courtesy of the Cornucopia Institute

Walker opens the book with his childhood memory of driving with his parents through the Central Valley on summer vacations, when the windshield would be plastered with bugs. That doesn't happen anymore, as pesticides have eliminated the bugs along with most of the wildlife. California leads the nation with 76 different crops -- not just lettuce and grapes but also goat's milk and honey. According to Walker, the leading export crops of the Golden State are almonds and cotton, believe it or not.

THE THIRD VISION:
THE KING OF THE GOLDEN LAND

Mark Arax and Rick Wartzman of the Los Angeles Times wrote a book, called *The King of California: J.G. Boswell and the Making of a Secret American Empire*. They tell the story of the biggest farmer in America, who owns 200,000 acres of America's richest farmland in the Great Central Valley of California. J. G. Boswell is the world's largest cotton farmer. He also grows more irrigated wheat, safflower, and seed alfalfa than anyone else in the country.

Water and Massive Government Subsidies: John Muir visited the Great Central Valley in the 1850s during the months of March, April, and May. He described it as "one smooth, continuous bed of honey-bloom, so marvelously rich that, in walking from one end of it to the other, a distance of more than 400 miles, your foot would press a hundred flowers at every step." And he described Tulare Lake, the largest lake west of the Mississippi, at 800 square miles.

It took 60 years for Boswell to drain Tulare Lake. And then he got the government to dam the rivers that once flowed into the lake, to create huge ponds for irrigation. This project made Boswell a billionaire but created an environmental disaster in the region. Many of the waterfowl die from the toxins in the standing water and their offspring hatch without eyes, beaks, or wings.

Chowing Down, Courtesy of PETA

In order to dam the rivers, Boswell purchased the water rights from the poor Portuguese farmers who once lived along the river.

The Boswell family started farming back during the New Deal, when their land was exempted from acreage limitations. The Boswell family has continued to control the water resources with government support.

THE FOURTH VISION

Another Vision: In his book, *Photographing Farmworkers in California* (2004), Richard Street portrays farm workers from times past with pictures of the lettuce fields in the Manzanar camp, where Japanese Americans were interned during World War II, to pictures of Mexican workers being sprayed with DDT in the 1950s.

The photos include helmeted sheriffs arresting a 16-year-old picketer, Marta Rodriquez, during the United Farm Workers grape strike at Giumarra vineyards in the 1960s, to Guatemalan farm workers in 1989 sleeping on a hillside above bustling Interstate 5 north of San Diego.

THE FIFTH VISION:
AN AGRI-CULTURE OF CORN

Corn is one of the main reasons for the obesity epidemic in the country. We grow thousands of tons of corn using heavy duty chemicals on land which was once in grassland. Up until 2008, corn was cheap to grow and cheap to purchase and process for use as corn syrup, corn oil and thousands of food products. Today, the main sweetener in our soft drinks is no longer sugar but high fructose corn syrup. Prior to 1970, very few manufacturers used it in their products.

Earl Butz, who studied agriculture at Purdue University in West Lafayette, Indiana, became the Secretary of Agriculture under President Richard Nixon. In the early 1970s under his urging, corn was grown from "fence row to fence row," -- a choice that we have come to regret. One needs to remember that Butz grew up during the Great Depression of 1929, when millions of people were going hungry.

* This information was taken from the documentary King Corn, described earlier.

WHEN YOU CONNECT THESE FIVE "VISIONS," YOU GET THE "BIG PICTURE" OF MODERN AMERICAN AGRICULTURE.

THE FARM MARKETING SYSTEM

Let's move from the farmer to the Farm Marketing System, the second element in the Structure of Modern Agriculture. It lies at the heart of CAIM, the Corporate-Agricultural-Industrial Machine and includes the assembling, processing, packaging, storing, transporting, marketing, and selling of food products. Supermarkets and restaurants are the next step in the food chain, with your dinner plate being the final step.

Do you know that on average 91 cents of each dollar spent in a traditional food market goes to suppliers, middlemen, and marketers, and only 9 cents goes to the farmer? The result is that the family farm is going out of business. It's clear someone's making a killing, and it's not the farmer. It's none other than the corporations comprising the Farm Marketing System.

EXAMPLES OF CORPORATE MODELS IN THE FARM MARKETING SYSTEM

Food Companies: Conagra, Cargill

Food Processors: Phillip Morris, Dean Foods, Suiza Foods & Products General Foods, Heinz

Food Retailers: Wal-Mart, Kroger, Albertson's

Restaurants: McDonalds, Denny's, Burger King. Hardee's, KFC, Olive Garden

* Sometimes, Food Processors are called Food Companies.

Most of the food available at your local supermarket was grown, packaged, and shipped by the large food corporations mentioned above. They are all part of the globalized food economy and form the backbone of CAIM. Ten percent of food money spent in the U.S. goes into the coffers of tobacco giant Philip Morris, now called Altria, which owns Kraft Foods. The other corporate food giants take an increasingly large share of your food dollar. Just six multinational food processors account for half of the wholesale and retail food sales in the United States: Altria, ConAgra, PepsiCo, Coca Cola, Tyson, and Anheuser-Busch, recently bought out by a European beermaker.
Source: Leopold Center for Sustainable Agriculture
Iowa State University.

IT'S ALL IN THE MARKETING, FOLKS

CAIM is a real smart cookie. They know how to sell and market their goods just like the shrewd grocer in the country store does, except in CAIM's case, the profit is in the billions. Take the new wave of drinking water products. It turns out consumers are willing to spend more for a bottle of zero-nutrition water with a couple of minerals and a fancy label than a bottle of milk.

That bottle of Evian drinking water comes all the way across the ocean from France. In 2006 the European-sounding Dasani (bottled by Coca-Cola) sold for $.95 per quart, as did Poland Springs water (owned by French Nestle SA). The Latin AquaFina (bottled by Pepsi-Cola) sold for $1.60 per quart. Most milk sold for about $1.00 a quart before 2007. Soda pop sold for $.75 per quart.

Consumers today pay high food prices because of slick labeling on prepared and convenience foods. Much of the prepared food sold in supermarkets like mixed greens is washed, chopped, and bagged in industrial packing-houses.

OLD MCDONALD'S SAVED A FARM E-I-E-I-O

Even milk has recently enjoyed an upsurge in demand because of skillful marketing. McDonald's has done this better than anyone else. I'm not surprised. In 2006, they sold 2 percent milk in half-pint containers for over $1.00 - which works out to a per-quart price of $3.96 or $15.84 for a gallon compared to the supermarket price of $4.00 a gallon. Wendy's has also increased sales of milk. Both McDonald's and Wendy's have replaced their paper milk cartons with plastic bottles, and sales have soared.

Martin Harris, an opinion writer for "Farming, The Journal of Northeast Agriculture," asks why the consumer would pay so much for a half-pint of milk at McDonald's. Harris says it could be for convenience, but skillful marketing may have more to do with it. McDonald's also sells apples these days, as it is now part of the up-and-coming health food movement.

Hoard's Dairyman reports that restaurant consumption of milk has gone up 10 percent. What's going on here? Has McDonald's taken the place of Elsie, the Borden Cow? One thing's for sure -- the food industry has shown a thing or two to the dairy industry. After all, marketing is what the food industry is good at. Just look at all the fancy labeling of organic food that "makes you feel better about yourself."

Smart Marketing in Our Schools: Another example of smart marketing is taking place in the schools. A recent milk industry study shows that children drink more dairy products when the containers come in round plastic bottles. Many schools now display the bottles in glass-front coolers just like convenience stores. Steve Taylor, former Agriculture Commissioner of New Hampshire, put it succinctly when he said, "Those damn square containers are awfully hard for kids to open." Now, 320 schools in New Hampshire carry milk in plastic.

In 2002, the National Dairy Council discovered that milk consumption increased 18 percent in schools that used bottles versus cartons. Hopefully, farmers, not just the dairy processors, will benefit from this increase in milk consumption. Overall, this is a positive change, as Americans had been drinking less and less milk since the 1970s. In 2001, more than 82 percent of the nation's milk was packaged in plastic, up from 15 percent in 1971. And much of that plastic ends up in our landfills. Another downside to this is that many of the milk drinks sold in schools are processed with lots of sugar and flavors like chocolate.

GRAIN CONTROL: CARGILL AND ARCHER DANIELS MIDLAND (ADM)

Two of the giant U.S. food processors are Cargill and ADM: Supermarket to the World, the world's largest private food corporation. A study by a group of rural sociologists at the University of Missouri found that four processors own 60 percent of U.S. terminals for grain exports. Two of these are agribusiness giants ADM and Cargill.

Cargill reported sales of $56 billion for 1996. It clears nearly $2 million a day in profits after taxes, operates in 1,000 locations in 66 countries and employs 76,500 workers; with more than 40 product lines, it handles just about every kind of food you eat, from salt and sugar to grains and meat. You will seldom see its name at the retail level; it remains behind the scenes as the supplier of raw materials and ingredients to the food industry worldwide.

Cargill controls about 35 percent of grain production (corn, soybeans, wheat) in the U.S. It is also one of the world's largest producers and distributors of synthetic fertilizers and pesticides. Whoever controls agricultural inputs controls the market.

In 2000, bacteria-contaminated poultry at the Cargill processing plant in Texas resulted in a number of deaths, miscarriages, and stillbirths.

The Top Six Supermarket Chains: The total food bill in the United States is $458 billion. Out of this Americans spend $320 billion at supermarkets. Ninety percent of this food is processed. The top six food retailers' share of the U.S. market grew from 24 percent in 1997 to 42 percent in 2000.

Farmsanctuary.org

There are only a dozen major food retailers in the entire world; the largest two are Kroger and Wal-Mart. In 2004, Kroger was the leading food retailer, with 4,169 stores and $56 billion in sales. Wal-Mart was third on the list, with 1470 stores and $31 billion in sales. In 2007, Wal-Mart surpassed Kroger in sales.
Source: www.supermarketnews.com

Market Share: In the past 40 years, the 50 largest food companies in the U.S. have increased their market share from 45 percent to almost 80 percent.

By the time you get to the supermarket or restaurant, dozens of decisions have already been made about your food basket. Like it or not, we are all part of the global market place.

LIMITED CHOICE AND LACK OF DIVERSITY

You don't have much control over that head of lettuce that travels by refrigerated diesel trucks all the way from California to Vermont and costs 25 cents just to ship. Or take the mighty spud. Most supermarket chains stock the same two or three potato varieties from coast to coast. The control of these industries by a small number of companies has led to fewer vegetable varieties across the agricultural landscape.

Today, apples in mid-western supermarkets come from China and New Zealand. The same is true in France, an apple producing country where one can find as many New Zealand apples as local ones.

Potatoes in Peru's supermarkets come from the U.S., even though Peru has more varieties of potatoes than any other country in the world. In Mongolia, a country of 25 million milk producing animals, the butter in the markets come from Germany. What a strange world, indeed.

* *See the LiftingTheYoke.com, part 1, The Loss of Vegetable and Fruit Varieties.*

THE ANIMAL POOL

The animal genetic pool is shrinking. More than 90 percent of all turkeys in the world come from three breeding flocks. According to William Heffernan, a rural sociologist at the University of Missouri, "Biotechnology eliminates diversity, and there's a lot of uncertainty about what results from the homogenization of breeds and the concentration of production that generates new pathogens." The national poultry industry is dominated by four large companies.

PESTICIDES

Many pesticides approved for use by the EPA were registered before extensive research linking these chemicals to cancer and other diseases had been established. Now the EPA considers 60 percent of all herbicides, 90 percent of fungicides and 30 percent of all insecticides carcinogenic. These chemicals pose serious health risks to farm workers and food handlers of non-organic produce.

A study by the Consumers Union in 2002 tested chemical residues on conventional and organic produce and found that "Overall, across 8 fruits and 12 vegetable crops, 73 percent of USDA's conventionally grown samples had pesticide residues. (Pesticides include herbicides and fungicides.) For five crops (apples, peaches, pears, strawberries, and celery), more than 90 percent of samples had residues." The report concluded that consumers who wish to minimize their dietary pesticide exposure should use organically grown foods.

Vermont State House

GENETICALLY MODIFIED CROPS

Monsanto has promised to feed the world with genetically engineered (GE) crops and to develop miracle drugs spliced into genetically engineered (GE) corn.

However, all is not well in the biotech lab. A three-year study published in 2008 showed that genetically modified soy produces ten percent less food than its conventional equivalent. The research was done by University of Kansas Professor Barney Gordon. He grew Monsanto GE soybeans and an almost identical conventional variety in the same field. The GE crop produced 70 bushels of grain per acre, compared to 77 bushels for the non-GE variety.

 * If you want to learn more about Monsanto, check out the documentary "The World According to Monsanto." It shows how Monsanto is out to destroy the diversity of the plant kingdom which has served mankind for thousands of years.

P.S. Monsanto produced the dangerous herbicide Agent Orange (dioxin), during the Vietnam War.

THE GREEN REVOLUTION

Do you remember years ago how the so-called "Green Revolution" promised to be the answer for feeding the developing world? It turned out to be a disaster for small farmers. The new "wonder" seeds did succeed in increasing the yields of corn, soybeans, wheat and rice but there was a price to be paid. Super hybrid rice, wheat and other grain varieties were introduced, however, there were problems right from the start. Peasant farmers could not afford the high cost of seeds and large amounts of chemicals needed to grow the crops.

OMINOUS TRENDS IN THE ORGANIC FOOD INDUSTRY:

Many folks in the organic movement are raising questions about the future of organic food. In the last five years, the number of corporate organic farms has increased. When you have tens of thousands of free-range chickens let out of their chicken houses for 10 minutes a day, one begins to wonder what organic means anymore. How about the 2,000 organic cow farms or the thousand-acre California organic lettuce operations? And that's just the tip of the iceberg, and I'm not just talking lettuce. There are dire warnings being sounded about the future of the organic food industry.

For the past five years, the organic food industry has grown 20 percent a year. In 2005, organic products accounted for 2.5 percent of all grocery spending or about $14 billion dollars a year. If additive-free, "natural" foods are included, the share jumps to 10 percent.

The estimate for the end of 2006 was $16 billion, $18 billion in 2007 and projections of $35 billion by the year 2010. The fastest growing **Organic Food Categories** in 2005 were as follows:

- meat sales: 55.4 percent
- sauce and condiment sales: 24.2 percent
- dairy product sales: 23.5 percent
- packaged and prepared food sales: 19.4 percent
- bread and grain sales: 19.2 percent
- snack food sales: 18.3 percent
- beverage sales: 13.2 percent
- fruit and vegetable sales: 10.9 percent

Overall, non-food organic products grew 32.5 percent; organic flower sales grew 50 percent in 2005 as well.

Source: Organic Trade Association

Seventy-three percent of U.S. consumers reported they used organic products occasionally in 2005, up from 55 percent in 2000, according to the Hartman Group.

The Hartman Group reported that one of the main reasons people gave for choosing organic food products was to avoid hormones in the food, especially in dairy and meat products, which could affect their children's health.

ORGANIC FOOD HAS GONE MAINSTREAM

The organic foods industry has taken off like a missile to the moon: demand outstrips supply from fresh produce all year long to frozen foods, TV dinners, junk and snack foods, cereals, and sauces. There is a lot of money to be made with organic food products. Most of the nation's major food producers are hard at work developing organic versions of their best-selling products, like Kellogg's Rice Krispies and Kraft's Macaroni and Cheese. Kellogg already has introduced organic Raisin Bran and organic Frosted Mini Wheats.

There are currently an estimated 10,000 organic farms in the U.S. This number is increasing but not fast enough. As a result, manufacturers are looking for organically produced food outside the U.S. in places like Europe, Bolivia, Brazil, Sierra Leone, Mexico, Venezuela, China, and South Africa. Currently, the U.S. imports far more organic food than it exports.

Organic Food Warehouse.

Most of the hundreds of organic products we buy now are processed, canned and bottled by large mega-corporations that bought out small organic/natural operations that purchased even smaller "mom and pop" businesses. These acquisitions are fueling greater growth for mainstream companies. Kraft purchased Boca Burger; Nestle bought out Power Bars; Kellogg's bought out Kashi and Morningstar Farms; Unilever bought out Ben & Jerry's. The best way for the mega-food corporations to deal with the organic movement is to take it over.

And that's exactly what they're doing. Coca Cola, Wal-Mart, Gerber's, Heinz, Dole, ConAgra, ADM, and Philip Morris might seem like unlikely matches for organic and natural food. But these large corporations, accused of contributing to obesity, diabetes and heart disease -- have taken the organic foods industry by storm.

In 2004, Kraft Foods, maker of processed cheese and Kool-Aid, bought Back to Nature, a small cereals maker. Kraft is a subsidiary of Altria Groups, which owns Philip Morris, one of the world's largest cigarette makers and beer brewers. Coca-Cola bought out Odwalla, which produces premium juices and nutrition bars. Stonyfield Farm Yogurt was taken over by Groupe Danone, the French parent of Dannon. White Wave, maker of Silk Soy Drink, is now owned by Dean Foods, the largest U.S. milk processor.

Earth's Best, maker of baby foods, which originated in Vermont as a small business by a couple of friends of mine, the Koss brothers, has been bought out several times. It's presently owned by Heinz, which also owns Arrowhead Mills, Garden of Eatin, Celestial Seasonings, Rice Dream, Little Bear Corn Chips and Hain Pure Foods.

Organic baby food accounts for a small portion of the overall baby food market, but it's rapidly growing. Organic baby food sales soared 21.6 percent to $116 million in 2007. Whole Foods Market Inc. says that it has tripled the space allotted to organic baby products in the last five years.

In 2006, Gerber broadened its organic line; it replaced its Tender Harvest brand in 2006 with a line called Gerber Organic and added products such as cereals, juice, and food for toddlers. Gerber's organic baby food sells for about 30 percent more than its traditional line of baby foods. There is now an organic version of Similac baby formula.

When interviewed as to why they bought their babies organic food, mothers said they felt better using it. They said they were willing to pay more knowing that the fruits and vegetables are not grown with chemicals and organically grown food doesn't hurt the environment. The USDA doesn't claim that organic food is safer or more nutritious than conventionally produced food.

The major food corporations have gained a large "market share in the organic food industry. Can you blame them when you consider that the price of processed organic foods is 20 to 40 percent higher than the price of conventional foods? Increased pressure for a greater slice of the organic pie has come from Wall Street and stockholders.

What was once a cottage industry of small organic family farms and food processors has now become "big business". Cascadian Farms bought out the organic tomato company, Muir Glen. General Mills, the third largest food conglomerate in North America, then gobbled up Cascadian Farms. At one time in its early history, Cascadian Farms couldn't afford to use the berries grown on its land, as there weren't enough berries to process. Cascadian Farms ended up selling these berries at a local roadside stand and buying berries to freeze from farms as far away as Chile.

Cascadian Farm, a division of the $17.8 billion giant General Mills, has a product called Country Herb: a TV dinner made up of rice, vegetables and grilled chicken strips with a savory herb sauce. There are 31 organic ingredients in the TV dinner, including natural chicken flavor and natural grill flavor (tapioca maltodextrin). What does natural flavor mean, anyway?

The organic broccoli is from California. It is then trucked to Alberta, Canada. There it has a rendezvous with pieces of organic chicken, which have already made a stop at a processing plant in Salem, Oregon, where they were defrosted, injected with marinade, cubed, cooked and refrozen.

Michael Pollan, the author of The Omnivore's Dilemma, put it well when he said, "In the eyes of General Mills, an organically grown fruit or vegetable is not part of a revolution but part of a marketing niche, and health is a matter of consumer perception. You do not have to buy into the organic "belief" system to sell it."

Tracy Frisch, founder and executive director of the Regional Farm & Food Project in Albany, New York, says, "Overall, organic agriculture is starting to mirror the rest of the agricultural system, with industrial farms, contract farmers, and a small number of powerful food processors, distributors, and retailers controlling the marketplace."

According to Frisch, an organic version of high-fructose corn syrup, the major ingredient in Coca-Cola's high-priced flavored and sweetened water beverage, has been approved for use in certified organic foods. Never mind that high-fructose corn syrup is related to the explosion of obesity, heart disease, and diabetes.

Change: Twenty-five years ago, when you went to your local food co-op or natural foods store, you could buy grains, rolled oats, peanut butter, and tofu from five-gallon containers, as well as honey, oil, whole wheat flour in bulk, and perhaps a jar of processed apple sauce from a local cannery. These items weren't offered in your local supermarket. Now, that's all changed. Even though you can still buy whole food items, like whole wheat berries, flour, oats and brown rice in bulk, they're now located at the "back of the bus" at many food co-ops.

Source: www.corporganics.com

THE ORGANIC DEBATE

Some would say that the entry of organic food into supermarkets, ranging from apples to milk to hamburgers, means the industry is finally getting the recognition and sales it deserves. Advocates say that Wal-Mart's efforts will help expand the amount of land that is farmed organically and increase the quantity of organic food available to the public at lower prices. Bob Snowcroft, executive director of the Organic Farming Research Foundation in Santa Cruz, California says, "It will bring organics to a whole new economic stratum that our farmers' markets and natural food stores have been unable to reach."

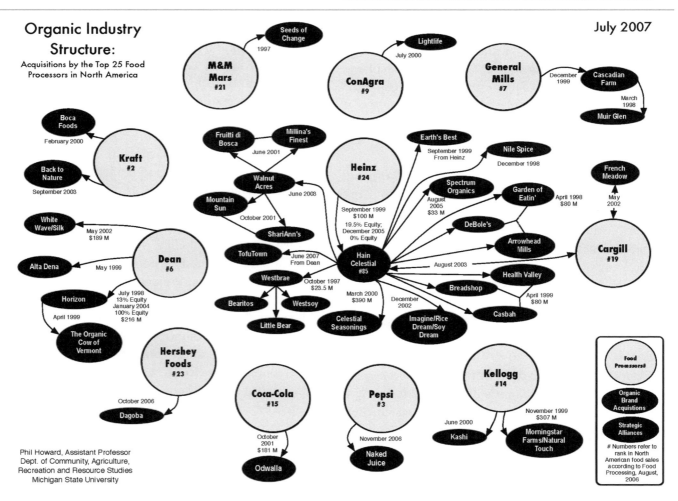

Organic Industry Structure: Acquisitions by the Top 25 Food Processors in North America

July 2007

Phil Howard, Assistant Professor
Dept. of Community, Agriculture,
Recreation and Resource Studies
Michigan State University

Side Notes:

Stonyfield: In 1983, Gary Hirshberg was invited to join the board of the Rural Education Center, an organic farm and school in Wilton, New Hampshire. The Center was founded by Samuel Kaymen, a back-to-the-lander, who had turned his attention to organic food. One night, as the school's trustees were sitting around eating yogurt that Samuel had made -- they discussed how to raise money to support the school. They decided to sell small batches of the plain yogurt.

Going back in time, I remember in the 1970s when Samuel liked to "get up on his high horse" and talk about the virtues of organic farming all over southeastern Vermont. Back then, we were both small-time organic vegetable growers. Samuel was a natural-born sales-man. Give him credit for furthering the cause of organics and helping to start the Northeast Organic Farming Association in Vermont.

Gary Hirshberg is now the Chariman and CEO of Stonyfield and Kaymen has retired to Maine. In 2006, Hirshberg said that Stonyfield's expansion is the price you pay to compete in the supermarket world.

There is a concern in the organic movement that corporate empires will wipe out small, independent farms and rely on imported food from countries with questionable standards, eroding the principles on which organic food production was built. A handful of mega-food corporations specializing in organics are already importing organic foods from South America, China and elsewhere. According to the USDA, 10 percent of organic food consumed in the U.S. is now imported, most from Mexico.

Ronald Cummins, national director of the Organic Consumers Association, says that he's talked to many organic farmers who are angry because they've started losing contracts to China. Cummins says the mega-food corporations are "getting into the organic market because they want to make a lot of money and they want it fast." He goes on to say that such companies couldn't care less about "family farms" making the transition to organic farms.

What will happen to Pam and Jeff Riesgraf's small organic dairy farm located in Jordan, Minnesota where cows graze on lush green grass during the growing season?

Will they be pushed out of business by the corporate-owned feedlot operations with thousands of cows that are fed organic grain but get little chance to graze?

There are serious concerns that large operations will muscle out smaller family farms. This is producing a backlash, including a boycott by the Organic Consumers Association against the country's biggest organic milk brand, Horizon Organics. Horizon, part of Fort Worth-based Dean Foods Co., sells about half the organic milk in the country, through retailers like Wal-Mart. Joe Scalzo, the CEO of Horizon, says that his company is a strong supporter of family farms, but the demand for organic milk outstrips the supply by 20 percent -- so they need large dairy operations to meet the demand.

Mark Kastel, a senior policy analyst at the Cornucopia Institute, the nation's most aggressive organic farming watchdog group, says that most consumers in the organic community consider factory farms the antithesis of organic farms. Organic farmers and consumer groups are hoping that the USDA will level the playing field by mandating that cows on organic dairy farms have access to more pasture land.

Source: Steve Karnowski, "Large Organic Farms Spread Ripple of Fear," Associated Press, June 28, 2006.

The organic debate continues...

Many say the pastoral ideals of the organic movement are being trampled as organic food goes mass market. For example, Stonyfield is the largest maker of organic yogurt in the U.S. What started out as a small farm on a rocky New Hampshire hillside with seven cows, has grown into a state-of-the-art industrial plant off an airport strip in Londonderry, New Hampshire.

Canada: Canada's organic food industry was worth $1.3 billion in 2003 and is growing 20 percent a year, the same percentage of growth as the U.S. Canada is also involved in organic exports -- about $63 million worth in 2003. Just as in the U.S., organic retail sales have come to occupy a greater niche in Canadian supermarkets as consumers are looking for healthier lifestyles.

Wal-Mart Goes Organic -- Or Does It?: Many of the changes in the organic food movement are taking place in part because Wal-Mart is selling more organic food. The nation's largest grocery retailer, Wal-Mart has decided that organic food will help to modernize the company's image. Currently, the nation's largest seller of organic foods is Whole Foods, but Wal-Mart with its 2,000 supercenters could easily overtake Whole Foods.

Wal-Mart says it wants to democratize organics to make it more affordable by lowering the prices. The idea is to carry organic Cocoa Puffs and Oreos at 10 percent above the conventional brands, making them available to tens of millions of food shoppers. How can Wal-Mart get the price of organic food to a level just 10 percent higher than conventional food when most organic foods are 20 to 40 percent higher in cost.

Another concern is that organic standards will be weakened and that small organic farms will go out of business and organic produce will become a commodity with prices dictated by agribusiness. Ronald Cummins, mentioned above, says, "This model of one size fits all and the lowest prices possible doesn't work in organics. Wal-Mart's business model is going to wreck organics the way it's wrecking retail stores, driving out all competitors."

Part of the problem, Cummins says, is that Wal-Mart is making a push into organics at a time when there is already heavy demand and not enough supply. He says, "They're going to end up outsourcing from overseas with places like China, where you've got very dubious organic standards and labor conditions that are contrary to what any organic consumer would consider equitable."

The Cornucopia Institute has filed a legal complaint asking the USDA to investigate allegations of illegal "organic" food distribution by Wal-Mart Stores, Inc. Cornucopia says it has documented cases of non organic food products being sold as organic in Wal-Mart's grocery departments.

"We first noticed that Wal-Mart was using in-store signage to misidentify conventional, non-organic food as organic in their upscale-market test store in Plano, Texas," said Mark Kastel of the Institute. Subsequently, Cornucopia staff visited a number of Wal-Mart stores in the Midwest and documented similar improprieties in both produce and dairy sections. Wal-Mart responded by saying that the cases cited by Cornucopia were isolated incidents.

* Go to Cornucopia.org for more information
Source: Jake Whitney, "Agribusiness: Organic Erosion," San Francisco Chronicle, January 26, 2007.

Whole Foods: Whole Foods was once the largest purveyor of organic food in the country, but now Wal-Mart is number one. Whole Foods opened in 1978 with a single counterculture vegetarian store in Austin, Texas. They're now the fastest-growing retailer in the U.S. with 181 natural-food supermarkets, including the acquisitions of Wellspring Grocery (1991), Bread & Circus (1992), Mrs. Gooch's Natural Foods (1993), and Fresh Foods (1996). In 2004, Whole Foods crossed the Atlantic and acquired six Fresh & Wild stores in London.

* At the beginning of the Food Crisis of 2008, Whole Foods began to cut some of its food prices, as they were beginning to lose market share.

Aurora, Colorado Organic Dairy Factory Farm Photos

Did you know that Aurora produces a good share of the organic milk in the U.S..?
Where does your organic milk come from?

Aurora factory farm photos, Courtesy of Cornucopia Institute

Personally, I would prefer a live lobster to a shrink-wrapped, frozen-pre-cooked, organic fish that comes from Chili. So what are New York City shoppers to do when they buy their weekly produce at Whole Foods? Buy the conventionally-grown New Jersey tomatoes or the organic tomatoes grown in Mexico? Of course, the tomatoes from the Garden State will be cheaper, fresher and will not need to be flown thousands of miles, and what about buying local, anyway? Plus, I would rather pass fields of tomatoes than condominiums in New Jersey.

Although the Whole Foods banner reads "Help the Small Farmer, Buy Organic," most of the produce from Whole Foods is grown in California on mega-farms. Earthbound Farm, for instance is a major supplier of greens to Whole Foods. Its website states something like -- Eating organic is like a spiritual quest -- we honor the fragile complexity of our ecosystem -- the health of those who work the land -- and, the long-term well-being of customers who enjoy the harvest. Most of the lettuce in local food co-ops and natural food stores also comes from Earthbound Farms. I would prefer to eat local greens rather than purchasing organic baby lettuce from Earthbound Farms sent across the country in a big semi that gets 5 miles per gallon.

Even though Whole Foods pays decent wages, it's anti-union. And did you know that you can purchase a $6 bunch of organic asparagus, grown in Argentina and air-freighted 6,000 miles to the U.S.?

In June, 2006, Whole Foods announced they would no longer carry live lobsters, as it was a "quality of life" issue. This was not good news for the lobstermen and women of Maine. It seems rather ironic that Whole Foods doesn't mind selling organic hamburger from steers in giant feedlots or salmon raised in pens, but objects to lobsters walking around the ocean floor for seven years in a natural habitat. Whole Foods changed its mind in early 2007 after taking a lot of flack from the people of Maine, sometimes called, Mainiacs.

More on Earthbound: Back in 2007, you could purchase a five-ounce plastic container of Earthbound Farm organic baby arugula salad for $3.98 or six and three-quarter ounces of Earthbound mini-peeled carrots with Ranch Dip for $2.98. Earthbound grows more than 70 percent of the organic lettuce sold in America. Compost is trucked in and spread on laser-leveled Earthbound fields. Earthbound's whole supply chain uses only 4 percent less energy than it takes to produce conventionally grown iceberg.

Earthbound sells greens at Whole Foods, Wal-Mart, and Costco, as well as at local supermarkets, food co-ops, and health food stores. It started two decades ago as a three-acre roadside farm in a valley 90 miles south of San Francisco. It's now the country's largest grower of organic produce, with more than 100 types of fruits and vegetables on 28,000 acres in the United States and abroad. The company's extraordinary success is a visible example of how organic farming is changing. Small family organic farms, once an alternative to conventional agriculture, are giving way to large-scale operations like Earthbound. Earthbound Farm, the California producer of organic greens, fruits and vegetables is owned by Natural Selection Foods.

Source: Melanie Warner, New York Times, May 12, 2006 Organic Food News
* Organic food -- whether it be produce, meat, or grain -- must be grown without pesticides, chemical fertilizers or antibiotics. The food cannot be treated with artificial preservatives, irradiation, certain flavors or colors.
See LiftingTheYoke.com, "Organic Certification Standards" Part 2.

A Question of Size: If you travel to California today, you would observe baby spinach, mesclun and other greens growing in endless flat fields, with no animals, hedgerows, or wildlife in sight. You would see migrant farm workers harvesting these greens in the evening hours when it' cool. Some of the fields would be filled with chemically grown greens in close proximity to fields of organic greens. Take, for example, Greenways Organic, a successful 2,000-acre organic-produce operation tucked into a 24,000-acre conventional farming area outside of Fresno. You probably couldn't tell the difference between the conventional and the organic farms.

In 1999, one of the largest U.S. conventional lettuce producers, Tanimura and Antle (T-&-A), purchased a 30-percent share of Natural Selection foods, a parent company of Earthbound Farms. You could visit that 1,500-acre farm, or maybe you'd go to the Petaluma Organic Poultry Farm, where thousands of organic chickens are confined to sheds for most of their lives and set free to roam for only short periods of time in order to meet the Organic Standards Act.

Contrast this with local, free-range chickens, which spend most of their lives on grassy fields. Is an organic label appropriate for eggs produced in 100,000 hen chicken houses where the girls rarely see the light of day?

Would consumers be willing to pay twice as much for organic milk if they knew that thousands of cows were spending most of their short lives in confined feedlots? Horizon Organics has 8,000 milkers in the Idaho desert where they eat organic grains, hay, and grass; where the cows produce mountains of manure which can pollute the earth with phosphates and nitrates and the air

OTHER ORGANIC TIDBITS

- Ten percent of organic food consumed in the U.S. is imported from Mexico. Source: USDA

- What happens when organic Coke comes on the market and tens of thousands of acres of organic corn are used to make high-fructose organic corn syrup as a sweetener?

- Already, the demand for organic milk exceeds the supply. To meet this demand, there are organic dairies with 1,000 cow herds and more.

with methane, carbon dioxide and nitrous oxide. Large amounts of water are being pumped from the earth to grow pastures in this drought- ridden climate.

Products approved for pest and disease control on organic farms may not have been designed for mega-farm operations. If you're spraying large amounts of organically approved copper-based fungicides, you may end up with heavy metals in the soil. Too much sulphur powder -- used on organic farms to control fungi -- can play havoc with the soil, as can the over-use of the organic pesticide - rotenone.

The giant corporations that control the organic foods industry know how to play up concerns about health and the environment with slick "niche marketing" to the middle and upper classes who feel good about buying organic foods. Corporations don't claim organic food is better for you -- they don't have to. To them, it's more of a lifestyle question than a nutrition question. Their spiel is that organic tastes good, and it's better for the earth and your well being. Just knowing there are no harmful sprays on those apples makes you feel better.

A RABBI GOING BACK AND FORTH

On one hand, isn't the increase in the availability and diversity of organic foods in supermarkets good for our health? Greater convenience and accessibility have given more people the opportunity to try organic foods. And what about the fact that the organic tomatoes at Greenways, when compared to the conventional tomatoes, received higher scores at the local cannery for more sugar and flavor? The conventional crops grown on nitrogen fertilizer take up more water, which dilutes the nutrients, sugars, and flavor. This could explain why chefs swear by organic ingredients. Organics means fewer chemicals being spread on the land and less soil erosion. Isn't it more efficient to buy from a 1,000-acre organic operation than a 10-acre farm?

THE LOCAL ORGANIC ETHIC

On the other hand, organics has never been about 1,000-acre fields of organic lettuce grown in California and shipped cross-country. Or giant 2000-cow organic-cow dairy operations that ship ultra-pasteurized milk from the western states to the Northeast. That's a lot diesel fuel being used to transport lettuce and milk across the country.

Local organic farmers foster biodiversity by using open-pollinated heirloom seeds, practicing crop rotations, using compost from animal manure and applying biological controls for pests. Their fields resemble quilts, not giant 1,000-acre squares.

Small scale organics is an opportunity for farmers to care for the soil, plants and husband the animals for future generations. Organic agriculture holds the promise of preserving the agrarian landscape and building community. It's about treating farm workers with respect and fair compensation. Organic farmers need to make a decent living. At the same time, families should be able to purchase healthy organic food at affordable prices. This is the real challenge.

On a personnel level, I'd prefer to buy organic local eggs, local free-range chickens, raw milk, local fruits and vegetables. But sometimes I don't have the gelt to buy organic food, so I have to purchase what I can afford. On March 29, 2009, Alice Waters, the famous organic food guru, said on 60 Minutes that "Good food should be a right, not a privilege". What she says is correct, but again, most low-income and some middle class families cannot afford organic food.

This once young hippie, whose beard has turned grey and white, might long for the good "old days" when we lived off the land for part of the year and ground our grain once a week for homemade bread. Actually, it wasn't always that great and we didn't grind all of our grain. But there is something to be said about baking bread; growing your own food, and canning and freezing fruits and vegetables. Of course, not everyone can do those things. That's why we have farmers' markets, farm stands and other local food outlets.

Vermont Chicken Lover

FINAL ORGANIC NOTES:

• **Demand & Supply:** The demand for organics is outpacing the supply. In 2008, close to 20 percent of dairy farmers in Vermont were organic. According to a Washington State University study, organic tree fruit acreage increased by 54 percent in 2008.

• **Certification and Transitioning:** To be certified organic by the USDA, growers must raise their crop free of chemical pesticides and fertilizer for three years. Because the cost of transitioning from conventional to organics is costly, Ronald Cummins of the Organic Consumers Association believes the solution for transitioning to organics is to pay a premium to the farmer during the 3-year transition period from conventional to organic. A label is needed that would state - transitioning to organics.

• **Dropping Out:** Many small organic farmers, especially those who raise animals for dairy, eggs, and meat, have become disenchanted enough with the organic certification system that they are choosing not to become certified as organic, even if their methods meet or exceed organic standards.

Some companies like Artisan Naturals have chosen to sell their fruits as not-quite-organic in an effort to receive a higher price.

ORGANIC WEBSITES

Organic Trade Association
www.ota.com

Organic Consumers Association
www.organicconsumers.org

Horizon Organic
www.horizonorganic.com

Organic Valley
www.organicvalley.coop

Whole Foods Market
www.wholefoodsmarket.com

USDA Organic Program
www.ams.usda.gov/nop

USDA Organic Standards Board
www.ams.usda.gov/nosb

CORNUCOPIA
INSTITUTE

Mark Kastel,
co-director of the Cornucopia
Institute

The Cornucopia Institute
www.cornucopia.org

I highly recommend this site. It provides up-to-date information on the takeover of organics by the corporate global food system. The institute has a dairy "report card" that describes those companies that are buying from local farmers. The report card showcases ethical family farm producers and exposes factory farm producers. The report card lists 68 different organic dairy brands.

Newsletter of the Cornucopia Institute

ANOTHER VISION

It's critical to provide another vision, an alternative to the global corporate food system or what I call CAIM. In the local marketplace, there's a connection between farmers and consumers, where the products in one's food basket are grown close to home. Consumers want to know the story behind the food as well as the farmers who grow it. They want community.

In *The Unsettling of America*, Wendell Berry points out the disconnect between culture and agriculture and how the U.S. has gone from an essentially agrarian society to an industrial farm model where the family farm and rural America are no longer relevant.

Ken Taylor, the late founder of the Minnesota Food Association said, "People who live in urban communities for the most part don't want to get their hands dirty, but they surely want to shake the hand of someone who does."

Consumers want to support local, small and mid-size farmers and producers who:

1. produce food using sound conservation practices

2. provide their animals with the opportunity to live as nature intended

3. preserve the identity of food products by processing them locally

4. make these food products available in the local market-place

Photo Courtesy NOFA, Vermont

* Part III of the book is devoted to local, sustainable change. It is entitled Sustainable Markets & Regional Solutions. I describe in detail a number of alternative models and solutions such as Farmers' Markets, Community Gardens, CSA's (Community Supported Agriculture Models), Enclosed Public Market, Value-Added Products, Food Co-ops, Natural Food Stores, and Local Restaurants.

Photo Courtesy of the
Vermont Food Bank

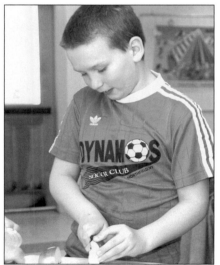

Photos Courtesy of the
Vermont Campaign to End
Childhood Hunger

PART II

THE BATTLE OF THE BULGE

A. A NATION OF FAT PEOPLE, FAST FOOD, POOR NUTRITION AND HUNGER

Today, we've added on enough pounds to be considered a nation of fat people. We're literally eating ourselves to death; a rise in diabetes and heart disease proves the point. Diabetes alone has doubled in the past ten years and obesity is the number two killer in the country.

Today, young fast-food lovers consume more fats, sugars and carbohydrates and fewer fruits and non-starchy vegetables than youngsters 25 years ago. They consume 187 more daily calories, which adds up to about six pounds a year -- translating into a country of overweight kids.

Control and Prevention:

Seventy-two million Americans are counted as obese -- 34 percent of the adult population or one out of three people. Obesity rates jumped from 15 percent in 1980 to 30.9 percent in 2000. Our adult population, on average, has gained 25 pounds in the last 35 years. The current rates of overweight and obese people are highest in the Southern region of the country and lowest in New England. (Obesity is defined as being 30 pounds overweight for a 5'4" person.) In 2004, nearly two-thirds of American adults were overweight.

What this adds up to is an epidemic of huge proportions -- the main reason being the eating of fast and junk-processed food. Once a day, one-fourth of Americans eat a meal from a fast food restaurant. Thirty-nine percent of our food spending is on meals away from home.

Since 1982, consumer spending on fast food has grown by almost 7 percent per year. Fewer families have a parent who prepares healthy, nutritious meals. The number of families that eat dinner together has dropped by a third since the 1970s.

Ensuring that families have access to a consistent supply of healthy food is essential to addressing the epidemic of obesity, especially in children.

Pepperoni Pizza

IT'S NOT JUST THE AMOUNT OF FOOD WE EAT, BUT THE QUALITY AS WELL.

Michael Pollan, the author of *The Omnivore's Dilemma* and his recent book, *In Defence of Food: An Eater's Manifesto*, asks the following questions. What are we feeding ourselves and what does it have to do with nutrition and how can we live in such a health-conscious country and be in such poor health? Take for instance Cheerio bars layered with synthetic milk, Cocoa Krispie Cereal Straws or those Go-Gurt yogurt tubes with their twenty ingredients. Pollan's basic message is that there can be no healthy people without a healthy diet and there can be no healthy diet without a healthy agriculture.

Michael Pollan, just like Steiner, believes that the blame can be placed on a narrow, reductionist ideology he calls, "nutritionism." Nutritionism is based on the principal that the parts are greater than the whole. It holds that food can be broken down into its parts: carbohydrates, fats, proteins, vitamins and minerals. The corporate food machine processes corn, soybeans and other food staples into their parts, sugars and fats and then puts them all back together again like Humpty Dumpty.

The "natural-organic" food machine spews out food substitutes like omega-3 fatty acids, beta carotene from carrots, oat bran from oats, vitamin this and vitamin that and adds them to processed foods to make people feel good about what they're eating. The problem is that you can't put Humpty Dumpty back together again.

Humpty Dumpty sat on a wall.
Humpty Dumpty had a great fall.
All the king's horses and all the king's men
Couldn't put Humpty together again.

Baby formulas are good example of "nutritionism": Food scientists create new baby formulas from processed foods, flavors and additives. According to Michael Pollan, these baby foods aren't nutritious and they lack vitality.

Pollan goes on to say that Americans obsess about food and yet they are in such poor health. Pollan observed that we eat 300 calories more per day than we did in 1980 and we're fatter and sicker than we've ever been.

The corporate food giants can't make money selling good, old-fashioned, whole grain oatmeal to people at 89 cents a pounds -- when they can turn oats into Cheerios with just a few cents worth of grain and charge $4 a box. Pollan says that at every step of the process, those oats become less nutritious even with vitamins and minerals added. He urges folks to stop thinking about nutrients but get back to eating nutritious, whole foods and to return to the cultural tradition of the past by preparing homemade meals. In other words, let's eat carrots instead of beta-carotene.

TOO MUCH FOOD: CALORIE FACTS

- It is recommended the average adult male needs 2,200 calories, the average female 1,800 calories and the average child, 1,500 calories per day.

- The average American male consumes 3,000 calories per day; the average female consumes 2,000 calories; about 700 calories a day more than in 1980. From 1971 to 2000, the average daily calorie intake for U.S. adults increased by 335 calories in women and by 168 calories in men. About 40 percent of those calories come from unhealthy, bad fats.

- The typical American diet provides more than enough calories, but not enough nutrients. Refined or processed fats and sugars have almost no nutrients. If someone borrowed $1 from you and returned 15 cents, would you feel enriched? This is what food manufacturers do when they remove wholesome nutrients and fiber (real food) and replace them with small amounts of artificial nutrients (fake food).

Chronic diseases such as diabetes and heart disease are increasing because of obesity. The problem is not only the large quantities of food that we consume, but the poor food quality as well. Our processed food is filled with high amounts of sugars, refined grains, and bad fats like trans fats. There is a direct connection between processed food, industrial agriculture and our overweight nation. This will be explored later on page 97 in Corporate Profits in the Face of Obesity.

Blame and Responsibility: Who's responsible for our overweight nation? This is a complicated question, and one that carries a lot of emotional baggage. I know many middle-class folks who put the blame on the individual. They say, for instance: "Just look at the people you see walking out of a convenience store with those half-gallon soda containers and big bags of chips. Why don't they buy healthy food?"

My response to them is simply that many families don't have the economic means to put healthy food on their plates.

Kelly Brownell of the Yale Center for Eating and Weight Disorders says, "Blaming people for being obese and hoping the situation will go away is a fantasy. Something dramatic needs to be done to change the environment, in order to prevent this problem from occurring in the first place."

In 2002, M. B. Schwartz and R. Puhl of the Department of Psychology at Yale University stated that in general the society holds parents and even their children responsible. Along with this goes the stigmatization of overweight children. Parents of overweight children are left in the difficult position of fearing the social and health consequences of their child's obesity. They are fighting a losing battle against the advertising industry and the constant exposure to eating nutritionally poor foods.

Schwartz and Puhl believe that childhood obesity is a societal problem. Take for instance the striking difference between childhood obesity and other child safety issues. Parents expect to see warning labels about the dangers of small toys to young children. Why aren't there labels on unhealthy food?

Poverty Leads to Poor Nutrition: The problem caused by poor eating habits is made worse for low-income folks, the disadvantaged population and some working people who lack accessibility to healthy food. Many studies show that low-income Americans, especially women, are heavier than middle or high income Americans. Current data also tell us that the middle-class and wealthy are also putting on the pounds.

THE EFFECTS OF HUNGER ON THE POOR

• The highest rates of obesity and diabetes in the United States are found among lower-income groups. Limited resources require low income families to purchase inexpensive foods that fill us up only for a short period of time -- typically, food high in bad fats, sugar and refined carbs.

• Families in poverty often skip meals to stretch the food budget and may overeat when food is available. Adults in low-income families often go without so the children can eat when food is scarce.

• Because adults in poor families often have more than one job, they have little time to prepare meals and may rely on convenience foods (such as chips and Coke) that are high in calories.

• Living with poverty causes high stress, which produces hormones that foster the accumulation of fat.

It's common knowledge in scientific circles that foods high in calories like snack foods, sugar, and refined carbs result in over-eating and weight gain. In general, when a family spends more money on food, they consume fewer calories and more nutrients. Conversely, families with less money to spend consume more calories and fewer nutrients.

Unemployed Man at Soup Kitchen, 1936
Photo Courtesy Food Security Administration

Comparison of two daily menus:
One low-cost and one moderate-cost.

Low Cost Menu	Moderate Cost Menu
Waffles with syrup	Cereal and Milk
Fruit Punch	Banana, Orange Juice
Bologna and Cheese Sandwich	Roast Beef Sandwich
Potato Chips Fruit Cocktail	Whole Wheat Pretzels
Fruit Punch	Carrot Sticks Orange Milk
Popcorn	Oatmeal Raisin Cookies Soda
Chicken Nuggets	Salmon
Macaroni and Cheese	Pasta with Cheese
Green Beans	Broccoli, Green Salad
Milk	Milk
Ice Cream Sandwich	Frozen Yogurt
Cost per person: $4.13	$9.28
Calories per person: 3,150	2,250

The results of the two menus are striking. The lower-cost menu has 900 more calories and is half the cost of the moderate-cost menu.

The moderate-cost menu costs more with fewer calories. When you compare the amounts of recommended nutrients for the low-cost and moderate cost plans, the results from the study are significant in terms of lowered amounts of the vitamin B complex, folate, iron, and vitamin D for the low-cost plan. The only area where the lower-cost menu had higher numbers was with the amount of fat.

The lower-cost menu was purchased in a Vermont supermarket with the amount of money the USDA has determined to be the minimum amount to feed a person adequately, which is based on the food stamp allotment.

Source: The menu information came from the Vermont Campaign to End Childhood Hunger, September, 2005. You can see the percentage charts for the two plans on the website, www.vtnohunger.org

Poverty in America: The poor in America are stretching their paychecks even further because of increases in energy, rent and food costs. Food costs increased 4.5 percent in 2007, partly because of higher fuel costs. According to the Bureau of Labor Statistics, egg prices were 44 percent higher, while milk was up 21.3 percent, averaging $4 a gallon. The average family spent $40 more per month on food. 2008 proved to be more stressful.

- A paycheck that once lasted five days might now last four days.
- Pay the gas bill but skip breakfast.
- Eat less for lunch so the kids can have a healthy supper.

Many working families, particularly those making less than $30,000 a year, can't afford to load up at supermarkets and are going to convenience stores to buy items such as bread, eggs, pasta, peanut butter, and hamburger meat. They are reducing spending on nutritious foods such as milk, fruits and vegetables.

Food pantries, which distribute foodstuffs to the needy, are reporting severe shortages and reduced government funding at the very time new families are signing up. The number of families served at the Bedford Styverson Food Pantry in Brooklyn went up 70 percent in 2007.

At the Chittenden Emergency Food Shelf (CEFS) in Burlington, Vermont, the percentage of clients who had jobs was 45 percent, a 10 percent increase from 2006 to 2007.

Photos Courtesy Vermont Food Bank, Barre, Vermont

Another factor is that food stamps don't provide adequate funding for a families food needs. Also, the Federal Food Stamp program doesn't provide adequate funding for food to feed a family. **"Low Food Security"** is measured by hunger and lack of food resources due to poverty. According to the current population survey of the U.S. Census, eleven percent of households were determined to have "low food security," meaning that in these households, adults were occasionally going without food altogether and the whole family was eating poor quality food. About 1/3 of these households were classified as **"very low food security,"** in which adults were frequently going without food and the children were sometimes going without food and the food was of low quality.

The lack of healthy food for the poor, along with all the other stresses associated with poverty, results in poor health. What's confusing is that some people gain weight when they don't have enough to eat and others do not. Some people will gorge when food is available and others will not. Did you know that fat is stored in the body as a defense mechanism for people who don't get enough food, or don't eat the right foods?

A women trying to feed herself and her toddler on food stamps shared her struggle with the Vermont Campaign to End Childhood Hunger.

She said, "I get $250 for the entire month. That comes to $7 a day for the two of us. It doesn't work. I was getting $200 of food stamps when I was pregnant.

Continued from page 93 …

Now I get $250 for me and my son. I just give him every crumb and scrap of everything I can find, and I just go without. I've found that I can get by not feeling hungry if I drink an entire 2-liter bottle of soda because then I'm bloated. And that's only a dollar! And, granted, I've gained 30 pounds in the last two months, but, you know, I'm living. I have about one real meal a day."

The first changes that occur in children when food is scarce are behavioral, including withdrawal, depression, aggression and anxiety. Children from **low food security** homes have been found to have more behavioral problems which significantly affect their ability to function in school.

Low food security has been shown to result in poor quality diets that are deficient in critical nutrients such as iron, which is essential for brain function and physical development. If poor nutrition is chronic, the immune system becomes compromised, along with loss of weight and a slowing of growth, which in some cases can result in the stunting of growth.

Hunger in the U.S. is not of the famine variety one sees on television of emaciated children in Africa. Poor people in the U.S. often suffer from episodic hunger -- going without food, or eating little food for a few days each month or living on diets that are low in critical nutrients.

Individuals with poor diets suffer from nutrient deficiencies and chronically poor health with detrimental effects on mental functioning.

Global Hunger: Malnutrition and hunger are also occurring in developing countries, creating obesity and stunting. Changes in diet and lack of physical activity are fueling an obesity epidemic around the globe. The world is moving toward a higher-fat and refined carbohydrate Western diet. Most countries in Asia, Latin America, Northern Africa, and the Middle East have experienced a shift in the overall structure of their dietary patterns over the past few decades. Those changes include a large increase in the consumption of fat and sugar, a marked increase in animal food products and a decrease in total cereal fiber.

The changes in nutrition in developing countries parallels a shift from a pre-industrial agrarian economy to a post-industrial model, which includes a sedentary, more leisurely lifestyle with less physical work. Two causes of this come from watching too much television and less food preparation due to labor-saving technology, like microwaves.

These changes have resulted in large increases in body mass and obesity in the general population, especially among the poor. New research has shown the phenomenon of both overweight and underweight people.

Some of the poor in the developing world are experiencing malnutrition (thinness) and hunger from not having enough food to eat. Others are experiencing obesity from a diet made up of more fat, sugar and processed foods. Both are occurring. One does not negate the other.

Source: Popkin, Barry M. The Nutrition Transition and Obesity in the Developing World, Journal of Nutrition, Department of Nutrition, University of North Carolina, April, 2000.

Wheat, Courtesy WPF, Photo by Mike Huggins

CHANGES IN THE AMERICAN CULTURE

Our culture is preoccupied with food and eating. In 1985, 5,500 new food products were introduced; in 1995, it was 17,000. One thing is certain. The American diet has changed dramatically in the past sixty years. Our society has gone from an agrarian to a modern post-industrial society with unforeseen health consequences. Our eating habits are nothing like those of our grandparents. Just look at the photos and compare the difference.

A whole generation of people have lost valuable knowledge that comes from growing, preserving, and preparing food.

We've basically had a "cheap food" policy in the U.S. for close to 60 years that subsidizes corn and soybeans.

The changes that have taken place at the dinner table have been dramatically influenced by the Corporate Agricultural Industrial Machine (CAIM), made up of the likes of Cargill and Archer-Daniels-Midland (ADM) -- Supermarket to the World, along with Coca Cola, McDonald's, Wal-Mart, and others. Where you eat, how much you eat, and what you eat is determined by who controls your food basket, including school breakfast and lunch programs.

ADM, headquartered in Decatur, Illinois, procures, transports, stores, processes and markets a wide range of agricultural products. They have manufacturing, sales, and distribution facilities in 26 states along with a network of offices, processing plants and distribution facilities on six continents. ADM ingredients are used in countless food products and beverage items from baked goods to dairy foods, from meats to confections, from soft drinks to sports drinks and just about everything in between.

AN AGRI-CULTURE OF CORN

Corn is big business in America. The U.S. leads the world in corn production. Over twelve million bushels were produced in 2007. Three million bushels went for ethanol production.

Since the 1970s, an "agri-culture" of corn has woven itself onto our dinner plates. (The word agriculture comes from the Latin agricultura: ager, meaning land plus cultura, meaning cultivation.) Most corn farmers use massive amounts of nitrogen fertilizer along with pesticides and herbicides to grow corn from genetically modified (GM) seed. In 2006, sixty one percent of corn planted in the U.S. was from GM seeds. A lot of this corn is ground up into livestock feed which is fed to cattle and ends up as hamburgers.

Corn syrup was developed as a cheap and sweeter version of cane sugar in the 1970s. It's found in everything from catsup to soft drinks to frozen foods. Americans eat more sweetener from corn syrup than sugar cane or sugar beets. Our consumption has grown from almost none in the 1960s to 62.6 pounds per person per year in 2006.

SUGAR AND THE WORLDWIDE OBESITY EPIDEMIC

Today, the "big three" -- burgers, fries and Cokes -- are costing more in terms of our pocketbooks and health. Many nutritionists believe there is a direct relationship between the rise in the use of corn syrup and type 2 diabetes and the rise of adult and childhood obesity. There is a giant battle taking place around the planet between nutrition experts and the crisis's key suspect: the sugar industry, especially from high-fructose corn syrup in soft drinks. A single-sized soft drink is the equivalent of 12-15 spoonfuls of sugar.

The World Health Organization (WHO) of the United Nations met at the 2004 Geneva Summit and came out with recommendations in a report for dealing with the obesity crisis. A panel of the world's top nutritionists was asked to determine a safe sugar level in our diet. Their report called for a diet restricted to 10 percent sugar. Angry sugar lobbyists and representatives from the Bush Administration sprang into action denouncing the report. Their point-man was none other than former President Bush's godson. The administration threatened to remove U.S. support for the World Health Organization.

THE CHEAP CORN
SCENARIO CONTINUES

The most popular sweetener today is not sugar, but corn syrup. And you may have guessed by now that most of it comes from genetically modified corn. If you check the labels in your local supermarket, you'll find sugar from corn in breakfast cereals, canned drinks, soda and processed foods of all kinds. Cheap corn, transformed into high fructose corn syrup, allowed Coca-Cola to move from the 8-ounce bottle of the 1970s to the larger 20-ounce bottle of today.

Cornfields in Iowa, Photo Courtesy USDA

When you sit down for an all-American steak, you may not think twice about how that steer came to take an important place at your dinner table. The bucolic image of cattle lazily grazing on green pasture land is an aberration in today's beef industry. Most cattle don't eat grass or hay any longer. They are fed on that most ancient of grains which the native people called maize.

Corn is fed to cows in giant feedlot factories that produce the meat in those fast-food burgers we love to eat. Corn is pressed into vegetable oil that cooks the fries we can't get enough of.

And the sugar from corn syrup sweetens all those shakes and sodas. Corn makes up 13 of the 38 ingredients in Chicken McNuggets, including the corn-fed chicken and the corn bulking and binding agents that hold it together. Of the 45,000 items in a typical supermarket, more than a quarter contain corn.

Author Wendell Berry said that we need to take the animals back to the farms and pastures, away from the giant feedlots, where manure pollution has become a national health and environmental issue. A study by the Union of Concerned Scientists confirms that milk from grass-fed cows contains higher levels of omega-3-fatty acids, the so-called beneficial fats -- that reduce the risk of heart disease and protect the immune system. Grass-fed beef also has fewer calories and is higher in conjugated linoleic acid (CLA), a fatty acid shown in animal studies to protect against cancer.

The tragic result of the above scenario is that when food like meat, corn and sugar is abundant and cheap, people eat more and get fatter. The large food companies continue to lobby for "cheap food" even as our calorie count continues to increase. A perfect example is McDonald's Happy Meal, which was originally 600 calories and is now 1,550 calories. This is only a little less than what an adult needs each day, which is 2,200 calories.

When you compare the costs of advertising, marketing, packaging and labor, the cost of added ingredients is trivial. All you need to do to create another highly processed, "value-added" food is to take some cheap raw materials like corn and soybeans -- add corn syrup, flour, oil and water and whatta yah got but another item on the grocery shelf.

KING CORN

The 2005 documentary, King Corn, by Ian Cheney and Curt Ellis, documents how corn has turned the American diet into a fast food nightmare. After college, the two friends decided to become Iowa corn farmers. With the help of friendly neighbors, genetically modified seeds, nitrogen fertilizers, and powerful herbicides, they planted and grew a bumper crop of America's most productive, most subsidized grain on one acre of Iowa soil. After nine months, the 31,000 seeds Cheney and Ellis planted on one acre turned into a 10,000 pound harvest, which yielded 57,348 cans of soda, 3,894 corn-fed hamburgers, 2,301 pounds of bacon, and 6,726 boxes of corn flakes. Cheney and Ellis turned 63 percent of their harvest into feed for livestock, 32 percent into ethanol and 5 percent into sweeteners, such as corn syrup. If it wasn't for farm subsidies, they would have lost money on that acre of land.

* See LiftingTheYoke.com Part 2. More on Cows, Corn, Sugar and Obesity

CORPORATE PROFITS IN THE FACE OF OBESITY

Marion Nestle, a nutrition educator and author, asks a critical question: "In whose interest is it for people to eat healthy?" She goes on to say, "I can't think of a single industry in the U.S. that would be better off if people ate healthily. Not the insurance industry, because prevention is as expensive as is treatment; certainly not the drug industry, the diet industry or the food industry. I can't think of a single one, and that's not good. So one tries to change societal priorities ... just as it has become socially unacceptable to smoke."

Nestle shows how the food industry promotes sales by resorting to lobbying, lawsuits, financial contributions, public relations, alliances, and philanthropy to influence Congress, federal agencies, and nutrition/health professionals.

Nestle describes the food industry's opposition to government regulation, its efforts to discredit nutritional recommendations while pushing soft drinks onto children via alliances with schools, and its intimidation of critics who question its products or its claims.

Nestle makes some other bold statements

including the following:

Marion Nestle

- Government nutritional advice is watered down when it might threaten food industry sales.
- Obesity is collateral damage on the way to corporate profits.
- Obesity is a matter of social policy as much as personal responsibility. It will take more than willpower to win "The Battle of the Bulge."

- Agribusiness and food corporations have more power than mom when it comes to what gets put on the grocery shelves.
- Obesity has become a problem in the last three decades as agribusiness has increased its pursuit of the consumer's dollar via ingenious advertising. The goal is to get people to eat and drink more and to switch brands.
- The U.S. produces twice as many calories as needed to feed the population. This is referred to as America's "paradox of plenty." The result of this food abundance leads corporations to do everything possible to broaden their market share, thus encouraging people to overeat.

Source: Marion Nestle is the chair of the Department of Nutrition and Food Studies at New York University. She is the author of two books. Food Politics: How the Food Industry Influences Nutrition *(2002) and* Safe Food: Bacteria Biotechnology and Bioterrorism *(2004).*

WHY DOES AGRIBUSINESS MAKE SO MUCH MONEY?

Farmers who sit at the bottom of the food chain are forced to over-produce because they receive so little for farm commodities, such as corn, soybeans, and other farm products. This benefits global food corporations who can purchase these commodities and create cheap processed foods like chips.

Prices received by farmers have been declining for a number of years. At the same time, farm costs have increased. In 2005, dairy farmers received $1.00 for a gallon of milk that costs the consumer $3.00, $.05 for a loaf of white bread that sold for $1.39. For every $1.00 spent on food in 1995, $.21 went to the farmer and $.79 to other costs such as processing, packaging, trucking, and the retailing of the product. Out of the $.21, the farmer had to pay for expenses such as labor, equipment and energy costs.

In 2003, the U.S. spent $18 billion on agricultural subsidies, but 70 percent went to large factory farms. Corporate agribusiness buys grain at reduced prices, processes it, and sells it to large food restaurants like McDonald's. The corn, soybeans, and canola that go into these processed foods come largely from genetically modified (GM) seeds. As stated earlier, GM corn is processed into corn syrup and corn meal and added to many food products. GM soy is processed into oil and meal and is used in lecithin, miso, tofu and animal feed. GM canola is used mainly for oil. GM food has completely infiltrated the marketplace. It's in everything from taco chips to soda.

Front Cover of "Fatal Harvest,"
USDA Photo by Ken Hammond

What this all boils down to is profit. The American food industry makes $900 billion a year. It makes more money when we eat processed and larger amounts of food. The industry invests billions in marketing and advertising to make sure we eat more processed foods filled with water, salt, sugar, corn, soy, canola, and wheat. For example, the cost of corn in those breakfast corn flakes is less than 10 percent of the retail price. Again, not only what we eat, but how much we eat is strongly influenced and controlled by CAIM.

NUTRITION AND HEALTH

Andrew Kimbrell follows the same line of thought as Marion Nestle in his book, *Fatal Harvest: The Tragedy of Industrial Agriculture*. It is filled with large photographs and descriptions of industrial agriculture.

On nutrition, Kimbrell writes, "While the industrialization of our food supply progresses, we are witnessing an explosion in human health risks and a significant decrease in the nutritional values of meals." There is a price being paid for eating processed food.

Frank Hu, an epidemiologist at the Harvard School of Public Health who tracks the effects of food on diseases in the American population, said, "During processing, a lot of beneficial nutrients like fiber, minerals, and antioxidants are lost, especially in highly processed, refined-grain products. Manufacturers also add in lots of sugar and trans fat to enhance taste. So you get rid of the good stuff and add in a lot of bad stuff, and that's the reason these foods are really detrimental."

Source: Hu Frank Hu. "Faux Foods." Eating Well Magazine, December, 2005.

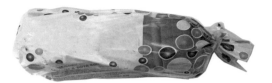

Commercial White Bread

Versus Whole Wheat Bread

Below: Eric Andrus Bakes Bread at Good Companion Bakery. Ferrisburgh, Vermont

Donald Davis, a University of Texas agricultural scientist, gave a report a couple of years ago to the American Association for the Advancement of Sciences. He compiled data regarding the nutritional value of food crops since 1955. The results showed that protein had decreased 15 percent, vitamin C 20 percent, and riboflavin 38 percent. Davis suspects this is due to an increase in the use of chemicals in industrial agriculture and the over processing of food.

Pot Pies, Faux Foods and TV Dinners: The award for an extreme example of processed foods and poor nutrition goes to Salisbury steak dinners from Banquet, which sold for $.79 at Wal-Mart in 2006. The multi-national company that makes the Banquet brand, ConAgra, is headquartered in Omaha, Nebraska. The ingredient list on their frozen dinners is 165 words long. You can't tell where any of them originated.

The Corporate Agricultural Industrial Machine: (CAIM) not only makes millions off processed conventional food, they're doing the same with processed organic food including TV dinners. Take a box of organic oat cereal, which costs around $4. The oats cost 15 cents. The fancy paper carton the cereal sits in costs more.

Commercial Bread: As an example of the demise of the American diet, let me tell you the story of a typical loaf of commercial bread. The loaf begins its young life in a five-story factory with a 2,500-pound "mother" dough-ball that contains 36 ingredients, including refined flour, dough conditioner for softness and cellulose gum for that easy feel in your mouth. A mechanized knife chops the mound into 27-ounce balls and another machine rolls the balls into logs and deposits them into pans. The pans are spiralled through an oven big enough to hold six full-size school buses and 16 minutes later the logs are baked. The oven produces 150,000 loaves a day, all sliced, packaged and distributed to stores. It takes 15 days for the loaf to mold.

Bread and Nutrition Facts:

Some of you may remember the anti-war song, "Where Have All the Flowers Gone?" Today, the title could be, "Where Have All the Nutrients Gone?"

•The modern grain mill crushes the raw wheat berries over and over, sifting and separating them between large screens, eventually stripping the nutrients and fiber-packed germ and bran from the starchy, bland endosperm.

- Throughout history, people considered white flour superior to coarse whole wheat but it wasn't until millers began using steel rollers in the 19th century that refined flour became cheap enough for everyone to afford.

- White flour contains only small amounts of fiber, vitamins or minerals, the building blocks of healthy food. One slice of white bread has 65 percent less fiber, magnesium and potassium than whole wheat bread.

- Twenty percent of the typical American diet comes from refined grains - in bread, pasta, doughnuts, chips, muffins, cereals, and crackers.

- Many studies have shown that a diet high in "refined" grains poses a higher risk of stroke, type 2 diabetes, and weight gain. People who eat more "whole" grains tend to have lower "bad" cholesterol (LDL) and higher "good" cholesterol (HDL).

Four Simple Nutrition Tips:

- Buy foods with fewer ingredients. For example, non-sweetened applesauce consists only of apples and water with no added sugar.

- Make sure the first ingredient in a bread or grain-related food begins with the word "whole."

- Avoid foods with "partially hydrogenated oil" in the ingredients, and choose low-salt varieties of canned, frozen and boxed foods.

- Eat more fresh fruits and vegetables. For example, peas from a can have 72 percent less vitamin C, 59 percent less niacin, 56 percent less B6 and 17 percent less potassium than the same amount of raw peas. Further, frozen foods are more nutritious than canned foods.

Side Notes:

In the early 1970s, I had an old, tan B-18 Volvo, the kind that looked like a late 1940s Ford coupe. I glued a hamburger from McDonald's along with some fries and ketchup, to the dashboard of my car. I was curious as to how long my "pop art food display" would last. It just grew old with age with no mold and lots of dust.

Today, I eat whole wheat bread from local bakers. The bread has fewer ingredients such as honey and canola oil and 38 percent less salt than the fluffy white loaf described above. A typical small bakery starts with a 100-pound "mother" dough-ball shaped into 27-ounce mounds. By the end of day, the bakers have made 400 loaves, each of which they estimate takes about a week to mold if left unrefrigerated.◥

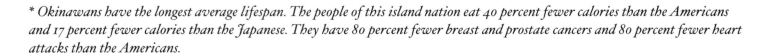

Okinawans have the longest average lifespan. The people of this island nation eat 40 percent fewer calories than the Americans and 17 percent fewer calories than the Japanese. They have 80 percent fewer breast and prostate cancers and 80 percent fewer heart attacks than the Americans.

FOODBORNE DISEASES

Along with the poor nutritional quality of our food supply is the increase in the number of foodborne diseases. You can't pick up the newspaper these days without reading about a new foodborne disease caused from bacteria in spinach, lettuce, seafood, hamburgers, tacos, peanut butter, or chicken. Bad food turning up in our restaurants, grocery stores and school lunches has become commonplace.

According to the Centers for Disease Control and Prevention (CDC), there are an estimated 76 million cases of foodborne illnesses, 325,000 hospitalizations, and 5,000 deaths each year in the U.S., The most common foodborne infections are caused by the bacteria campylobacter, salmonella, and E.coli 0157:H7.

Do you remember the headline-grabbing disease outbreaks in 2006 that killed three people from E.coli-infected spinach or the September 2007 recall of 21.7 million pounds of E.coli infected ground beef from Topps Meat Company?

Cargill Inc. announced in October of 2007 that it was recalling more than a million pounds of ground beef that may have been contaminated with E.coli bacteria. This was the second time in less than a month that the corporation voluntarily recalled tainted beef.

In October 2007, there was an outbreak of salmonella in pot pies processed by ConAgra Foods. The Center for Science in the Public Interest said ConAgra's delay in recalling the pot pies - linked to a nationwide salmonella outbreak - increased the risk that more people would become sick. The outbreak involved 165 cases in 31 states. Salmonella illness typically lasts four to seven days. Most people recover without treatment, but it can be life-threatening for the elderly, infants and people with compromised immune systems.

ConAgra initially issued a health alert asking stores nationwide to stop selling Banquet and other store-brand chicken and turkey pot pies.

It took a couple more days before they began to recall the pies. The recall included beef pot pies sold at stores such as Albertson's, Hill Country Fare, Food Lion, Wal-Mart, Kirkwood, Kroger, Meijer and Western Family.

On February 17, 2008, the USDA ordered a massive recall of 143 million pounds of frozen beef from a California slaughterhouse. Television pictures showed downed cows being bulldozed to slaughter. A lot of the beef went to school lunch programs. Officials said it was the largest beef recall in the United States, surpassing a 1999 ban of 35 million pounds of ready-to-eat meats. Secretary of Agriculture Ed Schafer said his department has evidence that the Westland Hallmark Meat Co. did not routinely contact its veterinarian when cattle became unable to walk after passing inspection, violating heath regulations.

According to Rep. Rosa Delauro, a Connecticut Democrat, "you're looking at the perfect example of a broken system." She introduced legislation that would empower the FDA to order mandatory recalls of contaminated food products, and establish fines for companies that don't promptly report the problem. Up until now, it's been up to the food industry to police itself.

Source: Quote -- Associated Press, October 15, 2007

WHAT ABOUT THE TAINTED TOMATO?

In the summer of 2008, it was the tomatoes' turn. How is it that salmonella, a bacterium that lives inside an animal intestines, gets on your tomatoes? Livestock, when kept in large numbers in confined spaces, can carry the bacterium without showing any symptoms at all.

The manure waste from these infected livestock could have spread, possibly from a rainstorm, to nearby fields where the tomatoes were grown.

Producers rinse their harvest with chlorinated water to remove most of the harmful bacteria, but some bacteria can be left over to make you sick. If the skin of a tomato is punctured when the fruit is picked from the vine or when it is pre-sliced for sale in a supermarket, salmonella bacteria can get inside and no amount of washing will make it safe to eat That is why on-the-vine tomatoes were exempt from the recent salmonella scare. The recent outbreak was the latest in a series of outbreaks of foodborne diseases and raised questions about the overall safety of our food.

By late July of 2008, the tomato scare was mostly over, but there was a hefty price to pay. It cost the tomato industry $100 million and left Americans with a new wariness about the safety of everyday foods. The tomato industry is worth $1.3 billion annually. An Associated Press poll found that nearly half of consumers changed their eating and buying habits in 2008 because they were afraid they could get sick by eating contaminated food. Eighty-six percent said produce should be labeled so it can be tracked through layers of processors, packers and shippers.

Michael Taylor, a former senior federal food safety official, said, "When you have almost half the population avoiding certain foods because of safety concerns, that's very significant from the standpoint of the economic impact for the people selling the food, and from the standpoint of peace of mind for consumers." Christy Taylor, a first-grade teacher from Sacramento, Calif., said she has all but given up on supermarket produce and is buying most of her fresh fruits and vegetables at the local farmers' market instead.

Source: "Tomato Scare Ends, But Fears Linger For Many," Associated Press, July 19, 2008.

The USDA inspects meatpacking plants every day. In contrast, the Food and Drug Administration (FDA), which is charged with regulating produce, might inspect a vegetable packing facility once a year and the number of inspections is shrinking.

In 1972, the FDA inspected 50,000 farms and plants. By 2006, that number went down to 10,000. Meanwhile, having increasingly centralized packing plants means that crops from a single contaminated field can mingle with clean produce and then be shipped across the country.

A salmonella outbreak sickened 1,200 people in 42 states in the summer of 2008. Initially, the FDA was not sure if tomatoes were the problem. They then stated that peppers were the source of the contamination. The peppers were found to come from farms in Mexico, a big supplier of produce to the U.S. The peppers were infected by irrigation water most likely contaminated by animal manure waste from nearby feedlots. It is still not clear whether tomatoes were also infected with the harmful bacteria.

In January of 2009, a salmonella outbreak from peanuts spread throughout the nation sickening thousands and killing nine people. The peanuts were traced back to a Peanut Corporation of America plant in Blakeley, Georgia. It was found that the plant shipped salmonella-contaminated products. The peanut tainted products included peanut butter crackers, granola, trailmix, and many other products including ice-cream and chocolate. The Blakely plant was found to be in filthy condition. The U.S. Drug and Food Administration (FDA) had not inspected the peanut plant on a regular basis.

Mercury was recently found in high fructose corn syrup (HFCS). Mercury is a residue in the production of caustic soda, a key ingredient in HFCS. If mercury proves to be at high levels, it could become a serious health issue in the nation. High levels of mercury in children result in Autism and Asperger's disease.

Did the cause of the flu pandemic (May, 2009) come from industrial pig operations in Mexico?

Factory Feedlot

B. SAD FAT FOOD FACTS, THE NEW EPIDEMIC

Baroque Painting, 17th Century, of Obese Man

Obesity and lack of exercise may become the leading causes of preventable deaths in the United States in the near future. Tobacco (smoking) was first in 2000 with 435,000, or 18 percent of the total number of deaths. Unhealthy diets and physical inactivity accounted for 375,000 deaths between 1990 and 2000. This was an increase of 65,000 deaths, and accounted for about 16 percent of the total.

THE NEW EPIDEMIC

OUR SUPER-SIZED FOOD CULTURE CELEBRATES EXCESS

"Super-Sized" is more than a catch phrase at fast-food restaurants, it describes America -- soft like a loaf of white bread. It's become so dire that Detroit may slap a "fat tax" on Big Macs and Whoppers. If approved, the Detroit tax would be the first to target fast-food outlets. In 2004, Detroit was considered the nation's fattest city by Men's Health Magazine. In 2005, it fell to No. 3.

The tax doesn't sound like such a bad idea, except it would place an undue burden on the poor. Others have suggested that we place a selective tax on sodas, cookies, cakes and snacks made from processed flour, sugar and bad oils. Fresh fruits and vegetables, 100 percent whole wheat products, dried fruits without added sweeteners, nuts, seeds, peanut butter without added oil or sweeteners, meat, fish, fowl, and dairy products would be exempt from the tax.

The state of West Virginia has one of the worst obesity problems in the country. Twenty-eight percent of West Virginians are considered obese. Nearly 43 percent of a sampling of children were overweight and more than 25 percent obese. The state has asked the Centers for Disease Control (CDC) to study the problem as it would investigate the spread of an infectious disease. The CDC teamed with state health officials to visit schools, grocery stores, restaurants, supermarkets, parks and more.

SUPER SIZE ME - A DOCUMENTARY

Filmmaker Morgan Spurlock decided to find out why people are so fat. He found out in two words: "fast food." So he made a film of himself eating three meals a day at McDonald's for a month. Spurlock said his body just fell apart. In his own words, "I started to get tired; I started to get headaches; my liver filled up with fat because there is so much fat and sugar in the food. My blood sugar skyrocketed, my cholesterol went off the charts, my blood pressure became completely unmanageable, and I was very lethargic."

Spurlock's doctors said his cholesterol went up 65 points, his liver became inflamed and hardened, his weight increased 25 pounds and he became angry and depressed. The doctors went so far as to say he was a good candidate for heart problems.

Spurlock said he was a disaster to live with. It didn't help that his girlfriend was a vegetarian. When he began the experiment, he was thin and healthy and all his vital signs were excellent.

Spurlock Continued...

Some would argue that Spurlock "pushed the envelope" by eating too many meals at McDonald's, but the fact is there are many people who eat more than one meal a day at a fast-food eatery. Super-Size Me aired all over the country. MSNBC showed it in its entirety on January 28, 2007. It received numerous awards.

In March of 2004, McDonald's decided to phase out its supersize fries and Cokes. The move came just before Super Size Me was being shown at movie theaters. Martin Spurlock has not gone back to McDonald's. He prefers a local burger close to home, which uses fresh ground beef.

McDonald's has been faced with a number of lawsuits related to the poor quality of its food. In most cases, it has won in court except for the lawsuit related to its trans fat fries. McDonald's has never denied that its menu is filled with sugar, fats and unhealthy foods. The company has pointed out that there are other reasons for obesity besides sugar and fat. And of course, it does have to answer to its stockholders.

Twinkies: The Golden Sponge Cake with Creamy Filling On April 20, 2005, Hostess "Twinkies" celebrated their seventy-fifth birthday Americans spent $47 million in 2004 on this junk food "they love to adore." Hostess makes 500 million of them every year. The little cream-filled yellow sponge cake is the same one I've been eating since I was a kid. I'm probably down to two a year. Everything in moderation. Twinkies contain no dairy products. They are basically flour, corn syrup, sugar, corn starch, corn flour, dextrose, water, vegetable and/or animal shortening, eggs, chemical preservatives, stabilizers and more. Each one has 150 calories, about a third of which is fat.

The Twinkie was invented in 1930.

IT'S OUR KIDS TOO!

FAST FOOD & WEIGHT GAIN

A 15-year study of 3,000 young people who ate a fast-food meal twice a week were found to be 10 pounds heavier than those who ate fast food less than once a week. The study was done at the University of Minnesota and reported by Tom Scneck of Minnesota Public Radio, December 30, 2004.

AGGRESSION

American children consume more than one-third of their daily calories in soft drinks, salty snacks and fast foods. Many of these foods cause school behavior problems. Children who are hungry are more aggressive in their behavior. Can healthy food reduce aggressive behavior? The answer is in the affirmative.

OBESITY

Food deprivation can trigger obesity as the body's physical response to hunger.

LEARNING

Many children who come to school are not able to learn because they are "nutritionally challenged."

EATING MORE

Eating more food doesn't provide good nutrition when the food is overly processed and filled with sugars, trans fats, and lots of cheap carbohydrates.

IT'S ESTIMATED THAT IF OUR CHILDREN'S POOR EATING HABITS CONTINUE THE WAY THEY'RE GOING, THEY WON'T LIVE AS LONG AS THEIR PARENTS. IN OTHER WORDS, THERE IS THE POTENTIAL FOR LIFE EXPECTANCY TO DECLINE IN THE UNITED STATES IN THE 21st CENTURY.

ADVERTISING FOR KIDS

According to research cited by Liz Kowalczyk, in the Boston Globe (February 25, 2004), 40,000 advertisements a year reach an average child, persuading them to eat more candy, cereal, heavily sugared soda and fast food. U.S. Food companies spend 10 billion annually to entice children to eat unhealthy foods.

A 2007 study done by the Kaiser Family Foundation found that of all food commercials on television for children, more than 40 percent were for candy, snacks and fast food. Nowhere to be found were commercials for fresh fruit, vegetables, poultry, and seafood.

COMMERCIAL BREAKDOWN:

Candy and Snacks	34 percent
Cereal	29 percent
Fast food restaurants	17 percent
Beverages	10 percent
Prepared foods	4 percent
Dairy	4 percent
Breads and pastries	2 percent

For years, health officials have warned that children were being inundated with commercials about unhealthy foods. Now researchers have attached numbers to such warnings. Children age 8-12 see on average 21 commercials a day or 7,600 a year.

Sources: Ludwig DS. "Childhood Obesity- the Shape of Things to Come." NEngl, J Med. 2007. Olshanksy, Passaro, Hershow, Layden, Cames, Hayflick, Butler, Allison, Ludwig. "A Potential Decline in Life Expectancy in the U.S. in the 21st century." N Engl J Medicine. 2005.

What's critical to understand is that eating habits begin early in a child's life. Food preferences are generally shaped between ages 2 and 3. If children are eating and drinking harmful foods at an early age, it's difficult to introduce healthy foods later on in life. Young people need good role models at school and in the home. Learning about and experiencing good nutrition at an early age can carry over to the adult years.

Photo Courtesy of the
Vermont Campaign to End Childhood Hunger

MORE INFORMATION AND STATS ON OUR YOUNG ONES

- The weight-gain trend in the U.S. clearly affects children and teenagers. A ten-year-old boy weighed 77.4 pounds on average in 1963, but 88 pounds in 2002.

Source: National Center for Health Statistics

- A recent nutrition study found that dairy products, despite their fat content, keep kids slimmer. Childhood dairy intake has been falling for 20 years because of the switch from milk to soft drinks. Soda consumption has risen 300 percent in the same period.

- Fifteen percent of U.S. children ages 6-19 are overweight or obese. In 1980, it was 7 percent and in 1965, 4 percent. The obesity rate among children ages 6-17 has tripled since 1975, from about 5 percent to nearly 16 percent.

- Every day nearly one-third of children ages 4 to 19 eat fast food, which likely packs on about six extra pounds per child per year and increases the risk of obesity.

- The prevalence of obesity in children between the ages of 6 and 17 years is currently estimated at 11 percent at the 95th percentile, with an additional 14 percent between the 85th and 95th percentile. These prevalence rates are a dramatic increase from 1963-70, during which only 4-4.5 percent of 6-17 year-olds were overweight.

Source: Schwartz and Pulh, "Childhood Obesity: A Problem to Solve." Obesity Review (2003-4).

STUDIES ON THE LIFELONG EFFECTS OF CHILDHOOD OBESITY

Two studies in the New England Journal of Medicine reported in December 2007 suggest that being overweight as a kid can lead to serious health consequences as an adult. The first study by Bibbins-Domingo estimates that by 2020, as many as 44 percent of American women and 37 percent of men, at age 35, will be obese and, therefore ill. By 2020, heart disease will rise 16 percent, and heart disease deaths will rise by as much as 19 percent for adults between the ages of 35 and 50 years. That translates to about 100,000 additional heart disease deaths among the 35-to-50-year-olds related solely to obesity, and that's a conservative estimate.

The second study compared the childhood and adult hospital records of 278,835 Danish citizens between 1930 and 1976. It found a direct correlation between weight and the risk for heart disease and heart-related illnesses, linking excess weight in childhood and health problems later on. The second study was reported by Dr. Jennifer Baker in Copenhagen. Baker said, "We can no longer sit back and wait, and think a child may grow out of it."

Other Kid Findings: A study of 6,212 youngsters was done by Dr. David Ludwig, Harvard pediatrician and Director of the Obesity Program at Children's Hospital in Boston. It was found that as a direct result of the over-consumption of fast-junk, over-processed, and restaurant foods such as Denny's, the nation is faced with a killer epidemic that has laid the groundwork for a dramatic increase in the onset of adult diseases in children, including Type 2 diabetes, heart disease, arthritis, and cancer.

These findings were taken from a sample of boys and girls in all regions of the country and different socio-economic levels suggest that fast-food consumption has increased five-fold since 1970.

See more on the Ludwig Study in www.pediatrics.org

Ludwig reported good news in May 2008: the percentage of American children who are overweight or obese appears to have leveled off after a 25 year increase. Ludwig noted that it is too soon to know if this really means we're beginning to make meaningful inroads into the epidemic. In 2003-04 and 2005-06, 32 percent of children were overweight or obese, and 16 percent were obese.

In another study, reported by the American Heart Association in 2004, it was found that more than 10 percent of children in the U.S. ages' 2 to 5, were overweight in 2002. That was up 7 percent from 1994. This is an indication that kids' weight problems are beginning even earlier according to Dr. Robert H. Eckel, President-elect of the Heart Association, who said the situation is probably even worse now.

Yale's Rudd Center for Food Policy and Obesity estimates that by 2010, almost fifty percent of all children in North America and 38 percent of children in the European Union will be overweight. In 2002, 28 percent of children (age 6-18) were overweight or obese. The number of U.S. children having obesity surgery has tripled in recent years, surging at a pace of 1,000 operations a year. From 1996 to 2003, 2,744 youngsters had surgery for obesity. This information came from a study at Robert Wood Johnson Medical School in Brunswick, NJ and Cincinnati Children's Hospital Medical Center.

Hate and Abuse: Overweight children suffer from severe self-hate. They're also stigmatized by their peers as early as age three and even face bias from their parents and teachers. Youngsters who report teasing, bullying, rejection and other types of abuse because of their weight are two to three times more likely to report suicidal thoughts. Kids are facing stigma from the media, school and at home.

This information comes from research on youth weight bias over the past 40 years from Yale University and the University of Hawaii at Manatoa.

The stigmatization of overweight children has been documented for decades. When children were asked to rank photos of children as friends in a 1961 study, the overweight child ranked last.

In a 1999 study of 115 middle and high school teachers, 20 percent said they believed obese people are untidy, less likely to succeed and more emotional. The research showed that another source of weight stigma towards youth comes from parents.

Source: Rebecca M. Puhl, Yale's Rudd Center for Food Policy and Obesity. Psychological Bulletin, July 2007.
* See Website Part 2 for more information: Other Sad Fat Facts about Adults, Immigrants, Rural/Urban Folks, Children and Teens

Junk Food Politics as Usual: In the last couple of years, the major food companies have been trying to convince Americans that they "feel the pain" of expanding waistlines, especially when it comes to kids. Kraft announced it would no longer market Oreos to younger children, McDonald's promoted itself as a salad producer, and Coca-Cola said it will not advertise to kids under 12. However, the Federal Trade Commission's chair, Deborah Majoras, declared that she would do nothing to stop junk food advertising to children. These hearings were held in the summer of 2005 by the FTC.

In June 2005, the USDA denied a request from the group Commercial Alert to enforce existing rules forbidding mealtime sales in school cafeterias of foods of minimal nutritional value -- referring to junk foods and soda pop. Stanley Garrett, head of USDA's Child Nutrition Division, said, "At this time, we don't intend to undertake the activities or measures recommended in your petition."

Conflict about junk food has intensified since late 2001, when the Surgeon General's report called obesity an "epidemic."

The Bush White House repeatedly weighed in on the side of the large food corporations working hard to weaken the World Health Organization's anti-obesity strategy. They questioned the scientific basis for "the linking of fruit and vegetable consumption to decreased risk of obesity and diabetes."

Former Health and Human Services Secretary Tommy Thompson, then our nation's top public-health officer, told members of the Grocery Manufacturers Association (GMA) to go on the offensive against critics blaming the food industry for obesity.

*It was reported in April 2009 that 25 percent of four-year olds in the US are obese.

THE AMAZING "OTHER" RESULTS OF OBESITY

Obesity also translates into absenteeism, pain, and disability. In 2001, according to the Surgeon General, illnesses associated with obesity cost the country $117 billion. The annual cost for smoking was $150 billion. That $117 billion could help fix a lot of social programs. Half of that money is in direct medical costs for weight-related diseases, such as diabetes, stroke, cancer, high- blood pressure, depression and kidney failure. The other half is in lost work time. Nearly a third of Americans, more than 73 million, have diabetes or higher-than-normal blood sugar levels. A third of the people who have diabetes, don't know it.

Costs of Poor Health: More than a quarter of the phenomenal growth in health care spending during the past 15 years can be attributed to obesity, according to Emory University researchers (2004). From 1987 to 2001, medical bills for obese people constituted 27 percent of the growth of overall health care spending. Treating obese patients was 37 percent more expensive than treating normal-weight people.

The only way to control medical costs is to begin prevention and treatment of the most costly weight-related illnesses, diabetes and heart disease. Emory research scientist Kenneth Thorpe says, "We've got to find ways to get the rates of obesity stabilized or falling, by developing effective interventions to deal with this on multiple levels -- the schools, home and in the work place."

SO, FOLKS, WHY ARE WE SO FAT, ANYWAY? TEN REASONS

REASON 1: WHY FRIES TASTE SO GOOD

The taste of McDonald's fries has been praised by customers and food critics alike. The taste comes mainly from the cooking oil the fries are cooked in. Some flavoring is added to the potatoes but this is insignificant compared to the cooking oils. For many years, McDonald's cooked its fries in a mixture of 7 percent soy oil and 93 percent beef tallow. The mixture gave the fries their distinctive flavor. After much criticism from the public regarding the large amount of saturated fat from the beef tallow, McDonald's switched over to artificial trans fat oil from corn and soy products in 1990.

Trans fat is the common name for the type of unsaturated fat industrially created by hydrogenating plant oils -- a process developed in the early 1900s and first commercialized by Crisco in 1911. The goal is to add hydrogen atoms to unsaturated fats, making them more saturated. Because these fats have a higher melting point, it makes them more attractive for baking and frying and extends their shelf-life.

Crisco was one of the first products made with a process called hydrogenation, in which manufacturers add hydrogen to vegetable oil in order to solidify it. Artificial trans fats, short for trans fatty acids, are listed on food labels as partially hydrogenated vegetable oil.

Americans have been baking with vegetable shortening loaded with trans fats since the invention of Crisco. Unlike frying oils, whose main purpose is to conduct heat, shortening is a major contributor to taste and texture. Not even Crisco is made from trans fats anymore, but from new reformulated ingredients.

Trans fat is neither essential nor healthy and, in fact, increases one's risk of coronary heart disease by raising levels of "bad" cholesterol and lowering levels of "good" cholesterol. Hydrogenated products increase artery-clogging cholesterol in the body and contribute to heart disease. Health authorities recommend that trans fats be reduced to trace amounts.

Trans fat is found in most snack foods, cookies, chips, the oil in fries, shortening, margarine, frying oils, pizza dough and pancake mix. Trans fat is similar to saturated fat in that it raises the bad cholesterol level (LDL). The trans fat oil in French fries have much more trans fat than the in fried chicken.

* See more on this by checking out BanTransFat.com -- a non-profit advocacy group that filed a lawsuit against McDonald's.

THE CHANGEOVER FROM TRANS FATS:

In 2001, McDonald's paid $12.5 million and issued a public apology to settle a lawsuit for advertising that its fries were cooked in vegetable oil, when in fact they were cooked in beef fat.

McDonald's Corporation agreed to pay $8.5 million to settle a lawsuit for failing to inform consumers of delays in a plan to reduce the fat in its cooking oil. The agreement required McDonald's to pay $7 million to the American Heart Association for education about trans-fat in foods. The remainder went to informing the public that it had not followed through on its 2002 pledge.

McDonald's attempted to make good on a three year-old promise to test a healthier blend of oil for its signature fries at a small number of restaurants. They vowed in September of 2002 to switch to a new oil that would halve the level of harmful trans fatty acids in its fries. On May 24, 2007, McDonald's Corp. executives said they would roll out a new trans fat-free oil within the next year.

In January of 2007, McDonald's selected a new trans-fat-free oil for cooking its famous fries. It did not say when it will be used in all of its 13,700 U.S. restaurants. McDonald's new oil is canola-based and also includes corn and soy oils. A March, 2008 Media Statement from McDonald's reads, "Reducing, and where possible eliminating trans fatty acids from our items continues to be a priority at McDonald's. Our goal is to provide our customers with significantly reduced or o-gram TFA (tran fat acid) fried products that meet their expectations of taste and quality."

Finger Lickin' Good: In November of 2006, Kentucky Fried Chicken (KFC) announced that it was phasing out trans fats in cooking its Original Recipe and Extra Crispy fried chicken, potato wedges and other menu items. The restaurant chain said it would start using zero trans-fat soybean oil in the U.S. immediately and have the transition completed by April of 2007. Crispy Strips, Buffalo Wings, and Crispy Snacker sandwiches, and other items, are also part of the change.

* The Centers for Science in the Public Interest (CSPI) withdrew a lawsuit when KFC dropped trans fats. CSPI has an informative web site. The organization is a strong advocate for nutrition, health, and food safety. They produce an award-winning newsletter, Nutrition Action Healthletter. For more information, go to the CSPI website.

Burger King announced in July 2007 that they would cut trans fat by the end of 2008. In tests, consumers determined fries and other items cooked in the new oil tasted the same or better than products cooked in trans fat products. The world's second largest hamburger chain said it is already using zero trans fat in hundreds of its 7,100 U.S. restaurants. CSPI said Burger King wasn't moving fast enough. Wendy's started using cooking oil with zero grams of trans fat in August 2006.

By early 2009, McDonald's had met the challenge of not using trans fatty oils. Wendy's was close and Burger King had not met the challenge completely .

Banning Trans Fats in the Big Apple: The New York City Board of Health voted unanimously on December 5, 2006 to prohibit restaurateurs from cooking with artificial trans fats. The city's 24,000 restaurants were given six months to stop frying foods in oils that contain high levels of trans fats -- and 18 months to switch to alternative ways of cooking pie crusts, doughnuts, and other baked goods. On June 30, 2008, New York became the first American city to officially ban trans fats. Almost all prepared food in restaurants, bakeries, cafeterias, salad bars and food carts are trans fat free. There was a three-month grace period before fines were slapped on violators. For more info, check out www.notransfatnyc.org .

In July 2008, California became the first state in the nation to ban trans fats. The legislation will take effect Jan. 1, 2010 for oil, shortening, and margarine used in spreads or for frying. Los Angeles officials have decided to ban fast food restaurants from an impoverished part of the city packed with roadside chains and battling high rates of obesity.

Dunkin' Donuts eliminated trans fats from in doughnuts in the fall of 2007. The company's cooks chose a replacement blend of oils made up of palm, soybean and cottonseed oil. In 2007, the state of Vermont was considering a ban on trans fats. Denmark banned trans fats in 2003, followed by other European countries.

REASON 2: THE FLAVOR INDUSTRY: IF IT TASTES GOOD YOU'LL EAT IT

One of the main reasons we're fat is because of the flavors added to food. According to Eric Schlosser, author of *Fast Food Nation*, the corporate food empires, especially the soft drink, snack and fast food segments, depend on how these products taste. About 10,000 new processed items come on the market every year and almost all contain food additives.

When you open your refrigerator and look at the labels on the jars and bottles, you will find the words "Natural Flavor" on many of the processed items, including the strawberry flavor in Stonyfield Yogurt. The canning, freezing, and dehydrating industries destroy most of food's flavor, so more flavor has be added.

Since the end of World War II, a vast flavor industry has arisen to make processed foods more palatable. Without flavoring, America's fast foods would not exist. Consumers know little or nothing about this highly secretive industry.

Most of the large flavor companies are located along the New Jersey Turnpike in an industrial corridor dotted with refineries and chemical plants. This area produces two-thirds of flavor additives in the U.S. Do you remember "comfort foods" from when you were growing up, like chocolate pudding? The indelible marks left by these foods on your taste buds still influence your food tastes. Childhood memories of Happy Meals can translate into frequent adult visits to McDonald's. The flavors in these foods from the past have been reproduced by the flavor industry.

According to Eric Schlosser, the human craving for flavor is a great force in history. Royal empires were built on it. Consider the spice and salt trades, and how Columbus sailed toward the East Indies in 1492 to find spices and seasonings. Today, the rise and fall of corporate food empires is determined on how products taste.

Kool-Aid: The flavor industry began in the mid-nineteenth century when processed foods began to be manufactured. Legend has it that a German scientist discovered a compound which later came to be the flavoring for grape Kool-Aid. Synthetic flavor additives were used mainly in baked goods, candies, and sodas until the 1950s, when sales of processed foods began to soar. By the mid-1960s, Pop Tarts, Hamburger Helper, Tang, Filet-O-Fish sandwiches and thousands of other new products came on the market.
Source: "Why Fries Taste So Good" came from Schlosser, Eric. Fast Food Nation: The Dark Side of the All-American Meal. Houghton Mifflin, 2001.

Aspartame: Diet Coke is a perfect example of a drink filled with flavors, caffeine and Aspartame (NutraSweet), a highly addictive substance. The story of NutraSweet and its approval by the FDA in the early 80s was a triumph of Reagan deregulation. It was an example of corporate profit over consumer safety. NutraSweet has been linked to migraines, seizures, fatigue, and has serious withdrawal symptoms. NutraSweet replaced saccharine as a sweetener. J. W. Childs Equity Partners purchased NutraSweet from Monsanto in 2000.

REASON 3: THE CLEVELAND CLINIC

Why are those Big Whoppers of Burger King fame served at the food court of the Cleveland Clinic, renowned for its research into heart disease? There are currently nine fast-food franchises in the food court. Are the officials at the clinic sending the wrong message by having all those fries, pizza, burgers, and shakes in a leading heart center that sees 205,000 patients a year?

By the way, McDonald's has franchises in 36 hospitals around the country.

Let's look at what's in all that franchise food: white bread, refined sugar, hydrogenated oils and carbs. Scientists say white bread and other refined grains go to the gut and hang out as belly fat. That was the result of a study at Tufts University in Boston, comparing people who eat refined foods and people who preferred more fiber in their diet, from whole grains, fruits, and vegetables. The belt size of the white bread group expanded about one-half inch a year. At the end of the three-year study, the white bread group had three times the fiber group's gain at the gut.

Dr.. David Ludwig, director of the Obesity Program at Children's Hospital in Boston, mentioned earlier, has found similar results in studying young people around the country.

The size of the waistline is important for health. A person with a bigger gut has a higher risk of heart disease than a person who weighs the same but does not carry extra weight around the belly. The same is true for diabetes.

REASON 4: SUGAR, CORN SYRUP AND SOFT DRINKS

Soft drink trends have marched in lock step with the growing obesity epidemic. About one-third of all carbohydrate calories come from added sweeteners, and beverages account for about half that amount. The main sweetener in beverages -- high-fructose corn syrup -- contains slightly more sweetening than ordinary table sugar. Table sugar (sucrose) is made from sugar cane.

Between 1970 and 2001, per capita consumption of 12-ounce cans of soda in the U.S. doubled from 230 to 460 cans a year. This averages out to more than one and a half cans for every American, every day of the year. There are 12-15 teaspoons of sugar in each can of soda.

A 2006 report in the American Journal of Clinical Nutrition stated that an extra can of soda a day can pile on 15 pounds in a single year. Dr. Frank Hu and others at the Harvard School of Public Health did the research. By the way, if you drink a 12-ounce can of soda every day for 22 days, you'll gain a pound.

The current beverage war is not between Coke and Pepsi, but between diet and regular. The highly competitive $64 billion soft drink industry is still dominated by regular soda, but sales of diet soda are surging because of America's perpetual diet craze. While regular soda is filled with high fructose corn syrup (HFCS), diet drinks contain artificial sweeteners, salt and flavors.

A 2008 University of Vermont study sponsored by the National Dairy Council says parents shouldn't worry about kids' sugar intake with flavored milk. It found that children who drink milk, flavored or plain, consumed more nutrients and had an equivalent or lower Body Mass Index than children who don't drink milk.

In addition, the overall sugar intake was no different between flavored milk drinkers and non-milk drinkers. Low-fat or fat-free milk offers a natural, high-quality source of calcium, vitamin D and phosphorous that is necessary for growth in children. It is recommended that children over the age of two drink the lowest-fat, lowest-sugar version of flavored milk.

More Soda Notes:

• One in every five calories in the American diet is liquid and one of the nation's single biggest "foods" is soda.

• Recent research at Yale and Harvard suggests that soda and other sugar-sweetened drinks are not only related to obesity, but may actually cause it. Barry Popkin, Director of the Obesity Program at the University of North Carolina and a professor of nutrition, also thinks that the consumption of sweetened sodas leads to obesity. He contends that the popular drinks might be psychological triggers of poor eating habits and cravings for fast foods. Popkin has called for cigarette-style Surgeon General warnings about the negative effects of soda. (Proving that something causes disease is not easy. Just look at how many years it took to prove that tobacco causes cancer.)

• Most people drink at least some sweetened beverages and get calories from other drinks such as milk and orange juice. Chocolate and strawberry milk drinks are also being sweetened with heavy amounts of sugar. People now drink more soda than milk.

Source: The information on More Soda Notes came from: Marchione, Marilyn. "Scientists Are Taking On Soda," Associated Press, 5 May. 2006.

REASON 5: CANDY ANYONE?

Some companies are now selling candy stating they help people lose weight, and claiming, for example, that the blueberries in the chocolate candies are packed with antioxidants. What they don't tell you is that there aren't nearly enough berries to make any difference.

In the last five years, manufacturers have introduced 56 snack foods and 42 confections with supposed health benefits. Have you heard about Snicker's Chewy Peanut Marathon bar, fortified with 16 vitamins and minerals, plus soy, for a long-lasting energy boost?

The food industry wants to make you believe you can have your cake and eat it, too, in terms of health, nutrition and weight loss. Perhaps, they've got something there, as nearly half of all women and one in four men are dieting at any one time. The food marketers are smart. The truth is that almost all diets fail. People go back to their old ways of eating, unless, of course, they make major lifestyle changes.

The Food and Drug Administration (FDA) regulates only those nutritional claims that draw a connection between a specific product and a particular disease. Claims that a particular ingredient is good for your health or that it will curb your appetite do not come under FDA approval.

REASON 6: IT'S NOT ONLY MCDONALD'S

Food choices for adults and children at table-service restaurant chains aren't any more healthy than the food offered at fast-food outlets. The Center for Science in the Public Interest (CSPI) found that the bulk of menu choices for kids at restaurants such as Applebee's, Chili's, and Denny's, are fries, chicken fingers, burgers and pizza. They all have enough calories, salt and bad fats to compete with McDonald's Happy Meals.

Ingredients:
Sugar, Marshmallow Fluff,
Chocolate Bits, Caramel,
Peanut Butter, Shortening, Salt,
And lots of Preservatives and
Flavors.

"Many parents appreciate the kid-friendly atmosphere and free crayons at places like Applebee's, but not many would expect adult-sized calorie counts in a children's meal," says Jayne Hurley, the center's senior nutritionist. For example, at Applebee's, the grilled cheese sandwich has 520 calories and 14 grams of bad fat. Add on fries and you have 900 calories. At Outback Steakhouse, the Boomerang cheeseburger with fries has 840 calories and 31 grams of saturated fat plus trans fat. The Agriculture Department recommends that low-active children ages 4-8 have 1,500 calories and 17 grams of saturated plus trans fat every day.

See www.cspinet.org for more information on chain restaurants.

REASON 7: SUPERSIZED PORTIONS

The food fight isn't just about McDonald's or Applebee's. What about the super-sized portions of popcorn drenched with butter at the local movie theater? It's everywhere -- at the local food mart, Ma and Pa convenience store, bowling alley, pizza joint, and at home.

REASON 8: DO OUR FRIENDS MAKE US FAT?

Do Birds of a Feather Chow Down Together? Nicholas Christakes and James Fowler, a doctor and political scientist made big news in the New England Journal of Medicine in August of 2007. The researchers found that people were likely to become obese when a friend became obese - their point being that social networks counted a lot more than family or neighbors even when friends lived a great distance from each other.

In real life we copy ourselves by our friends, fad by fad. Close friends affect our point of view. Just think about all the peer pressure that takes place in high school, such as the nose-ring phenomenon.

REASON 9: INDUSTRIAL CHEMICALS AND OBESITY:

An article in *Molecular Endocrinology* discusses the study of a class of industrial chemicals that disrupt the endocrine system and may cause obesity and weight gain. The chemicals, called organotins, are found in common household products such as pesticides and paints. Researchers have found in laboratory animals that exposure to certain organotins increased the fatty tissue in both fetal and adult animals. This is the first time that an environmental agent has been shown to increase fat by disrupting the function of the endocrine system.

FINAL REASON 10: INCOME DISPARITY

THE FINAL REASON IS THE INCREASING INCOME GAP IN THE U.S. BETWEEN THE RICH AND THE POOR. LOW-INCOME FAMILIES DON'T HAVE ENOUGH MONEY TO PURCHASE HEALTHY FOODS.

THIS MEANS THESE FAMILIES WILL PURCHASE WHAT THEY CAN AFFORD. IN MANY CASES THIS FOOD HAS LITTLE NUTRITIONAL VALUE. THIS CREATES THE "PARADOX OF OBESITY," WHERE THE MOST UNDERNOURISHED OFTEN LOOK THE MOST OVER-FED.

THE MONSTER ROLLOUT

Hardee's now has a Monster burger with 900 calories and 107 grams of fat. A day after the Monster's rollout Jay Leno said on the Tonight Show that the megaburger "comes in a little cardboard box shaped like a coffin." Apparently, it has succeeded beyond expectations in sales. This super-sized burger consists of two 1/3-pound slabs of all-Angus beef, four strips of bacon, three slices of cheese, and mayo on a buttered sesame seed bun. It sells for $5.49, or $7.09 with fries and a soda and exceeds the daily calorie and fat allowance for most people. (McDonald's came out with the McGriddle, which has more calories than the Big Mac.)

Eric Schlosser, the author of *Fast Food Nation,* says that McDonald's all-American Happy Meal has about 640 calories, counting the burger, fries and soda, but not including dessert. If we were on an Arctic expedition, each person would need about 4,500 calories a day as the cold, harsh conditions eat up calories, but we're not on an Arctic expedition.

THE NEW IMAGE:

Is McDonalds' striving for a healthier image? They are rolling out new meals with fancy salads, milk, and bottled water as well as fresh fruit instead of fries for our kids. But putting salads on the menu won't cut it when you add on those fat-filled Newman dressings. Anyway, most consumers go to McDonald's for the burgers, fries, triple-thick shakes, and Cokes, the backbone of the $6 billion-a-year operation.

Coca-Cola now includes natural Odwalla juices in its line-up. Frito-Lay is eliminating trans fats from Doritos and Kraft is reducing sugar, fat, and calories in most of its products. Kraft, the maker of Kraft Macaroni & Cheese, Oreo cookies and Oscar Mayer meats, also recently promised to eliminate in-school marketing to children, introduce smaller portions, and develop more nutritious products.

General Mills Inc., the nation's No.2 cereal maker, now makes all its cereals with whole-grain flour, and Coca-Cola labels some of its sodas with nutrition data.

What About Snack Foods?: America's snack-food makers are marketing smaller portions, using healthier fats and reducing sugar in some of the nation's favorite potato chips and cookies.

Did You Know?

- When you consume a Burger King Double Whopper with cheese, you're downing 130 percent of the saturated fat you're supposed to eat in an entire day. When you drink a Coke, you might as well be having a piece of chocolate cake -- the sugar intake is the same.

- For just 37 cents more, fast-food restaurants can super-size a regular soda to an extra-large, which adds 450 more calories. Research shows that when people are served larger portions, they eat more, regardless of intentions. When the Big Mac got bigger and juicier, folks bought into the two-for-one sale. This maximizes profits.

- A 32-ounce McDonald's vanilla shake has 1,110 calories -- more than two Quarter Pounders (840 calories).

- Ruby Tuesday has a 1,164-calorie Cuban panini.

- McDonald's has 30,000 restaurants in more than 100 countries.

Enough already! No more! No More!

While they're trying to make money off greater demand for more healthy grab-and-go food, they're also hoping the new products will help them avoid increased federal regulation and the threat of lawsuits.

Kellogg Co., maker of Pop-Tarts and Cheez-It crackers, has said that in the summer 2007 it will begin to reduce the amount of calories, fat, sugar, and sodium in products or stop marketing them to children under age 12. Kellogg's changes build on a move by Walt Disney Co. in the fall of 2006 to limit the use of its characters in marketing junk food to children. Nutritionists note that many of these products aren't health foods, but some of the changes are an improvement. Smaller servings, such as 100-calorie packs of Frito-Lay's Doritos and Kraft's Oreo thin crisps, can help people eat less. Sales of reduced fat, low-fat, and fat-free snacks fell 2.6 percent in 2006, while total snack sales rose 3.4 percent. Many kids don't like the taste of the fat-free snacks.

We'll see what happens.

Source: Tong, Vinnee. "Snack-Food Makers Feel Pressure to Cut Back on Fat." Associated Press, 21 June, 2007.

Supermarkets are also getting into the act of promoting healthy foods. A gold star rating system aimed at helping food shoppers make healthier choices seems to be working at Hannaford's. Shoppers are purchasing more Shredded Wheat and Raisin Bran, whole grain items, vitamins and minerals. The supermarket chain said sales of healthier items grew more than twice as fast as items deemed less healthy. The Center for Science in the Public Interest, a consumer advocacy group, said the findings are encouraging.

Hannaford is an American supermarket chain based in Scarborough, Maine. Founded in 1883, Hannaford now operates more than 150 stores in New York and New England. Formerly known as Shop `N' Save, Hannaford is owned by the American subsidiary of the Belgium Delhaize Group - Delhaize American, which owns over 1,500 stores along the eastern seaboard, mostly in the mid-Atlantic U.S.

C. CLAMOR IN THE CLASSROOM

A battle is underway across the country to improve school food and nutrition. From the cafeteria to the playground, schools must be more aggressive in fighting childhood obesity and poor nutrition and take a more active role in finding solutions.

Healthy food and nutrition education needs to be integrated into the school curriculum as early as elementary school and even kindergarten. Our young ones could be growing vegetables and herbs in school gardens, doing taste test-

Cooking Muffins in Vermont Classroom FEED
(Food Education Every Day) Program

Learning about food and nutrition could be at the center of a truly liberal education. Bread making could be part of the general curriculum, as could gardening, and beautifying school-yards by planting vegetable, herbs and flowers.

Parents and teachers need to persuade school boards to remove junk foods, set higher nutrition standards and develop more healthy school lunch programs. School nutritionists and food service managers need to work with local farm-

ing and food preparation in school kitchens, experiencing cuisine from different cultures in the classroom and visiting local farms and learning about the culture of farming in their communities.

Students need to learn through early experience that healthy food is delicious and good nutrition will make them feel better and lengthen their lives. By the time they reach their teens, they could be making wise food choices and be able to teach their own children what they have learned. What's clear is that kids that grow up with healthy food habits carry them over into adulthood.

ers to provide healthy school food.

There will be challenges along the way. The transition toward more healthy food offerings including the introduction of local produce, won't happen overnight. Some school kitchens are not equipped to serve local produce. The value of using locally grown produce in meals and learning how to prepare fresh foods from scratch can be a challenge. Some food managers may find it hard to locate local farm products and it's easier to open large cans of tomatoes for pizza sauce than to cut up a bushel of tomatoes, but much can be done at the local level.

A number of school food studies reported by the University of Minnesota News Service show that healthy food offerings are both practical and affordable.

- A 2007 study demonstrated that school age kids will eat healthy school lunches just as often as the less healthy options and school lunch sales don't decline when healthier meals are served. Previous studies had concluded that students prefer fatty foods and that healthier foods cost more to make. According to Benjamin Senauer, one of the three economists who wrote the Minnesota study, "The conventional wisdom that you can't serve healthier meals because kids won't eat them is false."

- Another study in 2007 reported that purchasing local food doesn't necessarily cost more than processed food when the food service staff is trained in using local, fresh produce. There is less waste from fresh local food purchases, but the labor costs of creating healthier food from scratch are higher. This was offset by lower costs for more nutritious foods such as fruits and vegetables compared with processed foods. Many school districts will need to upgrade their kitchens and train their food service staff to prepare these healthier food offerings.

- Finally, it was also found that when healthier meals are served, kids don't end up skipping lunch. It's clear from these studies that students will eat healthy food when given the option.

A study of 1,700 high school students found that those who ate healthy food with their families continued healthy eating habits throughout life. They ate more fruits and vegetables, drank fewer sodas, and sat down for breakfast with their families.

Students hankering for better school lunches took matters into their own hands in April 2007 at the first Vermont Junior Iron Chef Challenge. Twenty three middle school and 12 high school teams prepared lunches at the Champlain Valley Exposition Center. Judges graded the dishes on taste, use of Vermont products and ability to be replicated for mass consumption. The students' recipes were featured in a cookbook.

"It's empowering kids to allow them to cook and understand what their school-service people have to deal with," said Matt Tucker, an AmeriCorps volunteer for the Vermont FEED (Food Education Every Day) program.

Children Cutting Spinach Greens at Farm, Photo Courtesy of FEED

Children in School Kindergarten, Smart Growth Vermont

CHEZ PANISSE

Many years ago, Alice Waters, the founder of Chez Panisse, a well-known, upscale restaurant in Berkeley, California, began a school food movement. Who is this woman who cooked dinner for Bill Clinton and 30 of his top California contributors, each paying $25,000 for breaking bread with our former president? Waters is the California force behind "grilled" everything, hard-crusted bread, and support for local farmers. Her philosophy is simple: buy local and fresh, buy it organic whenever possible, and always buy in season. She says, "We've just gotten into such dishonesty about food. Consumerism is so powerful that it doesn't matter whether we're buying food that may be bad for us. We're paying for fancy wrappers."

So what does Waters have in common with children, school lunch programs and poor nutrition? First off, she told local chefs to simplify their cooking, show off their ingredients and demand pesticide-free products, grown and raised as close to their stoves as possible.

Alice Waters

Then, she told school principals the same thing. Why shouldn't healthy food be provided to school children? Children should know where their food comes from -- not from the milk shelf at the grocery store, but from a cow; not from the vegetable bin, but from the earth.

ALICE'S EDIBLE SCHOOLYARDS PROGRAM

While traveling the country, Alice Waters asks, "Do you know the most neglected schoolroom in America? It's none other than the lunch room." She tells us that kids fill up with sodas, pizza and snack foods. Waters began working years ago on a program in which kids serve each other food they helped to grow. The program includes a middle-school curriculum that teaches kids respect for the planet and for one another by having them work in the school garden and school kitchen. Waters has brought together teachers, chefs, food service managers, farmers, restaurant managers, and parents to work on the details of the program. She has set the right tone in the obesity battle, but the rest of the country is just beginning to wake up.

Dr. Barbara Frankowski, a Burlington, Vermont pediatrician and professor, serves on the board of the American Academy of Pediatrics and is a health consultant to Burlington schools. She is an evangelist when it comes to promoting nutrition and fitness. She says, "There are kids that are not just chubby but are quite a bit overweight in just about every class that I go into." When she talks about the federal "No Child Left Behind" program, she's referring to the kids' "behinds." Frankowski says, "What good is it if you pass all the tests, but die of a heart attack when you're 40 years old?"

Behavior, Too!: Many experts agree that nutrition affects children's behavior and their performance in school. Studies indicate that children who eat a healthy breakfast perform better academically and are less likely to disrupt class. Almost any school nurse will tell you that the children who come to school without breakfast complain of tummy aches and dizziness and exhibit learning and emotional problems.

You would think with all the information out there, we'd want to get rid of all that junk food and follow the advice of Alice Waters. What if all the schools in the country were ordered to purge junk food from their menus? Most likely, there would be a revolt. If you eliminate such popular items as burgers, fries and pizza, what would happen? Would the students make the transition from buying junk foods to healthier foods or simply brown-bag it?

The schools in Cohasset, Massachusetts tried to eliminate junk foods from their menus. School officials said, "No way." Because lunch programs must pay for themselves, messing with the menu can mean losing money. Joseph Gidzik, the town's health officer, in a well-to-do town of 7,300, admitted that the best of intentions can lead down the wrong road. He was concerned that if the school cafeteria turned quickly to healthy, nutritious food, there would be a backlash by the food managers and the students. There needs to be a transition in which everyone is involved, from food service personnel to teachers, administrators, and students.

According to Joanne Heidkamp of the Vermont Campaign to End Childhood Hunger, "The real problem is that foods come frozen on a truck, like those chicken McNuggets, and form the backbone of many school menus, as opposed to playing a minor role on the menu."

There's nothing wrong with burgers, fries, and pizza eaten occasionally as part of a varied diet that is based on fruits, veggies, and whole grains. Or, how about homemade meatless pizza, made with a little less cheese, and more vegetables?

Vending Machines: A Perfect Example of What Needs to Change

High-fat, sugary, and heavily processed food comes in a variety of ways -- in lunch bags from home, on school lunch trays, and from vending machines. Nationally, about 60 percent of our schools have vending machines that distribute candy and soda, the majority of sales supporting school programs. (Sugary soda is the largest source of teen calories.)

High schools are more likely to sell soda and candy bars than middle schools. In almost half of U.S. school districts, officials have allowed companies like Coca-Cola and Pepsi to sell soda in school vending machines or on-campus stores. In return, cash-starved schools receive up-front payments and in some cases, a percentage of sales.

Even though childhood dairy intake has been falling for 20 years, soda is now getting some healthy competition from milk. Milk vending machines are popping up across the country in an effort to offer students healthier alternatives to soft drinks.

Wisconsin leads the nation in the switch back to milk; two-thirds of the state's high schools now have milk vending machines. Nationwide, there are 7,500 machines dispensing milk in such flavors as chocolate, strawberry, and vanilla. Milk advocates have their work cut out for them, however, as there are 65,000 soft drink machines in the schools. The problem with flavored milk is the high amount of sugar added to the drinks.

The vending machine industry, taking heavy criticism from nutritionists and doctors, is launching an anti-obesity marketing campaign to improve its image and fend off efforts to remove vending machines from schools. Color-coded stickers on food items in vending machines separate the so-called healthy foods from the unhealthy items. The system is called the "Snackwise Nutrition Rating System," and was developed by Columbus Children's Hospital in Columbus, Ohio. The color green signifies a healthier choice than red. For example, a 1.25-ounce package of cinnamon-flavored Teddy Grahams is a green snack, and Grandma's Chocolate Chip Big Cookies is a red snack.

Pulling the Plug: In May 2006, it was announced that soft drink companies would begin pulling their high-calorie drinks from elementary schools. Former President Clinton, Governor Huckabee of Arkansas, and the American Heart Association helped to facilitate the change. As a result of this action, the Center for Science in the Public Interest (CSPI) dropped its planned lawsuit against Coca-Cola, PepsiCo, Cadbury Schweppes, and their bottlers. As good as the agreement is, schools, not nutritionists decide what to stock in their vending machines, and compliance by the beverage companies is voluntary.

There is, however, momentum building in Congress for legislation that would require the USDA to update its nutrition standards for foods sold outside of school meals (in vending machines, school stores, etc.) including: candy, cookies, fries, soda, potato chips, and other snack foods, as well as sports drinks -- standard fare in school vending machines and stores. We'll see what happens.
Source: The "Pulling The Plug" information was provided by the Center for Science in the Public Interest (CSPI).

Margo Wooten of CSPI came out with a report in June of 2006 that stated, "Although some local school districts have school food policies that are far better than state standards, they too often allow junk food in schools.

With junk food tempting kids at nearly every other public place in America, schools should be the one place where parents don't have to worry about what their kids are eating. States should continue to enact stronger nutrition policies, but since the school lunch program is, after all, a federal program, Congress should take action to ensure that all school foods are healthy."

CSPI recommends that the only beverages sold in schools should be waters, seltzer, low-fat or fat-free milk, and unsweetened juice drinks with at least 50 percent juice, and that beverage sizes be limited to 12 ounces. In snacks, CSPI recommends limiting the amount of saturated and trans fat, sodium, and added sugars.
* *CSPI is one of my top ten websites.*

Ditch the Fizz: It's been assumed that a high-intake of sweetened carbonated drinks contributes to obesity, but until the findings of a 2001-2002 study of 644 children, ages 7 to 11, in six primary schools in Christchurch, England, were published, there was no clear evidence. The one-year "Ditch the Fizz" campaign led to a decrease in the percentage of elementary schoolchildren who were overweight or obese. The improvement occurred after a modest reduction of less than one can a day. Representatives of the soft-drink industry contested the results.

3. FEED: FOOD EDUCATION EVERY DAY

Vermont School Children Making Pesto, FEED Program

FARM-TO-SCHOOL PROGRAMS

Over ten years ago, parents and educators in Vermont kept asking why schools weren't teaching children about good nutrition and why public school cafeterias didn't include local food products. From milk, meat, and cheeses, to vegetables and fruit, Vermont kids were missing out on high quality foods grown close to home.

In 2002-2003, schools in Vermont spent $13.4 million on food from distributors and wholesalers. Based on discussions with food service managers, only ten percent, or $1.3 million, of that total represents fresh or lightly processed produce. And less than five percent went for direct purchase of products from local farms.

Mitzi Johnson was frustrated when she saw children pass the local apple orchard on their way to school in South Hero, Vermont, knowing they were being served apples shipped from Washington State. She wanted to know why local farmers couldn't join forces with the schools to ensure that children were served fresh, locally-grown produce for snacks and meals. This would be a win-win scenario for the children, the farmers, and the entire community.

Johnson is a vegetable and apple grower and also a representative from South Hero in the Vermont House of Representatives. In 2006, she, along with other representatives introduced legislation whereby local schools would join forces with local farmers to improve the nutritional quality of food, and to teach the students about Vermont's agricultural heritage.

The 2006 Vermont Farm-to-School Funding Bill (H 456) passed both the House and Senate and was signed by the Governor. The monies provide grants to schools to purchase Vermont food products and acquire cafeteria equipment to process fresh produce. H456 also provided for professional development for teachers in the area of food, farming and equipment.

The Child Nutrition Program of the Vermont Department of Education works with the Food Education Every Day (FEED) program for training food service staff in purchasing and preparing Vermont food products in school meal programs.

There was also a one-time funding for a professional to process locally grown products for schools and institutions, and for equipment enabling farmers to process food. Strategies were developed to increase the use of locally grown products in Vermont schools.

Since 2006, programs to connect local farms to school cafeterias and classrooms to farms have begun to increase. The FEED program has trained many food service workers throughout the state. It is the most dynamic farm-to-school program in Vermont. FEED has developed individual farm-to-school programs in more than 60 schools since 1997 and had an impact on close to 20 percent of the students in Vermont.

FEED is involved in the creation of school gardens, farm-based field trips, student taste tests, community-based nutrition committees, nutrition and agriculture-education and purchasing local foods for cafeterias. The goal is to work with schools to build connections between classrooms, cafeterias, school gardens, local farms, and communities by involving food service workers, farmers, classroom teachers and other community partners. Teachers and students are also building school gardens as part of the FEED program. These gardens offer a place to study hands-on science, math, language arts, and social studies while providing food for the school cafeteria.

For more information on the mission and goals of the program, go to www.vtfeed.org or contact: Abbie Nelson, Vermont FEED Coordinator, (802) 434-4122, PO Box 697 Richmond, Vermont 05477

Recent efforts in Vermont have demonstrated that when children and food service personnel have relationships with local farmers and producers, they are more likely to try new foods and use fresh and less-processed foods. There is also a movement afoot to develop school gardens and to create an appreciation for the history of farming in local communities.

There are a number of pluses to increasing the supply of fresh local products in the schools. Studies show that bringing locally grown foods into schools benefits the regional economy. Farmers who work with the schools are able to extend the growing season, have outlets for their surplus, and sell produce that has surface blemishes but is perfectly nutritious. In an era where the outlook for the family farm is bleak, farm-to-school initiatives can be an opportunity for farms and a benefit to the community.

In the past few years, Vermont-grown vegetables including tomatoes, carrots, zucchini, and basil have started showing up in school cafeterias. Money that was once used to purchase food from out-of-state is now staying in Vermont's communities, and children are eating healthier meals.

Programs are sprouting up in cities and towns throughout the Green Mountains as food service directors, teachers and parents take steps to bring fresh, local foods into the schools. Vermont is considered a model state for farm-to-school programs across the nation.

Cooking for Life program, Vermont Campaign to End Childhood Hunger

2. A PRIMER ON SCHOOL BREAKFAST AND LUNCH PROGRAMS

Food Service Workers: It takes more than farmers to provide healthy food in the schools. Rachel Claffey, a food service manager, feeds 114 hungry youngsters at Newton Elementary in South Strafford, Vermont. Claffey lives across from the school. She serves food in the same room where she ate as a grade schooler and where she has spent the last 12 years as the food service manager. Her day begins at 4 a.m. when she starts baking bread for breakfast and prepping vegetables for lunch. Claffey leaves late in the afternoon depending on the amount of paperwork. She makes sure that the 30-percent-fat-or-less rule is followed.

CLAFFEY COMMENTS:

- We're not the dumb old kitchen witches that threw bad vegetable soup at you when you were younger.
- We try and incorporate as much local food as we can afford. Lots of times, it is just too expensive, such as local apples. That's unfortunate.
- The kids' favorite food is pizza along with apples, oranges, bananas, pancakes, sausage and fruit bars.
- We have always tried to maintain a healthy lunch program and to integrate new food on the menu. I dig into my Moosewood cookbook and make stuff with whole grains -- like tabouleh.

- Hot lunch has changed. It's more than the liver and onions we were fed as kids. We have standards we try to uphold, and we're trying to do it well on a very limited budget.
- People think of us as hash slingers, but we have to be really intelligent at what we do about obesity, diabetes and food allergies.

* I took some liberty with Caffey's comments. She is a positive role model as a food service manager. Source: Kardashian, K., Seven Days, August. 2007.

SCHOOL BREAKFAST AND LUNCH PROGRAMS

Every day the National School Lunch and Breakfast Program serves 28 million children in 98,000 public and non-for-profit schools -- about half of the nation's 60 million children. The program is administered by the Food and Nutrition Service (FNS), a division of the U.S. Department of Agriculture (USDA). (The USDA also administers Food Stamps, WIC, Summer Food Service Program and other programs.

Cooking for Life,
Vermont Campaign to End Childhood Hunger

FEED Program (Food Education Every Day)
Carrot Muffin Tasting

It Takes a Village to Lose a Pound: Somerville

The Boston suburb of Somerville went on a diet to curb childhood obesity. More fruits and vegetables were added to school lunches. Tufts University nutrition experts found that Somerville children avoided gaining about a pound of excess weight per year compared to counterparts in two nearby communities.

Researchers picked Somerville, a city of 77,500, because it had a large population of minority children in low-income families. The goal was to avoid meals high in sugar and fat, and the importance of physical activity was emphasized. Children began seeing more fresh fruits, berries and vegetables in the school cafeteria. School cooks started using fresh ingredients instead of frozen foods. They also turned to olive and canola oils and replaced fried foods with baked products. "If it looks good, they'll take it. And if it tastes good, they'll keep eating it," according to school food-service director Mary Jo McLarney. More than 90 teachers were taught a new health curriculum, including yoga, dance, and soccer.

Parents were sent newsletters offering health food tips, coupons for healthy foods, updates on the project, a physical activity guide and a healthy snack list. Somerville school nurses were trained to keep track of students' weight and counsel families of children at risk of becoming overweight. Some businesses supported the effort. Twenty restaurants agreed to offer more healthy meals, including low-fat dairy, smaller portions, and fruits and vegetables as side dishes. ✽

The National School Lunch and Breakfast Program subsidizes all meals, reimbursing schools with cash payments based on the number of meals served. Children from poor homes don't pay anything. Other students pay a reduced or full price based on their family's income.

In addition to cash payments, the government provides federal "entitlement" commodity foods to the schools. On average, the commodity food program provides about 10 to 15 percent of the food used in schools; however, the amount varies widely among schools and is determined by the total number of lunches served. Breakfast meals do not receive commodities, although lunch commodities can be used in the breakfast program.

The National School Lunch Program (NSLP), established in 1946, is a federally assisted meal program operating in public and nonprofit private schools and residential child care institutions. It provides low-cost or free lunches to more than 30 million school children each day. In 1998, Congress expanded the NSLP to include reimbursements for snacks served to children in after-school programs.

Afternoon snacks are provided to children on the same eligibility level as school meals. Programs that operate in areas where at least 50 percent of the students are eligible for free or reduced-price meals may serve all their snacks for free.

The New Food Pyramid

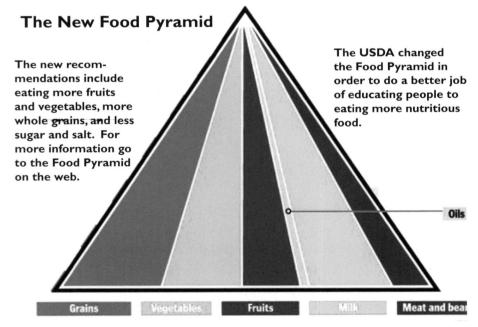

The new recommendations include eating more fruits and vegetables, more whole grains, and less sugar and salt. For more information go to the Food Pyramid on the web.

The USDA changed the Food Pyramid in order to do a better job of educating people to eating more nutritious food.

Oils

Grains Vegetables Fruits Milk Meat and bean

Farm to School Program   FEED: Food Education Every Day

Most of the support the USDA provides to schools in the lunch program comes in the form of cash reimbursements.

Here is how it breaks down:

```
---------------------------------------------
free lunches............................$2.47
reduced-price lunches .........$2.07
paid lunches............................$0.23
free snacks..............................$0.68
reduced priced snacks .........$0.34
paid snacks .............................$0.06

---------------------------------------------
```

School Breakfasts: The School Breakfast Program (SBP) was established by Congress in 1966 and made permanent in 1975 to assist schools in providing nutritious morning meals to the nation's children. Research shows that children who have breakfast at school eat more fruits, drink more milk, and consume a wider variety of foods than those who don't eat breakfast or have breakfast at home.

These students also displayed higher test scores.

Just like with the school lunch program, household income determines if a child is eligible to receive free or reduced breakfasts. The same application covers both lunch and breakfast. Households that receive food stamps are automatically eligible for free school meals. For the 2007-08 school year, schools are reimbursed $1.35 per free breakfast, $1.05 per reduced cost breakfast, and $0.24 per paid breakfast.

"Universal School Breakfast" refers to any school program that of offers breakfast at no charge to all students, regardless of income. These schools are still in the minority, and must seek local or state resources to cover any additional costs. In 2008, the Vermont legislature made free breakfasts available to all poor children by adding 30 cents to the federal reimbursement. About 7,500 Vermont children are eligible for the program.

FEDERAL ENTITLEMENT FOOD COMMODITIES

In addition to cash reimbursements, for breakfast and lunch programs, schools are provided with commodity foods called "entitlement foods," at a value of 17 cents per meal.

The individual states select the "entitlement foods" for their schools from a list of various foods purchased by the USDA and offered through the school lunch program. Schools can also get "bonus" commodities as they are available from surplus agricultural stocks.

The variety of both entitlement and bonus commodities depend on quantities available and market prices.

Group A Commodity Foods are seasonable and perishable, and include fruits, vegetables, poultry, fish, and meats. Most of those foods are purchased through the Agricultural Marketing Service of the USDA.

Group B Commodity Foods come from price support (subsidy) programs and include dairy products, cereals, grains, peanut products, and vegetable oils.

There are 160 food commodities, from regular and low fat cheeses, fruit and natural juices, meats, fruits and vegetables to butter and other dairy products. There is an ongoing process to improve the nutritional value of the food commodities. There is no longer any shortening on the list. Fruits used to come in heavy syrups and now come with lighter syrups. There is less sodium in the meat products. The local school districts have a choice of what they purchase. Milk must be offered as part of the school meals.

The Department of Defense (DoD) also provides schools with fresh produce purchased through DoD at a cost of $50 million a year.

Problems with the Feds: According to health professionals and food service managers, the two basic problems with the Federal Lunch and Breakfast Programs are that the nutrition guidelines need to be strengthened and the reimbursement rates increased.

One of the complaints about commodity assistance is that the program encourages an "institutional" approach to food service that emphasizes inexpensive, processed items and attainment of minimum rather than optimum nutritional standards. The foods in some cases are high in trans fats and loaded with refined starches and sugars.

The school lunch program helps dispose of surplus agricultural commodities, especially cheap feedlot beef and dairy products, both high in fat. The government is supposed to limit the fat content of foods sent to schools but that doesn't always happen. Again, it depends on the knowledge of the food service managers and how much they want to change the eating habits of the students. School systems have a say over what they receive and schools can choose not to receive any commodities at all.

The U.S. Department of Agriculture has a standard for what it calls Foods of Minimal Nutritional Values, and restricts the sale of those foods in the cafeteria during mealtimes. This 30-year standard focuses on whether the food has sufficient levels of nutrients, not on whether the food has excessive calories, added sugars, sodium, or saturated or trans fat. Bipartisan legislation introduced in early 2006 would have had the USDA bring its nutrition standards for foods sold in school vending machines, school stores, and a la carte in line with current nutrition science. Seltzer water for instance is not allowed under the current standard, but Twinkies and potato chips are. The legislation did not pass. What a world!

For more information visit the Federal Government's Food Commodity Program website.

NUTRITIONAL BALANCE

There is no guideline that says any given commodity has to be low in fat; after all, two ounces of cheese with a bowl of vegetable soup and a whole grain roll, along with a serving of fruit or vegetables, would still be an acceptable low-fat lunch. That makes sense.

The way I see it, it's okay to have a bowl of Ben & Jerry's ice cream, but it needs to be balanced with plenty of whole grains and veggies. It's the same with eating food items high in fat like cottage cheese and avocados. Those foods are good for you as long as you don't eat too much of them.

The federal lunch program requires a minimum of 3/4 cup of two different fruits and vegetables every day, which isn't a bad starting point. And the federal guidelines don't limit the amount.

There are programs with creative food service directors where kids routinely eat a variety of fruits, vegetables and whole grains and are choosing more healthy food commodities such as fish, walnuts, cheese, and whole wheat flour.

A parent-led campaign in Canada forced the Canadian soft drink industry to pull its carbonated soft drinks from all elementary and junior high schools in 2005. The same is happening in elementary schools in the U.S.

Cost: According to some food service managers, the problem is not with the federal nutrition guidelines but with the low reimbursement rates for federal breakfast and lunch. According to the Vermont Campaign to End Childhood Hunger, the federal reimbursement for meals is not adequate to provide healthy meals to children. Many schools sell "competitive" meals to support the federal program. These meals tend to be "junk food' because the mark-up is high. (Competitive foods are foods offered at schools, other than meals served through USDA's school meal program. Competitive foods include food and drinks sold in vending machines, a la carte sales and food offered through school stores and snack bars.)

In Vermont, where there are many small schools, programs lose on average 20 cents for every breakfast they serve to low-income students -- no small change.

The commody-entitlement foods provide 17 cents for school lunches. The reimbursement rate for free school lunch is $2.47, too low for some small schools.

The politics of school food is complicated. You would think all school boards would welcome the federal school breakfast and lunch program, but that's not always the case. The reasons are varied. Some school administrators say the federal programs cost too much, even though the cost is minimal when you look at the overall school budget.

Dorigen Keeney, a nutrition specialist at the Vermont Campaign to End Childhood Hunger says that federal food reimbursements are low and that food services in small schools have difficulty breaking even. However, some states make up the difference, as do some school districts. Some schools and districts don't want to be held to the federal requirements.

One of the determining factors of the school breakfast and lunch programs is the number of students served. Some small schools have high food costs and aren't able to serve meals for the amount the government reimburses them. In other cases, the number of students eating is low either because the food isn't appealing or because the meal is offered at a time that doesn't accommodate student schedules; maybe breakfast is over by the time the buses arrive. In some cases, students get only 15 minutes for lunch and the lines are too long to buy lunch and still have time to eat. Finally, there is a stigma attached to a breakfast and lunch program that serves the poor. Some schools use plastic cards that all students use to purchase food, so no one knows who's receiving free and reduced breakfast and lunch.

Vermont has a law that requires each community to offer both breakfast and lunch unless the local school community votes to opt out of the program. Each subsequent year, the school board must vote, allowing for public comment, in order for the school to not continue to offer breakfast or lunch. There is also the unfortunate fact that many school boards and administrators are willing to give the contract for the lunch program to the low-bid food service company who can save money by using processed foods, such as frozen chicken nuggets.

Despite all the issues with school meals, they are still more nutritious than what many poor children eat at home. They are also more nutritious than what children buy from school vending machines and snack bars.

From what I've learned, the money needed to supplement the federal school breakfast/lunch program is a pittance of the overall school budget. And why isn't the federal government footing the whole bill, anyway? What's happening in your school district? How much does your state government add to the pie? Some states make up the whole difference. Check out your state. As pointed out earlier, children don't learn when they are nutritionally challenged, that is, when they don't get enough of the right foods to eat.

Source: The above information came from Vern Grubinger, Overview Of School Food In Vermont, a report for the University of Vermont Extension and the Center for Sustainable Agriculture, September 2004.

The Good News

In May of 2008, the Vermont legislature made breakfast free for 7,500 low-income children. Many of these kids already received reduced-priced meals. Now, Vermont has become the 4th state in the nation to offer free school breakfast to all low-income students.

The states of Washington and Colorado passed similar legislation that uses state money to pay the child's portion of reduced price breakfasts. This legislation recognizes that families who qualify for reduced price meals cannot afford the 70 cents/day for each child to receive breakfast and lunch.

A family of four that qualifies for reduced price meals makes between $26,845 and $38,203; well below the $49,685 needed to meet their basic needs, according to the Joint Fiscal Office of the Vermont Legislature as estimated for a rural family with two wage earners.

Whole Wheat Biscuits, Edmunds School FEED Program

The Not-So-Good News

The "Food Crisis" in 2008 is putting the squeeze on the School Lunch and Breakfast Programs. Katie Wilson, president-elect of the School Nutrition Association, told members of the House Education and Labor Committee that we don't have the funds to sustain the school breakfast and lunch programs. Many schools in 2008 will charge more for full-price meals in addition to cutting staff.

Schools just can't put anything on a child's lunch tray. Because the government subsidizes lunches, schools are expected to follow new federal guidelines for healthy eating by providing lots of fresh fruit and vegetables along with whole grains. These are the foods hit hardest by the rising cost of food, as are milk and meat, two universal offerings in school lunch rooms. A one-penny increase in the cost of milk can cost the nation's schools another $54 million.

In 2009, Congress must re-authorize the continuation of the National School Lunch and Breakfast program and the Child Nutrition and WIC (Women, Infants, and Children) programs.

Murals in the lunchroom at Brewster Pierce School

A CASE STUDY: THE BREWSTER PIERCE SCHOOL OF HUNTINGTON, VERMONT

It would be helpful to look at one particular school to see how it deals with its food budget, the Federal Food Commodity Program, and the issue of health insurance for kitchen staff, which has a large impact on school budgets.

Allison Forest has been the food service director at Brewster Pierce for the past 19 years. The small school of 135 children is located in Huntington, a rural community 30 minutes south of Burlington, Vermont.

Allison said that the food program works fairly well at Brewster Pierce even though it's a balancing act to provide healthy nutritious food and at the same time meet the costs of the food budget. She said that overall, the school board and administration are very supportive. This is not always the case. Many rural schools don't have a proper kitchen or an enlightened staff and community, as in Huntington.

Allison Forest chooses the healthier commodity foods, such as ones with no trans fat, like pasta, flour and vegetable oil. For breakfast, she chooses milk, Rice Krispies and cold cereals. She would prefer to use more healthful whole grains, but the budget won't allow it.

Health insurance can have a profound effect on the food budget in a school. At Brewster Pierce, there is a line-item for health insurance in the overall school budget, not in the food budget. Some schools pay for health insurance in the food budget by using the profits from vending machines.

Allison Forest says health care costs are one of the greatest challenges that schools face. If the kitchen staff work more than a certain number of hours, the school is expected to provide health insurance. This is why many schools limit the number of hours for food service workers. What's needed is universal single-payer health coverage.

- **Auto companies spend $1,200 in healthcare costs to produce a car in the U.S. In Canada, healthcare costs are covered by the government. This is one of the main reasons more cars are built in Ontario than in Michigan.**

Brewster Pierce's $40,000
Food Budget

$16,000 in expenses goes for food costs, such as vegetables, milk and other food products; the remainder goes to pay salaries. Allison Forest works 30 hours a week, cooking and keeping the books. Every month she sends in a report to the Feds on the number of school breakfasts and lunches she has served for free, reduced priced, and full-pay students. Her health benefits are covered in the school budget along with the other teachers in the school. It took her 12 years to receive health care benefits. The other worker puts in 27 hours a week. She can choose a reduced health care alternative or receive a cash payment for health care as she has not worked long enough to receive health insurance.

Revenue: Of the $40,000 school food budget, $2,500 came from fund-raisers such as the annual Town Hall supper, community pancake breakfasts and bingo. About $10,000 was derived from federal reimbursements for school breakfasts and lunches based on the number of meals served. The remainder of the budget, about $27,500, came from payments by students and adults for school breakfasts and lunches. Breakfasts cost $1.00; lunches are $3.00 for adults and $2.00 for students. Some students pay a reduced amount or nothing, depending on family income.

The federal food commodity allotment is in addition to the $40,000 school budget. It came to about $2,400 but it's worth much more than that, as schools get a break on the costs of commodity food. For example, a 20-pound box of pasta costs only $5.

OBSTACLES IN THE USE OF LOCAL FOODS

The greater use of local foods in schools as part of an effort to incorporate fresher, less processed foods into school meals and snacks has the potential to improve childhood nutrition. This combined with nutrition education, farm visits and school gardens, can help children develop healthy eating habits. However, at the present time, connecting local farms with schools is secondary to the broader goal of improving the nutritional quality and variety of food that schools purchase and serve, wherever it comes from.

Vermont farmers are providing more dairy products, vegetables and fruits through Vermont food distributors to schools. One of the problems is that most of the milk produced in Vermont is sent to processing facilities in southern New England where it is mixed with milk from other states and then sent back to Vermont. Commercial bread, although baked in Vermont, contains few local ingredients, although that is beginning to change. Meats from Vermont tend to be higher in cost than from commercial sources. The free meats from the USDA commodity program make school purchases of local meat unlikely.

Farmers selling directly to schools need to have substantial liability coverage. However, when a farmer sells food through a commercial food distributor, the liability issue rests with the distributor. When Vermont farmers were questioned about the sale of food to schools, they indicated that school sales were a small part of their business at best and did not represent a profitable market for them at this time. However, they thought it was a positive way to connect to the community. Similarly, distributors said that distributing local food to schools is not that profitable for them because the orders are typically small and the length of travel too far. Sales to larger schools are more profitable.

Other obstacles to getting more local food into schools are limited school food budgets and insufficient storage and refrigeration facilities.

Vermont Farmer Planting Seeds with Children, Edmunds School, Burlington, Vermont. FEED

4. SUCCESSFUL SCHOOL MODELS - URBAN AND RURAL

URBAN MODELS

The Burlington Food Council: When Burlington residents were asked years ago to create a legacy for the future of their city, one of their top choices was to provide Vermont-grown food in schools to improve student nutrition and invest in the local farm economy.

The Burlington Food Council (BFC) meets on a monthly basis. It is made up of farmers from the Intervale, the Burlington Food Service manager, parent volunteers, teachers, and nutritionists. Other participants include representatives from the Burlington School District, the FEED Partners (Shelburne Farms, NOFA-VT, Food Works,) and the University of Vermont.

The Food Council's goals are to increase educational opportunities for school children and their families around food, farms, and nutrition; to help build the capacity for Burlington to better meet the food needs of students and to improve the Burlington School Districts access to food from local farms through improved communication and infrastructure.

One of the first steps of the BFC was to identify the challenges, opportunities, and resources inherent in these goals. In the winter of 2004, BFC collected data and produced a report entitled "Burlington Community Food Assessment." The report stated that 69 percent of Burlington teens between grades 8 and 12 failed to meet minimum USDA dietary requirements, 27 percent were overweight or at risk of being overweight and 40 percent spent three or more hours a day watching TV, playing video games, or using a computer.

Students at a Farm, Eating Cherry Tomatoes, Vermont FEED (Food Education Every Day)

THE EDMUNDS MIDDLE SCHOOL IN BURLINGTON

Bonnie Acker was a parent of a Burlington student and an active participant in the effort to improve school food at Edmunds Elementary School. She volunteered to work with students, inventing recipes and test-cooking healthy foods that might eventually be incorporated into the school menu. Bonnie is also a member of the Burlington Food Council.

Parent and community volunteers went into classrooms and worked with students to develop new recipes with produce from the Intervale in Burlington and other local farms. They also helped to host field trips at local farms where students visited, planted, and harvested crops to learn where food comes from. With the help of these volunteers, students performed taste tests and surveyed other students. If a recipe was a success, it was included in the school menu.

Acker worked with a group of middle school students to find the perfect whole grain oatmeal treat. Using local maple syrup and oats with government commodity eggs and oil, the kids tried over 30 recipes to find the best one. The winner was a moist, tasty muffin that included whole wheat flour, Vermont carrots, maple syrup, and apple sauce.

Acker, the Vermont FEED partners, and other community members worked closely with Doug Davis, Burlington's Food Service Director to change menus and improve nutrition in the schools as well as recycling food wastes to the local Intervale compost site.

Davis said, "This year there are fewer hot dogs and hamburgers and more veggies and fruits. Employees are slicing apples and oranges, rather than serving them whole because students tend to eat more fruit that way."

Cukes, sprouts, tomatoes and hummus are regulars at the new Edmunds sandwich bar. Sugary juices in vending machines are being replaced with less caloric versions. The school district is also working in partnership with organic farmers in the city's Intervale, which, Davis proudly reported, is bringing more local produce into the schools. "It's an amazing partnership that I feel will generate national models," he said.

Along with greens, peppers, and cucumbers, 650 pounds of zucchini and 900 pints of cherry tomatoes were brought into Edmunds in the fall of 2005 for salads and the sandwich bar. Davis said he does not believe a little pizza, now and then, hurts children, and he has no plans to change the once-a-week pizza at H.O. Wheeler Elementary. The pizza comes with salad and fruit.

For more information see the Burlington Food Council website.

Photo Courtesy Vermont Food Bank

RURAL MODELS

Hardwick: In the summer of 2004, the Hardwick school built an extensive series of gardens around the school. Students, teachers, and parents planted a wide variety of vegetables in the spring for a fall harvest. The gardens are used for classroom lessons -- everything from insect biology, to botany, to soil ecosystems. Much of the food that comes from the gardens is used for classroom cooking and nutrition lessons.

Beyond Food: The Burke Town School Project

Grade school teachers Jessica Simpson and Tracie Surridge named their unit "That was Then, This is Now: A Comparative Study of Vermont Agriculture 1800-2002." Students interviewed older relatives and neighbors about their farming experience. They watched movies and read books on agricultural history and methods, and went on field trips to a sugarhouse, a dairy farm, a cheese factory, a farm museum, and a sawmill. The children interviewed a sheep farmer who was also their school nurse, and a logger and mill owner who was a student's father.

Student Lettuce Picker, Courtesy of NOFA

To cap the unit, students chose research topics and presented their findings to a crowd of 150 at a community dinner. Eric Marcy and Kirsten Wilson talked about early milking methods: "In the 1800s it took ten minutes to milk a cow and farmers had to bring their milk to the creamery by horse." Tommy Vigent was motivated by his farm field experience to research the relationship between comfortable bedding for cows and increased milk production. Parents were delighted to learn something new about agriculture from their sons and daughters.

Fairfield: This rural school had a project called "Lettuce Celebrate." The third and fourth grade students worked with the Vermont Agency of Agriculture and Greenwind Farm to create a small working garden of their own. They started plants from seeds, composted school food-waste, and weeded and watered the garden. They learned geometry through garden design and biology through working with plants. They discussed nutrition as they ate produce from the garden and used budgeting principles in the sale of produce they had grown.

The students sold lettuce to the school cafeteria in June, and hosted a school-wide celebration. The project climaxed at harvest time with the selling of vegetables on the town common and dinner for their neighbors at the Fall Harvest Celebration. In the future, they plan to have the school garden supply vegetables to the town's senior center. "Anything except garlic and spice for the old folks," the center director says. Finally, the students studied apple varieties at the University of Vermont Horticultural Farm to start a school orchard.

The Brewster Pierce School: I consider this school to be the `Jewel in the Crown' when it comes to the ideal school/food program. (Earlier, I wrote about how Allison Forest manages the school budget.) It has been run for over 16 years by Allison Forest, who's been preparing meals for 150 kids. My good friend, Michelle Jenness, assisted Allison for many years. I would use the word innovative to describe the program, because the food program is so different in nature from most schools; and yet it makes such common sense.

Allison Forest said "Using local produce to create healthy meals that kids and teachers will eat is possible. Incorporating fresh greens and other healthy foods that kids like such as walnuts, salsa, dried cherries, and trail mix into meals adds to the mix." She said, "We have to work on all levels, on all ages, so that teenagers will be making wise food choices, and when, they're ready, having healthy babies, who will be given real whole foods at home and will eat them happily when they get to school."

Allison Forest avoids processed foods, and, instead bakes homemade bread in the school ovens four days a week and emphasizes the use of fresh fruits and vegetables rather than canned and frozen varieties. The kids eat beans once a week, grains every day, and homemade soups on Friday, all of which are eagerly anticipated by the kids. Ethnic meals are prepared in order to learn about foods from around the world and to appreciate the diversity of life. For example, a meal of millet, spicy vegetables, homemade pita bread and tahini shortbread came from North Africa.

This is carried over into the classroom, where Allison does food workshops. Michele Jenness taught a lesson on the historical relationship between slavery and sugar cane and Allison Forest taught a lesson on how to combine grains and beans as a healthy source of protein, as compared to meat, which has a higher percentage of fat. Tasting foods such as raw, red cabbage and red peppers in the safety of the classroom also prepares students for what they will find during lunch.

Allison Forest buys as much local and organic food as possible. For example, she purchases organic vegetables from Sarah Jane Williamson's Jubilee Farm in Huntington Center. The first and second graders walk over to the Jubilee Farm to harvest carrots in the fall. Black River Produce, of North Springfield, provides both conventional and organic fruits and vegetables throughout the school year to Brewster Pierce. Black River picks up Vermont produce and delivers to schools throughout the Green Mountains.

The results of the Brewster Pierce food program are a more varied diet, exposure to new foods and an understanding of what constitutes a healthy diet. According to Michele, it's an educational process that takes years to develop, boosted by exposure to new foods. When the kids don't shout, "Not that again!" you know you're doing something right. I don't believe Allison Forest would be there if they had to serve processed fish sticks or frozen Chicken McNuggets.

Mural in the Lunchroom at Brewster Pierce School

WHAT HAPPENS WHEN SCHOOLS CLOSE?

In Vermont, there aren't many affordable summer programs for low income children. Poor families can't afford to pay for camps, community recreational programs or child care centers to look after their children while they work. These parents must rely on neighbors or relatives to watch their children. The television is both baby sitter and entertainment for far too many children.

When schools close in Vermont, thousands of low-income children don't have access to free or reduced-price meals at summer meal sites like they have when schools are in session. In 2006 there were 52 summer food programs that served less than 1 in 5 low income children in Vermont. 5,500 of the eligible 42,000 school children received breakfast, lunch or snack in 2006. Many of these programs only served meals for 1 or 2 weeks during the summer.

It is not just food that kids are hungry for -- there are also recreation and educational activities included in the programs. When free meals are offered in conjunction with activities, the stigma of a kid going to a free program is eliminated.

The problem is that the federal programs that pay for summer meals were designed with urban populations in mind. Most areas in Vermont lack the large numbers of children needed for funding.

Vermont has steadily increased the number of children in the summer programs and ranks ninth among the 50 states. In Johnson, Vermont, coolers of sandwiches and snacks are sent from a school cafeteria to a day camp at an elementary school, a skate park in town, a reading program at a local library, kids in a court diversion program, and a theater camp at a local school.

* For more information on summer food programs, go to www.vtnohunger.org.

Summer Programs for Low Income Children

Campaign to End Childhood Hunger

D. FOOD INSECURITY, HUNGER AND RESPONSIBILITY

THE WORKING POOR IN CUTLER, CALIFORNIA

Iris Caballero lives and works in California's Central Valley, where most of the country's produce is grown. The valley also has some of the highest poverty rates in the State. Iris often has a hard time keeping the refrigerator and cupboard stocked with food. The working poor in that area, like Iris, who work in the fields everyday, often have a long walk to the supermarket, and not much time for cooking.

In Iris's neighborhood in the isolated town of Cutler, the only food store is a mini-market that offers an array of processed foods. It's ironic that most of the local fruit and vegetable pickers like Iris can't afford to eat the produce they harvest. Iris says that during the harvest season, she picks grapes and oranges in the fruit groves near her home. Most of the year, she feeds her husband and three children on the cheapest food she can get: bread, potatoes, and tortillas. As a diabetic from the age of 19, she knows that the sugar, starch and fat-laden diet from her local market is more than unhealthy -- it's dangerous.

Iris's children go to Cutler Elementary school. It has so many diabetic kids that the teachers held an emergency workshop on how to handle blood sugar highs and lows. This is a school where 100 percent of the kids qualify for the federal breakfast and lunch programs. Iris and other farm worker mothers attended a free nutrition class that addressed the problems associated with unhealthy diets, including issues such as smart food buying.

The mothers say they appreciate the tips on healthy eating, but they still have to scrape by just to pay for real fruit juice instead of the punch they know is mostly sugar and water. And they have to walk four miles, often with their children, to and from the nearest supermarket, where fresh produce is plentiful and less expensive.

Irene Flores, another farm worker, is having trouble putting healthy food on the table. Irene would like to feed her family of three children better. She stores large sacks of beans and corn to eat during the winter.

Homestead Food Insecurity: Millions of families like those of Iris Caballero and Irene Flores lack access to healthy food and the financial resources to put good food on the table. What an irony in such a rich country. In Vermont, more than 14 percent of children live in homes where parents, especially single mothers, run out of groceries periodically, as there isn't enough money for nutritious food. The term for this problem, **food insecurity,** was coined by the government. It originated as an agricultural term in international circles to assess how well nations feed their people.

The Suburbanization of Shopping: Most consumers want big stores where they can get bargains and variety. Big stores don't fit into dense urban areas, and rural towns can't support them. Many smaller stores have been forced to close because they can't compete with the large supermarket chains. During the 1950s, more than half of all grocery stores were mom-and-pop operations. Today, that figure is less than 17 percent. Jim Harrison, president of the Vermont Grocers' Association, said that Vermont has fewer than 70 grocers, down from 100 grocers, 15 years ago.

Take, for instance, the small general store in Weld, Maine run by Jerry and Dot Nering. This is a remote town of 400 people. The shop used to be stocked with meats, cheeses, and produce. Customers swapped gossip around the wood stove. Today, that's all changed. Now, the shelves have few items and fewer customers. Within the last couple of years, two Wal-Mart Supercenters opened within 20 miles.

The Grocery Gap: Urban & Rural

Most poor communities share low levels of income and education, inadequate housing and transportation, and limited access to food markets. Low-income shoppers in New York City pay close to 9 percent more for a basket of groceries than middle-class shoppers in other parts of the city. In poor neighborhoods there is one store for every 10,000 people. In wealthier areas, the average is one store for every 6,000 people.

In Hartford, Connecticut, 53 percent of low-income people who do not have cars say they have difficulty getting to a supermarket. Over two-thirds say a lack of transportation limits their choice of food markets.

Rural Vermont and New England:

Food Insecurity is more prevalent among rural people than urban people of the same poverty level. More than a few Vermont farm families qualify for food stamps.

There's a famous New England saying, "You can't get there from here." In Pittsburgh, New Hampshire, it's almost impossible to find healthy food at reasonable prices. Pittsburgh is a rural town of 870 people close to the Canadian border. Folks there have to drive a long distance to get to a supermarket. Many people who live in northern rural areas have nowhere to shop. The term for such places is "food desert." For those who have trouble driving long distances, that means sometimes buying pricey, fatty foods at convenience stores. "Food deserts" are also prevalent in poor urban areas; residents may have to take long bus rides or walk a mile to get to a grocery store. The U.S. Department of Agriculture estimates that groceries are 10 percent more expensive in "food deserts" than in suburban stores.

In 2006, a gallon of milk in Concord, New Hampshire, the state capital, cost $2.69. In Milan, New Hampshire, a rural town of 1,300 people 120 miles north of Concord, the price of milk at the local convenience store was $4.00. Today, the cost of milk in Concord would be $4.00 or higher.

HUNGER IN THE UNITED STATES

In the early 1960s, Bobby Kennedy, the Attorney General of the U.S., went down to the Mississippi Delta and interviewed poor black people who lived in shacks close to the rich soils of the delta. The cameras revealed shocking pictures of thin, malnourished men, women and children. The stark truth was that they didn't have enough to eat. The coverage of that event heightened consciousness about this national tragedy, and the "War on Poverty" began.

Today, if you were to travel to the Mississippi Delta and other poor rural areas throughout the country you would experience a different situation. You would still find thousands of families that don't have enough healthy food to eat. The difference between now and the early 60s is that many people have become overweight and obese from eating large amounts of overly processed foods.

Many people in Mississippi and other rural areas live with chronically poor-quality food and episodic food shortages resulting in nutrient deficiencies. Children in these homes have more developmental delays, poor health, and more hospitalizations.

Source: C-snap website. "The Impact of Food Insecurity on the Development of Young Low-Income Black and Latino Children."

Hunger Statistics: According to America's Second Harvest, the national hunger-prevention organization, in 2006, 10.9 percent of households, or 12 percent of the total population were **"food insecure."** This translates into almost 36 million Americans, including 13 million children.

Over four and a half million households experienced so much food insecurity that the USDA classified them as officially suffering from **"very low food security with hunger."** This includes 400,000 children, many of whom are overweight or obese. That comes to about 4 percent of all U.S. households. The percent of households with "very low food security with hunger" increased from 3.5 percent to 4 percent from 2003-2006. All of these percentages have increased in the past 3 years.

It should be clear that hunger is a fact of life in the U.S. Millions of people experience food insecurity, and one out of every six children is not getting adequate food. These statistics raise questions for the larger community as to how it will deal with the problems of nutrition and food insecurity, which go hand in hand.

Food Aid: Twenty-five million Americans depend on emergency food aid. According to a 2007 survey on hunger and homelessness by the U.S. Conference of Mayors, there was a 10 percent increase in overall food requests and half of all emergency requests were from families with children. The Conference of Mayors' report listed the main causes of hunger as: unemployment, low wages, and high housing and medical costs.

A 2004 analysis of data by the U.S. Census reported that 60 million Americans live on less than $7 per day. In 2006, 13 percent of the population were below the poverty level, which was $10,400 for one person or $28/day. *Source: Household Food Security in the United States:2006 USDA Economic Research Service.*

Lynn Parker, who heads the Food Research and Action Center, says, "More hunger and food insecurity means more children who have trouble at school, more illness among children and adults, less ability to purchase a balanced and nutritious diet and higher levels of anxiety for parents trying to make ends meet."

Thirteen million of the 38.8 million living in poverty in the U.S. in 2006 were children. Many of these children lived in homes with parents who worked on one job or many part-time jobs, which resulted in being paid too little to make ends meet. The high cost of housing and utilities often make it impossible for people paid the minimum wage to put food on the table.

What makes this all the more alarming is that our cities and states are now experiencing severe budget crises. At the same time, charitable giving is down. How strange this is considering we are the wealthiest nation in the world.

In 2002, the Walton family of Wal-Mart fame had a net gain of $8.5 billion, more than the total budget for Head Start, which serves 1 million children. By the way, most workers at Wal-Mart do not have health insurance. Wal-Mart's CEO's pay rose 1,767 percent between 1995 and 2003.

Golden Parachutes

The Food Stamp program enables low-income families to purchase food with coupons or electronic transfers at supermarket check-out counters. The Women, Infant and Children's (WIC) program provides nutritional foods to supplement diets, along with educational materials, to low-income women, infants, and children. The WIC Farmers' Market Nutrition program provides coupons that can be exchanged for eligible fruits and vegetables at local farmers' markets, roadside stands and CSA programs.

Many families on limited income run out of food or rely on cheap, often high-fat foods that promote weight gain. Good nutrition is financially out of reach for many families. The new federal diet guidelines promote more fruits, vegetables, lean meats, and whole grains, which are some of the more expensive items in your local supermarkets. The guidelines won't help unless low-income families receive more in food stamps.

Doug Hemming, a food stamp recipient at Highgate Apartments, Barre, says, "The Food Stamp Program, in my estimation, is by far our biggest and most important nutrition program in America. Literally there are no other food resources that even come close to it in scale."

Photo Courtesy of the Vermont Campaign to End Childhood Hunger

HUNGER AND SOLUTIONS IN THE GREEN MOUNTAINS

Even though Vermont is a small state, the problems of hunger reflect what's going on in the rest of the nation. A three-year average from 2004-2006 on food insecurity in Vermont taken from the last U.S. Census provided the following statistics:

- 9.6 percent of households were food insecure.
- 19,000 children, under 18 live in food-insecure households.
- 14.7 percent of all children live in food-insecure households
- 4.3 percent of all households were food-insecure with hunger.
- There has been a 100 percent increase in food insecurity with hunger. Since 2000, Vermont had the largest increase of any state.

All of these stats have increased since 2006.

Budgeting: In order to understand why it's difficult to provide healthy, nutritious food for a food-insecure Vermont family, let's look at a budget based on a four-member family living in a rural area of the state, with two adult wage earners and two children.

Total monthly income:.. $2,140

Total monthly expenses -- includes rent, heat, electricity, transportation, health care, clothing, personal expenses, dental care, insurance, and other costs: $4,921

Deficit each month without federal nutrition benefits: $2,781

Tax credits:..$268

The total deficit each month $2,160

Source: The above numbers were published in the 2005 Basic Needs Budget of the Vermont Joint Fiscal Office.

THREE VERMONT DOCUMENTARIES ON POVERTY AND HUNGER

Robert Dostis, the former Executive Director of the Vermont Campaign to End Childhood Hunger (VT-CECH), shared some thoughts on hunger in a 19-minute film called "Hidden Hunger" commissioned by VTCECH in 2005. The film begins by stating that 13 percent of all Vermont children live in poverty and one in five children live in homes without an adequate food supply.

Dostis says that poverty and hunger in the U.S. is a concept that many people have a hard time grasping; it isn't visible like the hunger and malnutrition in developing countries portrayed on television. If you work at a soup kitchen or as a school food service worker, you will see the challenges that families and children face in terms of receiving healthy, nutritious food.

In Vermont, children are not starving, but they are going without adequate nutrition, and that is having an impact in terms of their physical, mental and social growth. What's clear to Dostis and others is that the cumulative costs of housing, transportation, heat, clothing, child care, medical care and food place undue amounts of stress on families, especially children. We know that children require regular balanced nutrition in order to thrive physically, emotionally and intellectually. When they arrive at school hungry, they are more likely to be tired and not focused. This is why school breakfast and lunch programs are so critical.

Source: Hidden Hunger, a film by Anjalika Sharma on hunger in Vermont in 2005. Commissioned by VTCECH.

Another film commissioned by VTCECH called "Every Child, Every Day" was previewed around Vermont in the fall of 2007. The 14-minute film describes how Vermonters are tackling hunger with solutions such as subsidized meals in schools and day care centers, and nutrition education.

"Every Child, Every Day" was filmed and produced by Jim Ritvo and Dave Raizman. They interviewed individuals who are making a difference in the fight against hunger. The documentary opens with Brett Mashteare telling two stories -- what it was like for him growing up with food stamps and food shelves, and, then how years later he worked as a summer food program counselor, where he made a difference in the lives of kids who were facing the same food shortages his family had faced.

The camera takes viewers to a library that combines food and summer reading; to a day care center serving toddlers orange slices and scrambled eggs to ensure they have a healthy diet; and to an after-school cooking class where adolescents learn nutrition basics while having healthy meals. What's clear from the film is that every one of the options described above needs to be deployed in the fight against hunger.

In addition to the film, VTCECH launched a 38-member council called the Chittenden County Hunger Council in 2007. Chittenden County is the most populous county in Vermont. This is the second council set up by VTCECH in the state with support from the Northfield Savings Bank. One of the large holes in Chittenden County is the lack of nutritious meals served in child care centers.

A third documentary called "The Red Wagon: Facing Hunger," directed by Jim Ritvo and Dave Raizman, was commissioned by the Vermont Foodbank in 2006. It is the story of Vermonters struggling every day to feed their families. Many rely on the charitable food system of the Vermont Foodbank, soup kitchens, food shelves, community food kitchens, Boys' and Girls' Clubs, summer meal sites for kids, and senior meal sites to feed themselves.

After watching The Red Wagon, it was clear that hunger doesn't just affect people with low incomes. Many working families above the poverty line also cannot maintain a healthy food budget. Paying rent, a mortgage, utilities, car, and gas come first for many working families. In many cases, they take priority over food. If you can't afford to buy nutritious food to satisfy your child's appetite, you might buy junk food. If your car needs $300 for repairs and you have to go to work, what do you do? You pay the car bill and skimp on food.

Another response to the film was, "Why in this land of plenty, with such an abundance of food, is there so much need?" The USDA estimates 96 billion pounds of food is wasted each year in the U.S. Why is it necessary to have food banks, pantries and food shelves in the first place? We wouldn't need any if people were paid a "fair wage."

I began to wonder about the connection between tax cuts for the rich and food shelves for the poor, working-class, disadvantaged and disabled populations. The wealthy in this country are making more money and paying fewer taxes while the lower and middle classes are suffering. The richest 1 percent receive about 16 percent of national income, double the number from the 1960s.

The results of economic policies -- including low wages, loss of employment, lack of health care, unaffordable housing, lack of transportation, and little economic security for senior citizens -- have all contributed to this dire situation. What kind of country do we live in that has created this problem of hunger and need? Shouldn't access to healthy food be a basic right, just like health care?

Plenty of Food - We have plenty of food to feed everyone in this country. In my own community there are gleanings, which go unnoticed. As the coordinator, for the past ten years, of the largest community garden in Vermont (165 garden plots on about three acres), I estimate that we waste 15 percent of the vegetables grown there. One 30-by-30 foot plot can feed a family in the summer, fall and early winter. The positive thing is that many community gardeners and most local farmers donate fresh vegetables to the food shelf.

For copies of The Red Wagon, contact 132 Main Productions 132 Main Street, Montpelier, VT 05602 ❧

The Red Wagon documentary describes the network of volunteers and activists working to meet the essential food needs of the citizens of Vermont. It shows how food insecurity weakens one's sense of dignity and how experiencing hunger is more than just not having enough to eat.

The following comments, from both the providers and the recipients of the charitable food system in Vermont, illustrate what some Vermonters face everyday. I have taken the liberty to combine some of the comments and edit others.

PROVIDER COMMENTS FROM FOOD SHELVES AND PANTRIES:

- "We are more about community than poverty." Woodbury/Calais Food Shelf.

- In Randolph, a small working-class community, two factories employing over 200 people closed. "Where could they go for food except to the food shelf. I've seen many middle class people come in here, not just the poor." Randolph Food Shelf .

- "During the week, some of the kids that come in wouldn't have an evening meal if it wasn't for the club. What do they do on weekends when we're closed? I can sense their anger with the situation." Boys' and Girl's Club in Northfield.

- In Barre, the Community Food Kitchen takes donated food and prepares meals for the Foodbank's network. The kitchen works closely with culinary students at the local high school.

- In Morrisville, the 20/20 Club works with the mentally ill population in Morrisville. "Not having enough to eat is really hard on these folks. I'm glad we're here to provide food for them at our community gathering place."

- "With increasing health care costs and prescription drugs, many of the old people who come to the senior meal site need a good warm lunch. They wouldn't receive that meal if we weren't here." Montpelier Meal Site.

Provider Comments Continued...

• Pete's Greens in Craftsbury provides greens to the Vermont Foodbank. Volunteers and students from Sterling College cut the greens that are too large to sell to restaurants and food stores and provide the gleanings to the Foodbank.

• One volunteer asked, "Is this what we need, more food shelves? He went onto say, "I can't change the world, but I can help my neighbors. I know what it is to go without."

RECIPIENT COMMENTS:

• Wendy S. started coming to the Bethel Food Shelf two years ago. She said, "I didn't want to come to the food shelf but we don't have enough income. My child is autistic. I don't feel like an outsider."

• A middle-class single parent who worked was having trouble financially. She was afraid of the stigma attached to going to the Montpelier Food Pantry, but once she went, she felt okay about it, as she was accepted and treated with respect and did not feel ashamed.

• Two working adults who make less than $20,000 a year -- a school bus driver and a food service worker -- received food stamps, but not enough for all their food needs. They live in a trailer on his father's land. They couldn't make it if they had to pay rent. Woodbury/ Calais Food Shelf

• "I'm just one paycheck away from having to use the food shelf. I know about the food shelf because I volunteer there."

Senior Enjoying Lunch, Vermont Food Bank

Photo Courtesy of Foodworks in Montpelier

The Chittenden County Food Shelf (CCFS) is located in Burlington, Vermont. Wanda Hines, the former director of CCFS until 2006, can still see the faces of the people who frequented the place she directed for many years. Hines said, they aren't statistics; they are children, mothers and fathers, the homeless, the people with low-paying jobs, and the elderly whose cupboards are bare.

All day long Hines saw people who said they didn't have enough to eat. She said they were not here because they wanted to be. They are proud people. Thirty-five percent of the recipients at the Chittenden County Food Shelf (CCFS) are children. Forty percent are working people. Many have fallen on hard economic times due to illness or the loss of a job. They are hospital workers, truck drivers, and food service workers. They aren't paid enough to feed their children, and few of them have health care.

The people who have been coming to the Food Shelf are "your neighbors and my neighbors." Hines says CCFS never turned anyone away. She saw people there who worked for the State of Vermont. You can still work hard and not have enough for food.

CCFS couldn't operate without volunteers. In 2006 there were 493 volunteers providing over 12,000 hours a year.

Other Positive Signs: There are two directions that have shown promise in closing the food gap for poor families: one is through private, largely non-profit projects and the other is through public policy. The Hartford Food System in Connecticut founded the Holcomb Farm Community Supported Agriculture (CSA) farm that made a commitment to distribute 40 percent of its local and organic produce to the city's low income community.

Other models like the People's Grocery in Oakland, California use mobile markets to bring high quality, healthy food into communities under-served by supermarkets.

Non-profit organizations, such as the Philadelphia-based Food Trust have secured millions of dollars in state financing to develop food stores in under-served urban and rural Pennsylvania communities. As part of an overall economic development strategy, these stores are not only providing new sources of healthy and affordable food to low-income families, they are also expanding employment opportunities and the local property base.

Kitchen Worker, Chittenden County Food Shelf Photo

THREE POSITIVE ROLE MODELS
Library, Playcare, and Nutrition Class

"A library - its function is changing, its presence in the community. So I don't see food as something different, I see it as just expanding the services we have to offer. The summer program is food, and books, and crafts, all blended into one ... so if the shelves are empty, and their bellies are full, then I've accomplished what I intended for the summer."

Adrianne Scucces, Aldrich Public Library, Barre.
Photo courtesy Vermont Campaign to End Childhood Hunger.

"This is the most important job that I do. Feeding kids, helping them get a good start, helping them and their parents - particularly parents - understand the importance of the best food choices. This complements the school program. That they offer this in childcare is magical. It's magical because it makes a difference for a lot of kids and families."

Judy Pransky, Emerson Falls Playcare.
Photo courtesy Cooking For Life:
Vermont Campaign to End Childhood Hunger.

A parent nutrition class by the Cooking for Life Program, Vermont Campaign to End Childhood Hunger.

: OTHER VERMONT FOOD MODELS CONFRONT HUNGER

Healthy Food Being Served at a Senior Center.

I. Food Works at Two Rivers Center was founded in 1987 to address the root causes of childhood hunger. Food Works is a food and agricultural education center in central Vermont that works to strengthen local food systems, and empower families to grow, prepare, and preserve vegetables -- some of which they grow themselves.

The Farm-to-Table program at Food Works serves central Vermont schools and also distributes fresh-locally grown food to over 40 sites serving those who are "nutritionally at risk," including senior centers, assisted living facilities, nursing homes, hospitals, community mental health programs, and early childhood centers.

The program began in 2003 and has grown rapidly. In 2006, $46,000 worth of produce from a network of eighteen farms was sold at subsidized prices to schools, food shelves and senior sites. The produce was purchased at fair market value. In 2007, that figure came to over $56,000. Additional produce (10 to 15 percent) was donated to the Vermont Foodbank and area foodshelves.

Learning to Water at Community Garden at High Gate Housing, Barre

Private money and donations enables Farm-to-Table to administer the program, transport the produce, and offer subsidies on a sliding-fee scale. There are ten main growers and other supplemental growers. No costs are added for distribution.

Most food sites paid farmers 50 cents on the dollar of the market price they normally receive for their produce. The result is that more people enjoy the benefits of eating fresh produce, farmers make a more viable livelihood, and more land is put into sustainable production.

Joe Buley of Screamin' Ridge Farm in East Montpelier was just getting started as an organic grower in 2004 when he began to sell produce to Farm-to-Table. By 2007 he had quadrupled the amount of land he had put into production. Several other growers are cultivating more land, as well as investing in additional greenhouses and storage facilities.

More Programs at Food Works

Photos Courtesy of Food Works

THE GARDENS FOR LEARNING

The Gardens for Learning program began in the mid-1990s to deal with the increase in childhood hunger in the summer months when school lunch and breakfast programs are not available. There are now fifteen sites across Vermont with community-based gardens that provide at-risk children with hands-on-skills in growing and cooking nutritious food. The Two Rivers Center is the statewide demonstration and training site for all Gardens for Learning programs.

FOOD EDUCATION EVERY DAY (FEED)

-- This project is a collaboration between NOFA-VT, Shelburne Farms and Food Works designed to address the dramatic rise in childhood diet-related disease by focusing on food education in the "three C's": the classroom, cafeteria and the community (local farms).

GOOD FOOD - GOOD MEDICINE

Food Works' newest program takes a seasonal approach to exploring good health and nutrition through locally grown food and herbs. This program works with low-income families at two Section 8 housing sites in Barre, Vermont. The participants are involved in seasonal and hands-on cooking, nutrition and gardening. The classes include the entire family in the learning process.

2. The Foodbank Farming Network: In 2006, the Vermont Foodbank teamed up with Food Works to launch the first-ever statewide "Foodbank Farming Network" at Two Rivers Center. In the first year, over 40,000 pounds of fresh, nutritious food was distributed through the statewide Foodbank network, accompanied by classes in nutrition, education, food preservation and cooking for recipient families.

Two Rivers and other Montpelier area farms -- Riverside, River Berry, Littlewood, and Chappell's -- grew food for the Foodbank Farm. Some of the vegetables, such as carrots, potatoes, onions, red and green cabbage, watermelon, winter squash and beets, were grown on five acres of land at Two Rivers.

During 2007, the Foodbank Farm at Two Rivers and four additional local farms grew 46,000 pounds of food for 60 Vermont Foodbank Network Partners throughout the harvest season. Efforts are underway to expand this model to three additional regional sites in the next three years. The Network currently connects 66,000 Vermonters to the charitable food system.

In 2008, Two Rivers and six other farms provided 64,000 pounds of produce to the Foodbank Farming Network.

How Does it Work? Each network agency, such as a local food pantry, receives 200 pounds a month under a 1,025 pound/share agreement. Each share will cost $615, or 60 cents a pound. The agencies receive the produce for five months from August to December. The remaining costs are taken care of by the Vermont Food Bank from grants and donated funds.

Farmers are paid from 22 cents up to $1.30 a pound depending on whether the produce is conventional or organic, volume and the nature of the items. Obviously, tomatoes receive a higher price than zucchini. The average payment to the farmers is 72 cents a pound. In the future a storage area including a large root cellar will be built at Two Rivers.

As one elderly women put it when she watched a box of broccoli being unloaded at her assisted living facility, "This is why we still eat."

Photo Courtesy of the Vermont Food Bank

3. Salvation Farms: Salvation Farms is another program that's making a difference in meeting the hunger needs of Vermonters. For four years, Theresa Snow has organized volunteers to walk through farmers' fields and harvest the crops that would otherwise go to waste. The produce has been shared with hungry families in Lamoille County and additional produce given to the Vermont Foodbank in Barre.

Snow started Salvation Farms in 2004 while working for Pete's Greens, an organic farm in Craftsbury. Students at nearby Sterling College helped her glean the surplus vegetables from the fields. The produce was donated to the Craftsbury Community Care Center and the pre-school and senior centers in Greensboro.

During the next three years, Theresa used her time harvesting several farms' surplus, donating 88,000 pounds of fresh produce to 40 meal sites and the Vermont Foodbank. The Northeast Organic Farming Association of Vermont provided fiscal support by allowing grant money for Salvation Farms to pass through the organization. Snow and students from Sterling College in Craftsbury developed one-sheet educational materials with nutrition and food preparation information for food recipients. Without the overall support of the Vermont Foodbank, most of the surplus food could not have been distributed. (Salvation Farms provides its volunteers with harvesting tools, boxes and bags for collecting the produce.)

On April 11, 2008, the Vermont Foodbank merged with Salvation Farms and Theresa Snow joined the Vermont Foodbank as the Agricultural Resources Director to spread the Salvation Farms model statewide. She now oversees the program through Food Works in Montpelier. In 2007, Salvation Farms contributed 48,000 pounds of gleaned produce to the Vermont Foodbank. The amount of donated gleaned food increased to 150,000 pounds in 2008 with help from farms in Montpelier and Plainfield.

Gleaning Greens, Photo Courtesy of Salvation Farms

WHAT IS A FOODBANK?

A foodbank is not a food shelf. A foodbank secures large quantities of food and food-related products from commercial suppliers, concerned citizens, and the government. After the food is sorted, it is then offered to the foodbank's member agencies: food shelves, pantries, senior meal programs and other community meal sites, in exchange for a low per-pound maintenance fee.

A food shelf provides boxes of food to needy people for home preparation and consumption. A food shelf may obtain food from the foodbank, from individual donations, and through wholesale and/or retail purchase.

Food shelves provide take-home groceries, while community kitchens serve prepared meals. Some food shelves also provide meals. Most are run by volunteers. Foodshelves depend heavily on donations of supplies, labor, space, money and food.✴

Theresa Snow would like to see the Salvation Farms model replicated throughout the state. Her overall goal is "food sovereignty." Snow will be working in 2009 with farmers in the Brattleboro area to provide gleaned food for the foodshelves in the region.

Photos Courtesy of Salvation Farms

Salvation Farms logo

Rebecca Beidler,
Field Coordinator for the
Lamoille Valley Gleaning
Growers

Foodbank logos

America's Second Harvest
The Nation's Food Bank Network

IS NOW

FEEDING™
AMERICA

HOUSTON FOOD BANK
HELPING FEED THE HUNGRY

FOOD BANK OF THE ROCKIES
1978 — 2008
FIGHTING HUNGER. FEEDING HOPE.

NATIONAL ASSOCIATION OF LETTER CARRIERS
Stamp Out Hunger
FOOD DRIVE

RHODE ISLAND COMMUNITY FOOD BANK

NORTH TEXAS FOOD BANK

SECOND HARVEST FOOD BANK

GLEANERS COMMUNITY FOOD BANK of Southeastern Michigan

Vermont Foodbank
Gather   Share   Nurture

www.vtfoodbank.org

THE VERMONT FOODBANK AND AMERICA'S SECOND HARVEST - NOW CALLED FEEDING AMERICA

Each state has a foodbank. The Vermont Foodbank (TVF), begun in 1986, provides staples, canned goods, grains, and other items to the food shelves and food kitchens at reduced prices. On average, the Vermont Foodbank provides about two-thirds of the food available to the food shelves, pantries and kitchens. The Foodbank is the largest relief organization in Vermont, providing more than 6 million pounds of food to the needy.

The kitchen at the Vermont Foodbank also prepares low-cost meals for the various sites. It distributes food to 270 member agencies: food shelves, senior and day care centers, food pantries, and food kitchens. The Vermont Foodbank is supported by government programs, supermarket chains, individual donations and thousands of volunteers. (TVF also receives food from the federal government's food commodity program.)

The Vermont Foodbank serves 66,000 people annually through its member agencies or about 10 percent of the Vermont population. The foodbank is by far the single most important source of food for the member agencies.

Other Pertinent Foodbank Facts:

- 57 percent of food goes to food shelves and food pantries.

- 30 percent goes to the Community Supplemental Food Program.

- 3.5 percent goes to meal sites including senior centers.

- 2 percent goes to programs which serve children like the Summer Food Program. The remainder goes to group homes and homeless shelters.

- 16 percent of shelters are faith-based.

- Volunteers serve 92 percent of pantries, 75 percent of kitchens and 75 percent of homeless shelters.

- 33 percent of recipients choose between buying food and paying the rent or mortgage.

- 38 percent choose between food and paying for heat.

- 28 percent choose between food and medicine

- Over the past ten years, the number of families accessing the foodbank increased 50 percent.

- Ten percent of Vermont citizens use food from the Foodbank.

Source: America's Second Harvest and Vermont Foodbank

Volunteer at the Vermont Food Bank in Barre.

AMERICA'S SECOND HARVEST
- Now called *Feeding America*

This is the largest charitable food-relief organization in the U.S. It provides emergency assistance to 210 state foodbanks, including the Vermont Foodbank, and serves the nation's largest network of soup kitchens, and shelters -- 39,000 hunger-relief organizations, 80 percent of those in the United States.

Second Harvest serves 25 million people. If you estimate the amount of food they distribute, they would be considered one of the top five food distributors in the country. Requests for services went up 9 percent between 2001 and 2005, even though the amount of available food decreased.

The nation's foodbanks are scrambling to serve the growing demand at a time when government food donations and private cash contributions are falling. More people are asking for food even as the amount of available government commodities -- milk, cheese, canned goods and other staples -- is down 55 percent from 2005. In 2001, $418.4 million was given to food banks throughout the country by the USDA. In 2006, that number fell to $201 million. The USDA buys fewer commodities when it has less need to boost farm prices. It gives 80 percent of its purchases to America's Second Harvest, which then passes them on to the state foodbanks.

The vast majority of foodbanks, soup-kitchens and shelters across the country are run locally by nonprofit groups. Second Harvest found that 36 percent of people seeking food came from households in which at least one person had a job. About 35 percent came from households that received food stamps.

* For more information, See the Feeding America website.

More on the Vermont Foodbank: There is a membership fee for member agencies. A smaller food pantry might pay about $500 a year.

There is also a shared-maintenance handling fee of 18 cents a pound for food shelves, pantries and senior centers. This goes to pay for salvage food. The money also goes for storage, handling and distribution. Three-quarters of the food at the food bank is similar to the type of food customers shop for at a supermarket except that produce is more accessible at the foodbank..

Depression Era Photo

The lagging economy has forced the Vermont Foodbank to find more creative ways to put food on its shelves, as more people request help and fewer can afford to donate. According to Foodbank CEO Doug O'Brien, the organization donated 6 million pounds of food to needy Vermonters in 2007 through its member agencies. O'Brien said, "More than 1 in 10 Vermonters qualify for additional food resources; an independent research survey conducted for TVF indicated more than one-third of the people the organization served were forced to choose between fuel oil and food. That was back when fuel oil was $50.00 a barrel. Now its over $100.00."

Increasingly, the smaller food shelves and pantries in Vermont are having a hard time maintaining volunteers as folks are getting older. The other challenge for the small operations is to raise funds to purchase food, whereas TVF, with its large staff, is successful at raising money. Some food shelves cannot afford even the cost of food from the Vermont Foodbank because of lack of funds.

In 2007, it was reported that there was a 25-30 percent increase in the demand for food from charitable food system in Vermont. This food system is a complement, not a replacement, for the government's safety net of programs for low-income people, who receive food stamps, WIC, and school meal programs. These programs are the first line of defense; TVF and its network partners are the last line of defense.

When a family's food stamps run out or when children don't receive lunch during the summer months, their turn to the charitable food system. In Vermont, an estimated 14,500 people are served each week in the charitable food system. Vermont has a population of 621,000 according to the 2007 census.

The Chittenden County Food Shelf, the largest food shelf in Vermont, purchases one fourth of its food from TVF. It buys two types of food: salvaged and wholesale. Salvaged food costs 18 cents a pound including delivery. Salvaged food might include a case of canned tomatoes with tarnished labels or a case of dry cereal with creased boxes. The amount of salvaged food has decreased in the last few years because big jobbers have begun buying up damaged caselots of food from wholesalers and selling them in cheap food outlets. The majority of food purchased by food shelves comes from the Vermont Foodbank -- like cases of tuna or macaroni and cheese. Many smaller food shelves, like the one that serves Woodbury and Calais, purchase food at wholesale prices from the larger supermarkets in the area, as they can get better deals than going through TVF. The Chittenden County Food Shelf, like the other food shelves, has to raise money through the local United Way, as well as relying on private donations, donated food and many volunteers. It uses the Onion River/City Market Co-op wholesaler for food purchases. Smaller food shelves and pantries rely on volunteers, food and private donations.

AT NO TIME SINCE THE GREAT DEPRESSION OF 1929 HAVE THERE BEEN SO MANY HUNGRY PEOPLE.

A Mother of 7 Children During the Great Depression, Photo by Dorothea Lange. Courtesy of National Archives.

The book, *Sweet Charity?: Emergency Food and the End of Entitlement* by Janet Poppendieck exposes the institutionalization of the emergency food system by the private food sector in the U.S. Poppendieck says the National Food Relief System has not adequately helped those who live on the edge of hunger, the reason being the lack of money to purchase healthy, nutritious food. The National Food Relief System has allowed us to believe that we have solved the problem of hunger. This is a myth.

Poppendieck explains how the large corporate food companies receive major tax write-offs for food donated to Second Harvest and the food banks. They also don't have to throw the food away and pay dumping fees to haulers. In order for the emergency food system to operate, large warehouses are needed, along with refrigeration units and administration to transport food around the country.

Poppendieck doesn't say that food banks, food shelves, and soup kitchens shouldn't exist, but she makes the case that their proliferation points out the real problem of hunger in the wealthiest country in the world. One solution she proposes is to increase the amount of food stamp money given to low-income people. She also provides insight into the nature of volunteerism and the ways our "moral hunger" serves those who are less fortunate. We all know people who volunteer to help the homeless in food kitchens at Thanksgiving. What happens the rest of the year?.

Another concern of the smaller food shelves is the quality of food donated to TVF by large food companies and supermarkets, such as diet soda. The reality is that the Vermont Foodbank takes what it receives.

COMMODITY SUPPLEMENTAL FOOD PROGRAM

The Vermont Foodbank warehouses, packs, and delivers 31 pound packages of community food overwhelmingly to seniors and families under the Commodity Supplemental Food Program (CSFP) --a USDA nutrition program that offers free monthly nutrition information and nutritious food such as canned fruits and vegetables, fruit juices, cereals and cheese. Each person receives a 31-pound box of food. People can participate in other commodity programs, but cannot be enrolled at more than one CSFP site.

The program is basically a safety net for low-income seniors 60 years or older. It also serves children under 6 years of age not already in the WIC program and women who are pregnant or in postpartum for less than a year and not already in the WIC program.

Under the 1990 Farm Bill, another federal food program, the Emergency Food Assistance Program (EFAP) was authorized to distribute surplus commodities to local food providers through the Vermont Foodbank. This is the primary source of federal food for the Vermont Foodbank -- about one quarter of the total amount. Second Harvest is not the primary source. Again, most of the food comes from donations within Vermont -- from supermarkets, food distributors and private donations.

FEDERAL FOOD PROGRAM NOTES:

• Federal Programs include: Food Stamps, National Lunch and Breakfast Programs, Summer Food Service Program, Women, Children and Infant Program (WIC), Emergency Food Assistance Program (EFAP), and Community Food and Nutrition Program (CFNP)
.

• The 2008 Farm Bill will serve an additional 23,000 Vermonters under the Food Stamp program.

• The government program for Women, Infants and Children (WIC) managed by USDA went through a major overhaul in 2007, the first major change in 30 years. Today, families are receiving more fruits, vegetables and whole grains and less milk, cheese, eggs and juice. The reason for the change is that most WIC recipients have diets deficient in whole grains, fruits and vegetables. The new WIC foods have less saturated fat and cholesterol.

Side Notes:

1. Food Stamps EBT plastic food stamp cards can be used at some farmers' markets in the state. This initiative was spearheaded by NOFA of Vermont. The following markets can take EBT cards: Old North End Market in Burlington, Rutland, Montpelier, Newport, Winooski, Brattleboro, and Bellows Falls, plus a couple more. The EBT system is still being tested at markets throughout the state.

2. NOFA Vermont's Farm Share Program This program assists limited-income Vermonters in obtaining farm fresh products. Farm share participants receive partially subsidized shares from Community Supported Agriculture (CSA) farms.

The program has been serving Vermont since 1994 when it was established as a way to link food producers with low-income Vermonters. Each year, the Farm Share Program subsidizes the cost of CSA shares, providing a season's worth of fresh farm products (vegetables, eggs, bread, and meat) to low-income families and children.

This program is an in-house project which is funded in three ways: NOFA pays 25 percent with money raised through the "Share the Harvest" initiative every fall from members of the community. The shareholder pays 50 percent of the cost or whatever they can afford. Most pay the full amount. The CSA farm provides 25 percent of the cost. NOFA leveraged $10,000 in 2007 for $40,000 worth of CSA shares. The program provides anywhere from $200 to $400 for a CSA share for the season. Seventy eight low-income families participated in 2007 and support also went to a number food shelves and drop-in centers.

3. The Seniors Farm Share Program This program helps limited-income seniors who live in housing projects. It's a USDA funded project that's funded through the Senior Market Nutrition Program. The money passes through the Vermont Department of Aging and Disabilities and is administered by NOFA Vermont. In most cases, a CSA farm is located near the housing project. If one can't be found, a local farmer is contacted. The funds provide $5 a week for ten weeks. Last year it was $100 but the funding was cut in 2008. For more information contact Jean Hamilton at NOFA Vermont at (802) 434-4122.

• WIC serves about 8 million people. Under the program, people receive vouchers averaging around $39 dollars a month. Products such as tofu, soy beverages, tortillas, and brown rice are also being offered to meet the demands of culturally diverse populations. The WIC program is administered through the Vermont Department of Health. The School Breakfast and Lunch Programs are also administered through the Vermont Department of Health.

OTHER FEDERAL & STATE PROGRAMS

Coupons: and EBT Cards: Public policy advocacy has leveraged federal and state funding to provide special farmers' market vouchers to low-income women, children and elders through the Farmers' Market Nutrition Program. These small denomination coupons have opened an increasing share of the nation's 4,500 farmers' markets to a wider demographic of shoppers.

VERMONT FARM-TO-FAMILY COUPONS

Farm-to-Family coupons help low-income seniors and low-income Vermonters buy locally grown fresh vegetables and fruits at one of the 40 farmers' markets in the state. The federal Farmers' Market Nutrition Program provides support for the 5,000 households that use the program -- $30 per family/summer for a total of $154,000. Each coupon comes in $3 denominations. This amount is low compared to the 140,000 Vermonters who receive $5 million a month in food stamps.

Eligibility is available for families enrolled in the Vermont Department of Health's WIC Program and individuals or families at or below 185 percent of the federal poverty limit. Seniors are included. The coupons are valid for just one market season and are given out on a first come, first serve basis. The program -- now in its 21st year -- is administered under the Economic Services Division of the Vermont Department for Children and Families.

The local community action agencies handle the referrals.

The program is intended to be a stimulus to eat fresh fruits and vegetables, not to feed a family. In a recent state survey of 500 people, it was found that 28 percent of the participants visited a farmers' market for the first time, 80 percent began to eat more fruits and vegetables than before, 52 percent learned new ways of preparing and storing fruits and vegetables, 78 percent spent money for more fruits and vegetables than before the program, 82 percent planned to eat more fruits and vegetables year round, and 78 percent spent more money at the market after using the coupons.

World Hunger Facts

- **Hunger and malnutrition kill more people than AIDS, malaria, and tuberculosis combined.**

- **One child dies every five seconds from hunger- related causes.**

- **And finally, more people die from hunger than war.**

GLOBAL HUNGER

Hunger is increasing globally. After declining for years, the number of people in the developing world who are going hungry is on the rise, according to the United Nations. A 2004 report called "The State of Food Security in the World" found that 842 million people were undernourished. That's three to four times the population of the United States. It's much worse today.

In order to gain a better perspective on current hunger and world wide food prices, one needs to understand the current rise in food costs. The United Nations reported that food prices went up 40 percent and more from 2006 to 2007. For example, the price of Thai rice went up from $243.37 per ton in 2006 to $635.63 in 2007.

In 2008, according to the World Food Program (WFP) of the United Nations, future wars may be fought over access to basic natural resources, such as land and water. One of the solutions is to protect small farmers in the developing world from loosing their land in order to grow food crops. This will help reduce food Conflicts, and years of drought have made conditions worse for millions of people in the developing third world. Today, denying farmland to people is being used as a weapon of war, especially in Africa.

In Paraguay, peasant farmers and indigenous people are fighting in what has come to be called, "the soybean wars." One percent of the population owns 77 percent of all arable land. Wealthy Brazilians are buying up large holdings and planting genetically modified soybean crops - pushing peasants off the land and into the cities. Peasant farmers who live next to soybean fields are being driven from their fields and homes from chemical pesticides, which pollute the water, kill their crops and animals and cause illness. Since the boom in soybean production, 100,000 small farmers have been relocated.

Frances Moore Lappé, Director of the Small Planet Institute. For more information on her writings, go to smallplanetinstitute.org.

A decade ago, poor coffee-producing countries like Kenya retained 30 percent of their coffee revenue. Today, their share of that revenue has shrunk to 10 percent due to control of the industry by the global coffee corporations that have drained the wealth from the poorest countries. This type of manipulation kills the open market and consolidates power in so few hands that it inevitably corrupts governments.

The winners in this battle aren't the peasant farmers but the Nestles and Philip Morrises of the world. Does any of this sound familiar? It takes place not only in the Kenyan Parliament but also in the U.S. Congress, where corporations are "in bed" with the FDA and USDA.

In Kenya and Paraguay and the developing world, the key is through land reform programs in which the "people' take more control of their lives and their local food supplies.

Poverty can be overcome through democratic movements in which indigenous groups empower themselves. Take, for example, Brazil's Landless Movement, in which workers have secured legal title to more than 20 million acres for 250,000 formerly landless families, creating self-governing communities that are feeding themselves.

Diet For a Small Planet: Thirty years ago in *Diet for a Small Planet*, Frances Moore Lappé asked the question, "Why is there hunger in a world of plenty?" She said, "What I learned was shocking. All around me experts were predicting famine, saying we'd reached the earth's limits to feed ourselves." "More chemicals! Bigger farms! More technology," were the mantras of the day.

As Lappé studied the problem, she realized the experts were dead wrong. She said, "Not only was there enough to feed us all; there was more than enough. Worse than that, the strategies touted to bring us plenty of food through chemicals, large-scale farms, and technology might actually make the food crisis worse." One example of those modern strategies was the "Green Revolution," hyped as the agricultural solution to end world hunger.

The Green Revolution: The Green Revolution began as early as 1945 with the introduction of high-yielding corn varieties into Mexico. In the 1960s, the program reached into India and other south Asian countries, where loans, equipment, and technology were offered to farmers who would make the transition from their present farming systems to more intensive market-oriented production. The program was largely funded by the Rockefeller and Ford Foundations.

The "high-yielding" hybrid varieties of corn, rice, wheat and other staple grains came from U.S.-funded research institutions located throughout the world.

They produced higher yields for two reasons: the dwarf varieties produced more seeds on smaller stems, and second, the grains showed greater responsiveness to mechanical cultivation and applications of chemical fertilizers. However, those new varieties were more susceptible to pest infestations and required greater amounts of chemical insecticides.

Governments that supported the shift toward mechanized, chemical-intensive agriculture were rewarded by the U.S. government and the World Bank with favorable loans and economic aid. Farmers received free seed and other benefits, however, they soon found themselves increasingly dependent on the use of costly equipment and chemicals. In many regions, agricultural productivity increased dramatically, but within a decade it began to level off and even decline.

There was also a problem with water shortages in agricultural regions along with lower water tables due to an increase in water usage for the new hybrid crops. Many new irrigation systems were paid for with funds from the World Bank. Farmers growing dwarf varieties of rice and other crops produced less straw and no longer had enough fodder to feed their livestock. The new grain monocultures replaced the traditional cropping systems that had sustained people for hundreds of years. The Green Revolution enriched some farmers and plunged others into debt and dependency. Many farmers were forced to migrate to over-crowded urban areas. Today's biotech advocates often describe their new genetic technology as the harbinger of the "new Green Revolution."

Source: The information on the Green Revolution was taken from a book edited by: Toker, Brian. Gene Traders - Biotechnology, World Trade and the Globalization of Food, . Toward Freedom, Burlington, Vermont.

A LACK OF DEMOCRACY

Lappé makes other more provocative statements in her book, *Hope's Edge*. She asks, "What belief systems allow people to tolerate the devastation of nature and the starvation of millions of people, and allow others to benefit from cheap food and fuel?"

Lappé details how hunger occurs because people don't have access to food, land, and water because of limited income. She says, "Hunger is not about being left outside the dominant economic system. Hunger is actively created by that system - economic life divorced from democratic values and driven by a single rule: highest return to existing wealth." Lappé is referring to control of the world's food supply by the wealthy global food giants and other multi-nationals. She says that the key to lifting the poor out of poverty is not by the rich world assisting them up the economic ladder but rather by the ability of the poor to empower themselves. Lappé destroys the myth that hunger is caused by a scarcity of food; in reality, it is caused by a lack of democracy.

Judy Wicks, the owner and founder of Philadelphia's White Dog Café and co-founder of the nationwide Business Alliance for Local Living Economics (BALLE), has a similar way of looking at the question of food, hunger and democracy. Wicks says, "A socially, environmentally and financially sustainable global economy must be composed of sustainable local economies. Yet, tragically, from American `Main Streets' to villages in developing countries, corporate globalization is causing the decline of local communities, family businesses, family farms, and natural habitats."

Wick's said, "Wealth and power are consolidating in growing transnational corporations that wield alarming control over many important aspects of our lives -- the food we eat, the clothes we wear and the news we hear. By working cooperatively, locally-owned businesses and conscious consumers can create an alternative to corporate globalization that brings power back to our communities by building sustainable local economies ... "

SELF-EMPOWERMENT MODELS

With a per-capita GDP of less than two-thirds of India's, Bangladesh has a child death rate nearly one-fifth lower than India's. The reason Bangladesh is making progress despite its deep poverty and hunger is in part due to what's called "democracy in action." Lappé describes how citizen action networks have spread to almost 80 percent of Bangladesh's villages, providing basic health training, schools, and capital.

Through the largely self-financed Grameen Bank and the Bangladesh Rural Advancement Committee, founded in 1976, peer-backed micro-loans have gone to about nine million poor people, mainly women, who have created their own village-level enterprises. A rather revealing statistic is that these local, self-directed enterprises have freed more than twice as many from poverty as the number employed in export garment sweatshop factories in Bangladesh. Mohammed Yunus, the man who began the Grameen Bank, providing small loans at low rates to poor people who otherwise had no access to capital, received the Nobel Peace Prize in 2006.

Throughout India, women have built a network of cooperative dairies that in 30 years have lifted the incomes of more than 11 million households and benefited more than 100 million people.

Source: The information on Global Hunger came from an article: Lappé, Frances Moore. "Hunger is Not a Place" Nation Magazine January 23, 2006. It is based on a recent book, Democracy's Edge.

Frances Moore Lappé reported in 2008 that almost two thousand Indian villages were embracing community-managed sustainable farming using natural pest controls. She said that one can find rural communities all over the globe developing GM-free, agro-ecological farming systems that are succeeding. A recent study looked at sustainable practices in 57 countries, involving almost 13 million small farmers on almost 100 million acres. It was found that after four years of production average yields went up 79 percent.

Source: Lappé Frances Moore, NPR Misses Real Story, Plants Wrong Seeds, August 11, 2008. From Lappé's Blog. Reported in the Huffington Post. Her most recent book is called Clarity, Creativity, and Courage in a World Gone Mad.

FAIR TRADE AROUND THE GLOBE AND THE U.S.

Coffee: The multinational coffee companies rule our shopping malls and supermarkets and dominate an industry worth over $80 billion, making coffee the most valuable trading commodity in the world after oil. Coffee is called "Black Gold" in the world of agribusiness.

While the cost of our gourmet Starbuck's espresso, mocha, and latte with coffee goes sky high, the price paid to coffee farmers remains so low that thousands of small farmers have been forced to abandon their coffee plots and move to urban areas. Nowhere is this more evident than in Ethiopia, the birthplace of coffee.

Tadessa Meskela is on a mission to save 74,000 struggling Ethiopian coffee farms from poverty. He travels the world looking for buyers willing to pay a fair price. Meskela is up against New York commodity traders, international coffee exchanges and trade ministers of the World Trade Organization.

Fair Trade Coffee: Fair Trade Certified coffee guarantees farmers a fair price, which means they can afford to feed their families, stay on the land, and invest in the quality of their coffee. Organic farmers who grow fair trade coffee are going back to the tradition of replanting coffee trees under natural shade canopies and enriching the soil with natural compost.

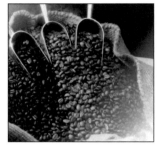

Currently, more than 600,000 coffee farmers in 32 countries benefit from fair trade. 300 companies sell fair trade coffee, including Green Mountain Coffee Roasters of Vermont. Many of these companies also sell fair trade tea and cocoa. Fair trade coffee is the fastest growing segment of specialty coffee, up 74 percent in the last five years. However, 25 million coffee farmers and their families continue to struggle throughout Latin America, Asia and Africa.

Sadly, many of the world's rainforests are being cut down and large plantations of non-shade grown coffee are being planted by global agri-business firms, forcing thousands of small farmers off the land.

Bananas: In 2004, the Food and Agriculture Organization of the United Nations reported that more bananas are exported than any other fruit. The U.S. imports 25 percent of the world's bananas, mostly from Central and South America. To meet the growing world demand, world production increased from 4,000 tons in 1961 to 70,000 tons today. As the demand for bananas has grown, competition has increased.

Historically, the way to reduce costs is to pay the farmer less. This has traditionally been easy in developing countries with fewer labor laws and high levels of poverty. Entire communities in banana-producing countries are often at the mercy of large global corporations that control the markets.

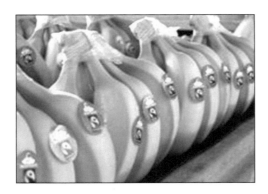

FAIR TRADE BANANAS

Oké bananas come from a new fair trade banana co-op in which the growers own a 30 percent share. The remainder is owned by fair trade non-profits, such as **Equal Exchange**. (Equal Exchange, founded in 1986, is the oldest and largest non-profit fair trade company in the U.S. Its mission is to build long-term trade partnerships that are economically just, environmentally sound and that foster mutually beneficial relationships between farmers and consumers.) The cooperative, called El Guabo Association of Small-Scale Banana Producers, consists of 339 producers from Ecuador.

Fair Trade standards guarantee a minimum price to farmers; in this case, $7 per box to the El Guabo farmers, as well as a Fair Trade premium used for community projects such as health care and clean drinking water. Many of the farmers used to receive $2 per box of bananas. The co-op farmers must meet certain requirements: safety regulations, no forced child labor, and using open, transparent, democratic procedures. Fair Trade is overseen by Transfair, a U.S. certifying organization.

Oké has encouraged growers to become certified as organic and stewards of the land. This sustainable model is a win-win situation for both farmers and consumers.

Domestic Fair Trade (in the U.S.): Recently, a group of food co-ops in the U.S. pledged their support to the **Federation of Southern Co-ops**, based in Georgia.

This organization is dedicated to saving land resources owned by its members. Family farms in the south, in particular, have been hit hard by the loss of farming.

Photo Courtesy of the
Federation of Southern Co-ops

The Federation of Southern Co-ops and Equal Exchange started to explore domestic fair trade in the U.S in 1968, when Equal Exchange floated the idea. Food co-ops across the nation were among the first partners to support the concept. The Onion River Co-op/City Market in Burlington, Vermont started purchasing domestic fair trade products under the "Red Tomato" label in 2008. Watermelons and pecans have also become available through Equal Exchange. The alliance between co-ops and Equal Exchange is in its infancy and support for domestic fair trade is growing.

Global Farm and Food Stats:

- Agriculture is the largest industry on the planet. It employs an estimated 1.3 billion people and produces $1.3 trillion in food products.

- Even though food production has more than kept pace with global population growth, 800 million people in the world are seriously underfed and many are starving.

- The top eight agricultural commodities -- with rice, corn, wheat and soy, being the top four -- provide more than 80 percent of the calories we eat.

SO, AGAIN,
WHOSE FAULT IS IT ANYWAY?

Do you remember Iris Caballero and Irene Flores, the two California farm workers described earlier? Is it their fault they are not putting healthy food on the table? Adam Drewnowski, an epidemiology professor and Director of Nutritional Sciences at the University of Washington, says that many farm workers are obese because they have little money, and therefore do not have a quality diet. He goes on to add that the message being sent out blames people for not making healthy food choices.

What society often forgets is that the poor are limited by finances, time, lack of transportation, and lack of access to healthy food. Drewnowski says, "We have been pretending that it is easy to replace a diet of soft drinks and fast foods with home-cooked meals, fresh fruits and vegetables. A growing body of research shows that the people who have gained the most weight in the last decade tend to have the lowest incomes, and often go without the kind and amounts of food they need."

Many poor, single mothers are placed in the situation of not having enough money to purchase healthy food. They, in fact, might go without eating in order to feed their children.

Side Notes:

I know, I know! No one is forcing it down anyone's throat, or are they? Do the folks at McDonald's tell you that Chicken McNuggets are more than just chicken fried in a pan? They are, in fact, a combination of various elements including chicken skin, hydrogenated oils and dimethylpolysiloxane, whatever that is.

Many of the foods we eat and drink are addictive due to the thousands of substances added to them, such as NutraSweet, caffeine, high fructose corn syrup, salt and flavorings. (I couldn't get my mom to stop drinking diet soda, with all its salt, NutraSweet and caffeine).

The Blame Game: I hear people blaming parents for their children's weight problem. In particular, they ridicule parents of poor children for their children's poor eating habits, with questions like, "Why can't they buy more nutritious food for their children?" "Why are they so fat?" Why don't they do something about it?" Yes, parents need to act as positive role models and they are not without responsibility when it comes to good nutrition for their children, but they can only do so much when they have limited resources.

It's assumed that consumer choice shapes what we eat. This way of thinking ignores all the other factors that have more direct and deliberate control over the food system -- including the decision-makers at global firms like Cargill that produce, market and distribute food. When parents are seen as solely responsible for their children's weight, it makes it difficult to discuss the roles of schools, community and policy makers in addressing childhood obesity. When obesity is attributed only to bad eating habits, lack of exercise or poor parenting, it is difficult to get people to think about food and nutrition policy change, because responsibility is again placed on the individual.

Increasingly, public health officials are identifying a range of public policies focused on improving nutrition and increasing physical activity that could reduce the level of obesity among American children. These policies include restricting the marketing of low-nutrition foods to children; improving school food programs; providing nutrition labeling in restaurants; increasing physical activity options in the community, such as walking paths, and walk-to-school programs.

In neighborhoods where access to fresh produce and other healthy foods is limited, it's difficult for parents to offer healthy diets at home. Initiatives such as community gardens and local farmers' markets can help make healthy food more available to everyone. ❧

A mother who has a limited amount of income to spend on food might walk to the discount convenience store to buy week-old Wonder Bread, where which she could get five loaves for the price of two. Today, those loaves would be double in price. With the addition of some low-cost margarine, she could "fill up" the hunger urges of her children and herself.

A poor family without transportation might pick up a frozen package of chicken nuggets at the local convenience store, as it's cheaper than fresh chicken. Besides, the local store doesn't carry fresh chicken. The poor are marginalized by a lack of healthy food, as they are by the lack of affordable housing, education and health care.

The broader problem lies with the growing income gap and a low minimum wage. Poor health and obesity are economic and political issues. Increasing the amount of money for food stamps would be a real boost to increasing the consumption of healthy food. That, along with workshops on preparing healthy foods, budgeting and smart food-buying, would be a help to low-income families. And if children can learn at an early age in school about good nutrition, they, in turn, can teach their children about healthy food.

DOUBLEWIDE

The following narrative describes a group of overweight middle and high school students who live in a rural farming community in Vermont. It's a true story.

A friend of mine, let's call her Sarah, worked as a mentor to these high school students. She was a student at a local college. Her goal was to introduce them to healthy food and meal preparation through positive social interactions. Sarah shared with me some of her experiences working with different students from 2003 to 2005.

Farms dot the landscape in this rural community. Some of the students lived on roads in "doublewide" trailers and are neighbors.

Although there is typically limited kitchen space in "doublewides," this in itself is not a prohibiting factor when it comes to preparing healthy food. The problem of obesity is connected in part to a lack of structure in the home resulting in a low level of self-esteem. This can happen in any socioeconomic class. Eating meals within the home is one of the most stabilizing aspects of family life.

Sarah worked with the students outside the classroom. She used a school-approved van to transport students to the local food co-op or supermarket to buy food, which they later prepared at Sarah's home or at the college's kitchen.

The breakfast of one of Sarah's students, whom we'll call Annie, consisted of Doritos and soda, while lunch was a bag of Lay's potato chips and a grinder with lots of mayo from the local store. Annie never ate in the cafeteria among her peers because she was embarrassed about her weight. What money she had, she spent on junk food, like candy bars.

Another student, Diane, went home to an empty, unstructured home. Her parents had divorced a few years ago, and she lived with her father, who was always at his girlfriend's house. Diane could usually be found at a friend's house. There was no reason for her go home, as she felt lonely and abandoned. No one was home to welcome her after school, nor was there any real food in the refrigerator or cabinets, and no one to share a meal with.

Outcomes of programs like Sarah's are often difficult to evaluate, but it was clear to her that the meals she made with the students were the healthiest meals they had ever had. She said, "They appreciated the quality of the meals they created with their own hands. I believe it gave them hope and a feeling that they were not stuck and helped to uplift their self-esteem by showing them of what they were capable."

Doublewide, continued....

One of the ironies of this story is that it takes place in the heart of a farming community. Most of the food consumed there is shipped in from thousands of miles away. If you were to talk to principals, food service managers, and school superintendents, you would find that it's not easy to change old food habits. Food preparation is a sensitive subject, especially to food service workers. It's easier to open a can of tomatoes than cutting up fresh local vegetables.

Questions and Solutions: Why are high school agriculture programs rapidly disappearing across the country? The school in the community where Sarah's students lived once had a Future Farmers of America program, but the teacher retired and no replacement was found. Why couldn't it be resurrected?

The focus of the college where Sarah went to school is experimental in nature with an emphasis on environmental stewardship, sustainable agriculture, outdoor education, and conservation biology. Because of its close proximity to the high school, the college is in a unique position to provide the type of experiences many high school students need, including practical activities in farming, meal preparation, and nutrition. Why not a culinary arts and food nutrition program that connects the resources of the college to the local high school? Why couldn't some of the students at the high school get involved in the sustainable farming program at the college?

This leads us again to the sensitive topic of placing blame on those who are overweight. The "Just Say No" advocates tell us that no one is forcing those cokes and snickers down anyone's throat and whatever happened to taking responsibility anyway. They say that consumers must bear some responsibility for being overweight. And its it's not the food industry's fault that people don't exercise, or that schools have cut physical education, or that people prefer Twinkies (500 million sell each year) to tofu.

If our supermarkets are overflowing with safe, wholesome food, why don't people make the right food choices? Aisle after aisle is filled with fresh and frozen fruits and vegetables, cheeses, grains, milk and other whole foods. What the "Just Say No-ers" don't say is that healthy foods cost a lot more than Twinkies and other processed foods.

Society blames the poor for their weight problems rather than providing the necessary support for them to learn about good nutrition. Families need to be educated about purchasing healthy food and preparing meals from scratch.

Empowering people to take greater responsibility is part of the solution. Education is the key. It has taken only one generation to lose the knowledge and experience of preparing healthy meals, canning, freezing and preserving foods. It will take a generation to reverse the harm that's been done. ✿

Families Prepare a Tasty Meal After Harvesting Fresh Greens at a Class Led By Anne Maule. Courtesy of Food Works

Courtesy of Vermont Campaign
To End Childhood Hunger

MODELS OF EMPOWERMENT

A group in Pennsylvania, The Food Trust, helps provide funds for the Fresh Food Financing Initiative, which places supermarkets in the urban core to provide healthy food to low-income families. The program also connects local farmers to local farm markets.

The Vermont Campaign to End Childhood Hunger (VTCECH) runs the Cooking for Life Program, which improves food security for parents, young adults and youth by providing classes that teach the skills necessary to make nutritious food choices, and instruction in meal planning, budgeting, shopping and cooking. The program is based on a national model of Operation Frontline, called Share Our Strength. The Cooking for Life program is a collaboration between VTCECH and the University of Vermont Extension's Expanded Food and Nutrition Education Program. (633 low-income participants were served in the six-week series.)

POLITICS AS USUAL - THE "PLAUSIBLE DENIABILITY" DOCTRINE

In January 2004, the Bush administration challenged a World Health Organization report that outlined steps for nations to take to reduce obesity. Administration officials questioned the science behind some of the recommendations, such as limiting food advertising aimed at children and limiting fats, salt and sugary sodas. Consumer groups say Bush is beholden to the food industry, some of whose executives are among his biggest fundraisers.

The Bush White House said in 2003 that the World Health Organization did not adequately address an individual's responsibility to balance diet with physical activities, and objected to singling out specific types of foods, such as those high in fat and sugar.

THE CENTER FOR SCIENCE IN THE PUBLIC INTEREST (CSPI)

According to Michael Jacobson, the executive director CSPI, the Bush administration mounted a war on obesity with "popguns, not howitzers." At a news conference held in March of 2004, the then Secretary of Health and Human Services, Tommy Thompson, likened the obesity epidemic to the tobacco epidemic. (Lawmakers require warning labels on cigarettes and in ads, levy steep taxes on cigarettes, and ban tobacco advertising to young people.)

Jacobson says that obesity is a far tougher problem than smoking, despite tobacco's addictiveness. The cigarette is a single, dangerous, unnecessary product whereas food is essential for life. He's recommended that our lawmakers approve legislation to require calories to be listed in menus; kick snack-food, fast-food and soft drink marketers out of schools; and stop food companies from aiming junk food TV advertisements at youngsters.

Jacobson added that government should become proactive by urging consumers to eat more fruits and vegetables and to cut back on candy, soft drinks and fatty meat. CSPI has been a strong advocate for nutrition, health, and food safety since 1971. Go on the web to CSPI for up-to-date nutrition and food news. They also have an informative Nutrition Action Newsletter.

Our politicians and the policies of the federal government and the food industry need to be held accountable for poor nutritional standards by being required to provide less high-fat, high-sugar foods with lots of carbs. As long as our politicians are beholden to the special interests of the food industry, little will change.

On July 14, 2005, a salvo was added to the war on sugar and fat. The Federal Trade Commission held hearings on childhood obesity and food marketing. The FTC made it clear that they would not regulate the sale of foods of minimal nutritional value, e.g., junk food and soda pop.

Why not cut back on federal farm subsidies to industrial farms which supply large food corporations with corn made into corn syrup. Why not use money for nutrition education, increasing the amount of funding for summer nutrition programs, the federal breakfast and school lunch programs, and the food stamp program.

Conflict about junk food has intensified since late 2001, when the Surgeon General's report called obesity an "epidemic."

Since that time up to 2009 the White House has weighed in on the side of big food. It has worked hard to weaken the World Health Organization's global anti-obesity strategy and has questioned the scientific basis for "the linking of fruit and vegetable consumption to decreased risk of obesity and diabetes."

What will President Obama and the 2009 U.S. Congress do?

E. FOODSTYLE CHANGES & ORGANIC CHALLENGES

HISTORICAL FOODNOTES

The modern food industry in the U.S. emerged at a time when malnutrition was the country's chief dietary concern. Food companies were asked to feed a hungry nation back in the 1930s. When saturated fat was the enemy, companies reformulated their products with trans fat products like Crisco, considered to be a healthy alternative.

Just before World War II, canned foods like Chef Boyardee began to appear on grocery shelves. However, it wasn't until the 1950s and 60s that amazing changes began to take place in the food industry. Technology came into its own with synthetic foods such as Cool Whip, Pop-Tarts, nondairy creamers, Tang, Carnation Instant Breakfast, and lots of indestructible baked goods, such as Twinkies and Wonder Bread. The burger joints such as White Castle and McDonald's were just opening. Kids began to have spare change for soda and chips, something unheard of in the past.

Is it the tail wagging the dog? The Grocery Manufacturers Association will tell you that in the 1960s and 1970s the consumer demanded convenience and bargains. Manufacturers responded with processed food in fast-food joints, supermarkets, and convenience stores. Over a period of time, the American diet became filled with an excess of fat, sugars, and processed food -- a change that radically altered our eating habits.

Or did this change occur because the food industry wanted to make greater profits? After all, they had an ample supply of raw materials like corn to make high fructose corn syrup for sweetening in soft drinks, plus a group of food scientists that could create synthetic foods like Kool Aid and Tang.

Evelyn Storm - 1947, Photo Courtesy Storm Family

EVELYN STORM OF LONG ISLAND NY AND ISLAND POND VT: A PERSONAL STORY

I want to share a story with you. These are not in my own words but those of Evelyn Storm, a woman I met when giving a gardening talk on June 8, 2006, in the town of Island Pond - way up in the Northeast Kingdom of Vermont, close to the Canadian border. Island Pond is one of those small, lovely, way off rural villages that are hard to find. Evelyn's story illustrates the major food and lifestyle changes that have taken place during the last 60 years.

Nassau County, Long Island: "My first recollection of food coming from a garden was when I was five years old and I accompanied my mother to the garden to gather vegetables for our dinner. From that time around 1938, until 1945, when World War II ended, my parents depended on the vegetable garden for much of our food. They also raised chickens, and one year, two pigs, all of which provided us with eggs and meat and a very small income called "egg money.""

"My mother preserved vegetables and fruit by canning; potatoes, carrots, etc. were stored in the root cellar and leaf vegetables were available all summer long. In the winter, Del Monte supplied whatever was not available from the pantry and root cellar. She was not employed and bore the brunt of tending the garden while my father went to his employment.

"This method of food production was performed by most families in my neighborhood, which consisted of blue-collar workers of different cultural backgrounds: Italian, Hungarian, Polish. I don't know about the white-collar workers of our town in regards to gardening, if they did any at all, their neighborhood being a mile away from where I lived. I do know that the farmland around my neighborhood produced great quantities of cabbage, string beans, potatoes, and possibly other vegetables, too, for commercial buyers and farm stands.

"The individual gardens of my neighborhood supplemented the low pay income of the families. Barter trading was not uncommon, since not everyone was fortunate enough to have as large a garden as my parents. For example, one of our neighbors had several bee hives, and we exchanged vegetables and eggs for honey. Other food commodities like flour, sugar and oil, were obtained from the local A&P market.

"Although refrigeration was not available in most homes, it was found in large refrigeration units in butcher shops, ice cream storage units and some homes of the more affluent. We had an icebox -- a porcelain, insulated, three-box affair. The middle box was made of tin into which was placed a 50-pound block of ice every week all summer long. It provided enough coldness for maintaining milk, butter and cooked meats.

It was not until 1949 that my parents could afford to purchase their first refrigerator where the freezer compartment contained only enough room for ice cube trays and a little ice cream.

"From the 1950s on, refrigeration for home use as well as refrigerated train cars and trucks was one of the innovations that quickly led many gardeners to stop gardening, for along with refrigeration came frozen vegetables, like Bird's Eye.

"When I was eight years old, our country entered World War II with the bombing of Pearl Harbor. We moved to a smaller house; the chickens came along, too. The garden was smaller. Both my parents went to work at Grumman's Aircraft factory. My father still gardened and my mother still canned, but potatoes were now bought at the A&P supermarket as the garden plot was too small for such plants. Of course, the war caused a great shortage of certain foods for us. We were issued ration books filled with coupons for meat, sugar, coffee, and butter. Oleo margarine came into existence.

"In 1945 the war ended and we moved to Vermont. The house in which we lived was situated on a very small plot of land; no space for a garden. Del Monte and the supermarket became our vegetable garden for four years.

"In 1949 we returned to Nassau County on Long Island. Most of the farmland had become Levittown, a reflection of what had occurred in many farmland communities surrounding urban areas. The city folk had moved out to the country. People commuted from the country and worked in the city, and in many cases, it was both parents. The local dairy farms were gone, the land converted to golf courses and country clubs.

Storm's Story Continued...

Both my parents worked now, so there wasn't much time to devote to a garden, and the need was no longer there. Wages were sufficient for buying all the food needed, and freezer storage was available right in your own kitchen. Any food you desired was available in the new supermarkets, which were everywhere. New highways brought vegetables and fruits from states further south and west, and eventually from California where the farmland was quickly turned into producing large amounts of fruits and vegetables with the use of chemicals. These farms were run by large corporations who employed many migrant workers from Mexico.

"Soon came the fast-food chains: McDonald's, Burger King and Kentucky Fried Chicken. Technology was rapidly advancing, especially in the area of television, and with it came TV dinners. Further advances in technology brought in the microwave oven. Now whole dinners could be prepared in a matter of minutes.

"By the end of the 1950s until the 1980s -- during which time I married, had my children and returned to work -- I, too, succumbed to a fast pace of living, and food became only a necessity to be consumed. I did stay away from prepared packaged food as much as possible, used frozen vegetables rather than canned, and didn't go to McDonald's, as many families were doing."

Sidenotes

As you can see from Evelyn's story, much has changed within her lifetime. In 1989, she retired from teaching, moved back to Vermont, built a house, created a garden, and for a period of time froze vegetables and stored some in her root cellar.

As time passed, she was not able to keep up with a garden. She told me she didn't know what to do anymore when it came to food and asked questions like "Do the potatoes I'm eating from the local supermarket come from genetically modified potatoes?" She said, "I'm really concerned about the food we're eating. I don't know where to turn. I'm old now and am not able to garden. I buy as much local as possible." Evelyn passed away in the summer of 2008.

When I was a kid in the late 1940s, my grandparents led simpler lives then we do today. They had fewer food choices. There wasn't much junk and processed foods then and most meals were prepared from scratch. I'm not trying to romanticize this time in my life, but, one thing is for sure -- looking at the pictures of my grandparents shows them to be anything but fat. Families ate more of what was in season. Many rural families canned, froze, and "put by" the food they grew in their gardens.

I remember a farmer named Guy Kelsey, who moved to the Green Mountains from Ohio in the early 1950s to work at the Putney Nursery with George Aiken. Aiken later became Governor and then Senator of Vermont. Guy Kelsey considered himself a rich man because he and his wife, Lula, had a large garden along with a milk cow and some steers. I remember Guy saying the only food they bought at the local grocery store in Brattleboro was the canned mackerel. The Kelseys would be considered an anachronism today.

I grew up in Louisville, Kentucky. My mother was a stay-at-home, cook-at-home mom. Women didn't work so much out of the house in those days. Once a month, we drove the big Chrysler from the city out to the rural town of Simpsonville where we ate at Sanders Home-Style restaurant. This was the home of Colonel Sanders of Kentucky Fried Chicken fame. His wife managed the farm and kitchen. Most of the food at Sanders' restaurant came right off the farm. And yes, the "Colonel" was real, not just a caricature.

My mom was a great cook. She won numerous baking contests. She learned how to cook during the Great Depression of 1929. Mothers in those days made most everything from scratch, except for such things as canned peas and corn, tunafish and Alaskan salmon for salmon croquettes. The Swanson TV Dinners, filled with all that gravy, didn't come in until the fifties. I don't remember any TV dinners when I was a kid. I do remember going with her to the "Haymarket" to buy fresh fish and vegetables once a week. We also went to the kosher meat market. My Great Uncle Ben was a baker, who brought loaves of warm, fresh pumpernickel, rye and challah to our home in a large brown bag once a week. 🖋

FOODSTYLE CHANGES FOR THE NOT SO RICH AND FAMOUS

So much has changed since my mom filled the kitchen with warmth and home-made food. Today, food has become a lifestyle question for the "time-starved and kitchen-challenged." Before mom gets home, the kids may be scarfing down chips and Coke and watching the tube. What's a mom to do when she gets home from work, a little frazzled, and all she hears is, "What's for dinner?" She may say to herself, "There are only so many hours in the day." There are always the cans of mushroom and to-mato soup with gobs of crackers. Or frozen pizza, or, the perennial favorite, macaroni and cheese out of a box, or, finally, a quick road trip to Burger King or KFC.

It's not only the poor and disadvantaged who are having health/obesity/nutrition problems. All classes of people need to look at their eating habits and lifestyles. Our current American culture lays the groundwork for our "death by doughnuts" lifestyle. It requires us to spend lots of time in the car. Work means sitting for hours, and recreation translates into watching the tube.

Walking off pounds: A three-year study of more than 10,000 people in Atlanta, published in the American Journal of Prevention in August 2004, found that walking to a grocery store 10 minutes away burns 50 calories. That means 100 calories back and forth. Over the course of a year that comes to about 10 pounds worth of weight. It was also found that Americans in urban areas took 84 percent of their trips in cars, compared to 42 percent in Italy, 45 percent in the Netherlands and 49 percent in Germany. Bicycling is more common in those countries than in the U.S.

Take-Out: In the restaurant business, almost all the growth over the past 15 years has been in take-out. Supermarkets have also gone into the take-out business. They have set up delis with kitchens and more processed take-out entrees. Supermarkets make lots of frozen din-ners and prepared foods for the "time starved and kitch-en challenged" and the rest of us can go to McDonald's or Applebee's.

The eating habits of the middle-class have radi-cally changed in the last 25 years. Going to fast-food restaurants is now routine. Research shows that home cooked meals contain more 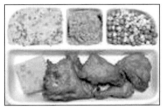 fruits, vegetables and dairy products than eating out.

- One in four meals served at home consists of frozen or prepared food.

- According to Whole Foods, the largest organic super-market chain in the U.S., prepared foods are its biggest growth item.

- A typical home-cooked meal for many families con-sists of a pre-cooked meatloaf and a container of mashed potatoes, heated in the microwave, all pur-chased at the local supermarket. Why not throw in a bag of California greens.

History and the Counterculture

Thirty years ago, healthy and organic food was called hippie food - referring to those crunchy-granola types like me wandering around the countryside growing carrots.

At the same time that junk and processed food came onto the food shelves, the counterculture of the 1970s was challenging the value of processed foods as a symptom of what was wrong with our post-modern industrial society. Naturally grown, organic vegetables and brown foods like whole grains were the foods to buy at the local food co-ops and natural food stores.

I used to buy wheat berries and grind them up in a hand-cranked metal grain grinder once a week to make bread. My girlfriend, Betsy, loved to make loaves of whole wheat bread and carry them around in a backpack to give to friends. They were so heavy she could have used them as a weapon, if attacked! My lifestyle in those days, along with that of many friends, was intimately connected to the back-to-the-land movement, and was strongly influenced by Helen and Scott Nearing and their writings, especially, *Living the Good Life.*

The "You Are What You Eat" phenomenon of the 1970s took on political overtones in the 1990s and the early twenty-first century, as more people became aware of how their food was grown, where it came from, and the increasing concentration of the food industry in the hands of a few multinational corporations.

From 2000 to 2005, new issues came before the dinner table. Eating organic changed from being a "hippie" kind-a-thing to one where the middle class began to buy organic grains and tofu at the local food co-op and the wealthier classes enjoyed organic asparagus and lattes from Whole Foods. In 2006, another change took place. Wal-Mart, the nation's largest grocer, decided to take organic food seriously -- by rolling out a complete selection of organic foods. How the world turns.

Me and My Buddy, Ethyl, Early 1970s

ORGANIC FOOD SHOPPING

DILEMMAS
Health and Nutrition and Cost

Is organic food healthier than conventional food? This is a contentious issue. Food safety and nutrition scientists say there is no definitive proof that organic foods are better for your health. However, a number of research studies indicate that organic food is healthier and more nutritious in terms of vitamin C content, mineral content, and higher protein content in grains. Critics will say those health benefits are unproven.

Two of every three shoppers believe that organic foods are healthier. Consumers also choose organics because they want to protect the environment and support the humane treatment of animals.

They are worried about pesticide residues and antibiotics fed to animals. They fear that hormones fed to dairy cows might cause young girls to race to puberty. There is also concern about all the additives in non organic food, as well as the question of the irradiation of food.

Linda Berlin, a nutritionist at the University of Vermont completed her doctoral dissertation on organic food buying. She found that consumers choose organics for the same reasons just mentioned.

Of course, the giants in the organic foods business know how to play up these notions of health and the environment with slick marketing. The pictures in their ads make you feel good about buying organic foods. They don't claim they're better for you; they don't have to. To them, it's more of a question of lifestyle than one of nutrition. Their spiel is organic tastes good, its better for the earth and your well-being. Just knowing there are no harmful sprays on apples makes you feel better.

As organic food moves from its health food niche into the mainstream, the higher premium prices are challenging many shoppers.

Health-conscious families are left to find creative solutions to eating well on a fixed budget. It can involve a bit of hunting and gathering, bulk-buying and purchasing whole food items on sale.

The Organic Food Shopper's Guide

Jeff Cox

Tips on Smart Shopping and Finding the Best Prices for Organics

- Buy fresh organic fruits and vegetables in season from local farms. Vermonters on food assistance can use Farm-to-Family coupons at Farmers' Markets.

- Buy a share in a Community Supported Agriculture (CSA) farm.

- Pick your own vegetables and fruit at organic farms.

- Buy a lot during the growing season. Can, freeze and store.

- Join a food co-op and work in exchange for a discount.

- Buy organic food when it's on sale.

- Buy whole foods like oats, wheat, and other grains in bulk and store them in glass and plastic containers.

- Buy organic meat in bulk from a farmer.

PART III

Cheesemakers at Crowley Cheese
Factory

NOFA Vermont Farm Tour

Woodstock Farmers' Market
Courtesy of Voltaire Santos Miran

PART III
SUSTAINABLE MARKETS & REGIONAL SOLUTIONS

A. THE TWENTY-FIVE PERCENT CHANGE

When it comes to food and farm issues, Vermont's not that different from other states. It faces many of the same production, marketing, and distribution challenges. And just like other states, Vermont is dependent on outside food sources, but it can make a sizeable dent in reducing how much food is imported. The good news is that Vermont has begun to serve as a positive farm and food model for the rest of the country. The question is -- to what extent can the regional, sustainable food model in the Green Mountain State replace the Corporate Global Food System?

Farmers' Market Courtesy Smart Growth Vermont

be revised since it was made back in 1976 by two University of Vermont professors, George Burrill and Jim Nolfi. Perhaps, we're closer to 90 percent food dependent. One must also consider the dairy, apple and maple exports along with all the value-added food being processed in-state.

No one to my knowledge has done any research since 1976 on how dependent the state is on outside food sources. It's hard to get information from supermarket chains on how much local food is sold.

In the last ten years, positive change has been taking place in Vermont. In 2008, there were 60 farmers' markets and 75 Community Supported Agriculture (CSA) initiatives - where consumers subscribe to a year's harvest from a farmer. Institutional buyers ranging from state government, to schools, to correctional facilities, to hospitals, are purchasing more local food. And the Internet has introduced Vermont products to the global marketplace.

I'm not talking about a 50 percent change towards greater food self-sufficiency. That would be unrealistic. A sustainable goal would be to cut the margin 25 percent by the year 2015. That would take Vermont from the current rate of 95 percent food dependent to 30 percent food self-sufficient.

For over 30 years, the figure of ninety-five percent food dependency has been used to describe the amount of food imported into Vermont. This percentage needs to

If there was a major loss of fossil fuel supplies in next five years, greater food self-sufficiency might occur more rapidly. (Agriculture currently consumes 17 to 20 percent of energy resources in the U.S.) Robert Constanza, the director of the Gund Institute for Ecological Economics at the University of Vermont, believes the end of "peak oil" is a reality. Pete Johnson of Pete's Greens in Craftsbury said, "If the fuel cost tripled, all of a sudden, there would be no price differential between the greens I grow and what a local restaurant buys from California. It would be a whole new paradigm."

Source: T. Johnson, Burlington Free Press, "Can Vermont Feed Itself," 11 June. 2007.

The Twenty-Five Percent Change would require cutting more ties to the global food system, increasing vegetable, fruit, bean, and grain production as well as a rise in beef, pork and chicken production. It would include the building of more infrastructure: processing plants, creameries, slaughterhouses, grain mills, distribution systems, and marketing networks. The change would require fewer federal regulations in regards to on-farm slaughtering and butchering practices and make it possible for consumers to purchase meat products directly from farmers.

Pete Johnson Loads a Seeder, Pete's Greens, Craftsbury, VT
Photo Courtesy of Vern Grubinger, Vermont Extension

Another change would include exporting more farm products and increasing the number of value-added foods made from local ingredients. The Vermont Agency of Agriculture has begun efforts to open markets of Vermont food products to ski areas, prisons, hospitals, and schools. Strategies are needed to protect farmland, provide farming opportunities to new and current farmers, and increase the number of training/apprenticeship programs.

SUSTAINABLE MODELS OF POSITIVE CHANGE:

In order to make a good stew, it takes the right ingredients. When most people think about agriculture, they see small farms and farmers' markets. There are other elements in the stew that are just as critical.

- Rural Vermont has played a central role in advocating on behalf of farmers on agricultural issues.

- The Center for Rural Studies has been doing research on Vermont agriculture for the past 30 years. Sound research is needed to assess and evaluate programs.

- The University of Vermont and the Vermont Agency of Agriculture have begun to take a more active role in sustainable farming and food issues.

- Non-profit educational organizations such as the Northeast Organic Farmers Association of Vermont (NOFA-VT) have played an important role in transforming the face of agriculture in Vermont.

- A necessary ingredient in the stew is the entrepreneurial spirit. Three successful examples are American Flatbread - a restaurant in Waitsfield, Red Hen Bakery in Middlesex, and the Neighbor Food Alliance-a group of Natural Food Co-ops.

- The Vermont Land Trust has conserved 110,000 acres of farmland since its founding in 1977. In the last four years 100 family farms have been saved. This has given farmers the opportunity to purchase additional land to pay off bills and repair machinery and fix-up the barn. to the next, or to a farmer outside the family.

* These models will be described further in the coming pages.

ORGANIZATIONS
RURAL VERMONT

Without groups like Rural Vermont advocating for the family farm and rural communities, the status quo would remain the same. Rural Vermont stands for a local food system which is self-reliant and based on reverence

for the Earth. The non-profit group educates farmers and the public on farm issues. They advocate locally on policies that strengthen the family farm and promote food sovereignty. Rural Vermont activates its Farm Policy Network on issues like fair milk pricing, promotion of raw milk. and protection for farmers and citizens on the labeling of genetically modified seeds and dairy products from the hormone rGBH.

Logo for
Rural Vermont

Jack Lazor, Butterworks Farm, Speaking to a Group of Farmers on the Labeling of Genetically Modified Seeds.
Photo Courtesy Rural Vermont

THE CENTER FOR RURAL STUDIES (CRS)

CRS is located in Morrill Hall at the University of Vermont. CRS is a nonprofit, fee-for-service research organization that addresses social and economic questions for rural people and communities. In 2008 it celebrated 30 years of service to the citizens of Vermont. The co-director, Fred Schmidt was honored for his 30 years of service and his commitment to Vermont agriculture.

In 2005, the Center developed an Agricultural Handbook for Vermont Counties based on the 2002 census, which provided information on land trusts and conservation in Vermont as well as links to agricultural resources. The Handbook offered an historical profile of Vermont agriculture, 1850-2002.

The work of CRS is critical because without good data and accurate research, it would be difficult to evaluate the increase of local food production and consumption in Vermont and the progress of local food and farming efforts.

The Center for Rural Studies works with NOFA-Vermont, the Vermont Agency of Agriculture, Vermont Fresh Network, the Rotational Grazing Network, CSAs and farmers' markets throughout the state. CRS is currently developing an Internet model that would connect consumers to farmers' markets, farm and food workshops, local farms and farm stands. This is based on the Internet model used by the Valley Food and Farming Network in Vermont and New Hampshire.

The Vermont Food Systems Leadership and Policy Council: This new organization was created in the summer of 2008 to create a more sustainable food system by providing healthy, safe, nutritious and dependable food for the people of Vermont. The Council is run out of the University of Vermont and is made up of farmers, academics, nonprofit leaders, food distributors, entrepreneurs, retailers and government officials. Its goal is to generate greater economic returns to producers, processors and retailers. It also promotes investment in and economic development of rural communities. The new focus of the group in 2009 will be on the research of successful farm and food operations in Vermont. It will be run out of the Center for Rural Studies at the University of Vermont.

UVM Center for Sustainable Agriculture

The University of Vermont's Center for Sustainable Agriculture (VCSA) has three programs. The Beginning Farmer Land Access Program hopes to increase the number of newly established farmers over the next five to seven years. The program provides business planning for young farmers, helps them gain access to land and capital and connects young farmers with more experienced farmers who are interested in renting, sharing or selling their farms. The program used to be called Land Link Vermont (LLV), but ended in May of 2008. Over the years, LLV had enrolled 688 participants, resulting in 23 documented matches, 10 of which are active today.

The goals of the Farm Enterprise Program of VCSA are to assure that more high quality, local foods are available to all Vermonters, to add income to those farmers producing the food, and to increase the marketing and needed infrastructure for processing the farm products. This program works closely with the Farm Viability Enhancement program that has provided sixteen farms with mini-grants for season extension, farmstead cheesemaking, and upgrading farm fiscal management to help with marketing Vermont products. The third program of VCSA is the Vermont Pasture Network, which provides grazing planning, technical assistance and support for small ruminant dairy production to farmers.
For more information, go on the web to the UVM Center for Sustainable Agriculture.

Vermont Agency of Agriculture

The Vermont Agency of Agriculture: In 2007, lawmakers directed the Agency of Agriculture to review food-buying practices at state institutions. Helen Labun Jordan was appointed as the new Agricultural Development Coordinator for the Agency of Agriculture. Her job is to focus on the State's buying practices. Jordan produced a report on the potential connections between agricultural producers, state government and state institutions, such as the state hospitals, prisons, and the Veterans' Home.

According to Jordan, no one had previously tracked the amount of local food being distributed and sold to state institutions. She said that one of the first steps was to bring farmers and state purchasers together to meet one another. Then a survey was made of government food purchases and a determination was made of the barriers to acquiring local food. One proposal allowed correctional food service supervisors to buy local crops which had been damaged in some way.

Jordan admits that when you see a "Buy Local" sticker, `**prison**' isn't usually the first thing you think of, but the Agency of Agriculture sees Vermont's nine correctional facilities as a potential market for Vermont farmers, food processors and state-sponsored farm-to-table initiatives. And unlike schools, prisons are in business year-round. Jordan says, "Correctional facilities are the primary place where Vermont government directly purchases food. It's a whole new frontier for the types of markets farmers can sell to."

The Northwest Correctional facility in St. Albans is a good example. The St. Albans Co-operative Creamery supplies dairy products. Sysco, a national distributor from Massachusetts has its food shipments supplemented by Vermont farmers who supply Black River Produce of North Springfield. The prison has a four-and-a-half acre garden that provides up to 40,000 pounds of produce annually, half going to the local food shelf.

Vermont currently awards half of its commodity contracts, which include food for state institutions, to Vermont companies. Another 35 percent are contracts that received no Vermont bids. It's clear the State of Vermont is now exploring new routes to buy locally grown food. Will more prison yards be turned into vegetable gardens? Will more Vermont food be on the menu at the statehouse cafeteria?

The Farm-to-Table program at Food Works in Montpelier supplies vegetables to the statehouse cafeteria through the Abbey Group, a Vermont food service company.

The Abbey Group (AG), based in Franklin County, provides food services to schools and institutional cafeterias, catering services, campgrounds and restaurant management. AG works in Vermont and New Hampshire and has 260 employees.

AG supplies 50 schools throughout Vermont and provides 20 percent of all the school meals, which are prepared by AG food staff within the schools. One of their priorities is to buy local, spending $100,000 a year or five percent of its budget on local food. If you go onto the AG website, they have a list of Vermont farms and food processors including Rosie's Beef Jerky from Swanton and Champlain Orchards. AG works with non-profit food groups such as Food Works of Montpelier and distributors like the Burlington Food Service.

The Abbey Group's biggest challenges are the lack of availability and higher prices of Vermont food products. Another challenge is distribution. For example, they are able to pick up 100 cases of apples from one orchard but it isn't practical for smaller amounts of produce like 5 cases of lettuce. Most of the time, they work with local food distributors. AG has a contract with the Vermont State House Cafeteria where they provide local beef.

As AG grows, they are able to exert greater buying power and more influence in using local food. The Burlington Food Service is their largest distributor. They now have a separate slot on their ordering form for either Vermont cucumbers or California cucumbers. It wasn't long ago that the Abbey Group did not know whether the cukes came from California or Vermont during the growing season.

(The three largest Vermont food distributors are Burlington Food Service, Black River, and Squash Valley. Other out-of-state food companies include Sysco, located in Massachusetts, and Fitz Vogt & Associates of Walpole, New Hampshire, which serves Vermont schools. Sysco is too large to serve small schools.)

The Northeast Organic Farmers Association of Vermont (NOFA-VT), founded in Putney in 1971, is the oldest organic farming association in the country There are NOFA chapters in all of the New England states, as well as New York. NOFA Vermont has spearheaded a number of initiatives in the State including farmers markets', CSAs and organic dairy farm initiatives. The farm and food economy of the State has been changed by the technical and educational expertise and initiatives of NOFA. They have led the way and the Vermont Agency of Agriculture has followed.

* For more information on NOFA-VT, see Part 2 under FEED (Food Education Every Day), throughout Part 3 and in the RESOURCES section in the Lifting The Yoke website.

Photos Courtesy of NOFA Vermont

NOFA Farm Tour

Bakers
at Red Hen Bakery

PROFIT AND NON-PROFIT BUSINESSES

American Flatbread, a successful restaurant in Waitsfield, Vermont and Burlington told the Vermont Cheese Company, from which it buys $400,000 worth of mozzarella each year that it wants all the milk to be free of the bovine growth hormone (rBGH). The synthetic hormone, when injected into cows, increases the production of milk. Consumers question the safety of the rBGH milk for their children. (Monsanto produces rBGH).

Red Hen Bakery in Middlesex uses organic grain in its bread. The bakery would like to find more local sources of organic grain and is working with the Extension Service of the University of Vermont and grain growers to increase the use of local wheat.

Randy George, the owner of Red Hen, currently buys 75 percent of his wheat grain and flour from Kansas. Another twenty percent comes from an organic flour mill in Milan, Quebec in the Eastern Townships called Meunere Milanaise. The mill, designed in the U.S., produces 110 metric tons of organic flour weekly. The grinding stones are of pink granite quarried in North Carolina. Stone milling is an art. While there were many stone mills in operation at the turn of the century, it is a trade that is now practically lost.

The Canadian miller, Robert Beauchemin, has worked closely with local wheat farmers for the past twenty years - developing a high quality, organic flour. He provides classes to the wheat farmers on weed control, the best planting times and the appropriate varieties to plant. According to Randy George, Beauchemin is able to equal the quality of Kansas wheat because of his dedication to the craft. George went on to say that the key to good baking flour comes from the variety of wheat sown, how it's grown and the milling process.

Red Hen buys a small amount of flour from Ben Gleason, a local wheat grower in Addison County. There are very few grain growers in Vermont. For more information on wheat growing in Vermont, go to page 191, The Wheat Challenge.

Robert Beauchemim, owner of the mill, Meunerie Mila-naise. On right, Gilles Audit, farmer in St. Lawrence Valley in Quebec. The mill serves 350 farmers. There are 5,000 acres of organic grains and 30,000 acres of pesticide free grains. Ninety percent of acreage is in wheat production.

Combines Harvesting Wheat

Bulk Food Containers,
Hunger Mountain Food Coop, Montpelier

NATURAL FOOD CO-OPS

The Neighbor Co-op Alliance is made up of 20 co-ops in Vermont, New Hampshire and Massachusetts which meet on a regular basis.

As a group, they are able to buy as one unit from suppliers and so receive a better price. They are beginning to leverage their dollars to command a certain quality in the products they purchase by working closely with local farmers and food processors. The alliance is working with CSAs, farmers' markets, the Vermont Fresh Network, and state agricultural agencies throughout New England. Their goal is to develop more local-food initiatives, such as community gardens, to distribute more locally grown food and support farm and food processing facilities like slaughterhouses.

They are also beginning to focus on questions of how to deal with the energy crisis, how to preserve farmland, how to provide education and training of new farmers and how to build a stronger food and farm infrastructure.

SUSTAINABLE FARM CENTERS

The Intervale Center: It takes more than markets and value-added products to change the agricultural landscape. Finding farmers and farms is just as critical. The Intervale is unique in that it combines farm initiatives and training for new farmers within a rare piece of rich bottomland soil in the city of Burlington.

The Intervale has been transformed into one of the most innovative and sustainable agriculture experiments in the northeast. The initiative was formed in 1988 to restore this valuable land resource to its agricultural roots and to produce local food for the Burlington community.

Over 350 acres of land have been reclaimed for agricultural use. Twelve organic farms produced food, worth over $500,000 in 2006, for the Burlington community, including fresh food for the low income and disadvantaged populations. There are 50 farmers, hired staff, interns and students who work the land. The farms supply Burlington with about seven percent of the fresh produce consumed in the city. That comes to about 550,000 pounds of fresh produce a year. The goal for the future is ten percent. Besides the farms, there are greenhouses, walking trails, and the newest initiative - a native tree and shrub nursery being developed for the protection of streambeds and rivers.

* *What's unique about the Intervale is that you have a number of diversified farms operating in a central location close to an urban population.*

The largest composting project in the State is located in the Intervale. Over 30,000 tons of food scraps and organic materials are composted each year. The raw materials comes from yard and kitchen waste, Ben and Jerry's leftovers, animal manures, leaves and discarded hospital food. The compost serves farmers in the Intervale, landscape companies, gardeners and homeowners. Some call it the "black gold" of Burlington.

The Fletcher Allen Hospital (FAHC) purchases vegetables from Intervale farmers which they use in their new healthy food program. The hospital serves 5,000 meals a day. According to Daria Holcomb, the manager of food services at FAHC, this change represents a major shift in providing nutritious food to staff, patients and visitors. You won't see a McDonald's at FAHC.

The Farms Program is the "bread and butter" of the Intervale Center. This Incubator program for new farmers, begun in 1990, supports practical, organic, sustainable farming methods. The project provides land, farm equipment, greenhouse space, irrigation, storage and compost for new, small scale farmers at reduced rates.

After completing three years as an incubator farmer, individuals graduate from the Incubator program and become Enterprise farmers. At this stage, farm enterprises are entitled to extended leases and their fees increase to cover the full operating costs. The program includes "mentor" farmers who volunteer their time by providing support to Incubator farmers. Some farmers continue to farm in the Intervale; others re-establish their businesses elsewhere.

One of the Enterprise farms is the Intervale Community Farm, a CSA (Community Supported Agriculture) farm. (The Intervale Community Farm is the largest CSA in Vermont and was the first CSAs in Vermont - started in 1989.) In a CSA, the farmer agrees to provide a wide variety of fresh, local organic produce through the growing season and the consumer agrees to purchase a "share" of the harvest, at a price set before the growing season begins. It's a contract; there are no middlemen. It's like buying stock in a company, but in this case, the benefits are a steady supply of vegetables and fruit during the growing season. If, for example, there is flooding in the spring and some of the crops are ruined, the community "share holders" must "share" the risk. For more information on the Intervale, go online to www.intervale.org.

Farm Worker and Andy Jones,
Intervale Community Farm CSA

CSA Shareholders Picking up Produce.
Courtesy Intervale Center

Photos Courtesy of the Intervale Center

The Intervale Center Office, the Calkins Farm House

Intervale Healthy City Youth Program, winter of 2008
Junior Iron Chef Title

Harvesting Garlic, Pitchfork Farm

Composting

Healthy City Youth worker.

CHALLENGES

With all the good news described above, there are many challenges that lie ahead. On one hand, agricultural production in Vermont is strong. In 2002, the USDA Census of Agriculture reported that Vermont farmers had raised $473 million worth of agricultural products or $767 per Vermonter, more than the U.S. average of $696 per capita.

On the other hand, a 2006 Master's thesis by David Timmons at the University of Vermont estimated that direct sales to consumers by Vermont farmers accounted for only 1.2 percent of the state's food expenditures. Believe it or not, this is a higher percentage than most states. Timmons found in 2006 that Vermont provided five times the national average of direct food per capita.

An earlier study in 1976 by two University of Vermont professors, study by George Burrill and Jim Nolfi, concluded that about 487,000 acres of farmland would be necessary to meet the food needs of the population of Vermont. The population at that time was 470,000. Today the population of the State is 620,000 and the amount of farmland is less than it was in 1976.

The Burrill and Nolfi study was prompted in large part by the energy crisis and oil embargo of 1973 -- a stimulus that is sparking interest in greater food self-sufficiency today.

Source: Burrill, George, and Nolfi, Jim. "Land, Bread, and History: A Research Report on Food Self Sufficiency in Vermont." University of Vermont, 1976.

What if a national emergency forced us to become more self-sufficient? Is this already happening? How much land would be necessary to meet the food needs of the average household? A study done around 1990 in the Netherlands compiled a list of 100 foods and calculated the amount of land required to produce those foods for the average household of 2.4 people for a year. For a household that consumed the full spectrum of meat, eggs, dairy, grains and vegetables, less than an acre was necessary.

Historical Notes:

Many important food crops have been raised in Vermont: wheat land in 1850 produced 536,000 bushels, the state's peak production year. Beef cattle peaked in 1840 at 384,341 head. Pork, wheat and bean production peaked in 1850 and oats in 1880. Other peak years and products were: corn for grain and apples in 1900, chicken and pears in 1910, sour cherries and strawberries in 1940, and eggs in 1960.

What spelled the 19th-century demise of food self-sufficiency in Vermont was the new market economy and the transportation system -- first the canals and then the railroads -- resulting in a shift from self-sufficient farms to commercial market-oriented production. When western agricultural lands opened up and transportation improved, cheaper products came onto the market. At one time, the major cities of Boston and New York served as major markets for Vermont products.

Farm Security Administration: Sharecropper, Walker Evans, Photographer

U.S. Government Farm Security Administration photos

The FSA was created by the Department of Agriculture in 1937 to combat poverty during the Great Depression.

1880 Hayfield

1900 Farm

1910 Mowing and Threshing Grain.

HOW MUCH CAN VERMONT FEED ITSELF?

If food trucks stopped running tomorrow, Vermont would have plenty of dairy products, but there would be shortages of most everything else. The fact is that most Vermonters, like people in the rest of the country, buy food from supermarkets that come from across the country and around the world.

According to researcher David Timmons, just mentioned, the Green Mountain state produces less than it consumes in every food category except dairy -- the supplies of local meat, poultry, eggs, grains, beans, fruits and vegetables are all less than the amounts consumed. Currently, dairy products make up 80 percent of Vermont's agricultural production and 85 percent of those products are exported.

By U.S. standards, Vermont's agricultural diversity is quite low. Thirty one states have more potential than Vermont to feed themselves (Minnesota ranking #1 at 88 percent), though Vermont leads all New England states except for the state of Maine. The main obstacles to greater food self-sufficiency in Vermont are twofold. Farmers would need to raise a wider variety of crops and livestock and industries would be needed to process these foodstuffs. Besides growing and processing more of their own food, farmers would need to continue to export farm goods.

While the challenges are many, there are positive signs. Vermont is at the center of a renaissance of farmers' markets, community supported agricultural farms, farm stands, and other forms of direct sales. Nationally, direct sales doubled between 1992 and 2002. (Direct sales exclude sales at grocery stores, food co-ops, restaurants, and sales of processed foods.) Vermont has the highest per-capita direct sales in the U.S., at 5.5 times the national average. While tourists assist in this effort, tourism does not account for most of Vermont's direct sales.

It is clear the demand exceeds the supply. There are great opportunities for local farmers and food vendors in the future.

Claybrook Farm,
Photo Courtesy of Vermont NOFA

Vermont producers have higher costs than their competitors outside Vermont -- many of whom grow on a much larger scale for national and global markets.

The question is whether Vermont consumers will be willing to pay higher prices for local products. In return, consumers can expect fresher food with higher quality, the preservation of local farms, greater food security and more money invested in the local farm economy.

Higher energy prices may one day favor local production and the price you pay for a head of lettuce from Vermont may be closer in cost to that head of lettuce shipped all the way from California.

The following research on the challenges and opportunities facing farmers, processors and consumers in Vermont was completed by David Timmons at the University of Vermont in the summer of 2006. These are the results of local interviews with Vermont co-op managers, farmers' market managers, wholesale food distributors, college food buyers, and farmers:

INTERVIEW RESULTS

In general, the supply of local food equals or exceeds the demand for vegetables like tomatoes, cucumbers, lettuce, and zucchini during the growing season. For almost all other products, the demand exceeds the supply.

• Some of the food co-ops report shortages of beef, chicken, and pork as well as cheese from small producers and local, organic milk in glass containers. Some of the farmers' markets reported that consumers would purchase more meat, poultry and local dairy products if they were available. Eggs sell out early at farmers' markets as do corn, asparagus, strawberries and blueberries. Potatoes, beets, turnips and carrots are available year round; and salad greens during the summer season and into the fall. Consumers continue to request grain and flour for home baking.

• With few exceptions, local food costs more, but in many cases the Vermont product is of higher quality. The co-ops reported that local food is more expensive; however, in-season produce like greens and root crops are sometimes cheaper. Local chicken costs more as does beef and pork. Vermont cheese and tomatoes are more expensive.

• The managers of farmers' markets reported that many vegetables like carrots, summer squash and beans are similar in price to supermarkets. They pointed out that when growers sell to grocery stores or distributors, the markups are higher because of the middleman. A major distributor reported that local products are slightly more expensive. Because the cost of trucking from California has doubled, some Vermont products are now more attractive to local distributors. One distributor said he can only pay local farmers the national market rate. In many cases, local farmers will sell to distributors only when they have a surplus or don't have another alternative.

• A Vermont grain grower said he sells his wheat berries and flour to a niche market because people want his local, organic product. He receives a higher price than the conventional commodity wheat price. He said he could never survive if he received the commodity price.

• A college purchaser said that prices vary product by product. Local apples are cheaper as are some dairy products those from a nearby farm, But in general, produce such as potatoes and tomatoes cost more.

OBSTACLES TO MORE LOCAL FOOD

Production costs are higher in Vermont because of the short growing season. Co-op managers reported prices are one obstacle to stocking local foods as consumers can purchase cheaper food at supermarkets.

• Connecting with a reliable supplier is a challenge for co-ops managers. Small farm and food operations may have trouble dealing with all the issues needed to market their products, like labeling, bar codes, and quality control. Most co-ops use more labor to buy local, dealing with many small suppliers. This is less efficient than conventional buying from large wholesalers.

• High land values are another obstacle. Farming does not provide the best return on the land and some farmers may not have the expertise to make farming profitable. Smaller farms also lack the economy of scale that favors larger operations. Vermont has high land prices, plus there is lack of processing, storage, and distribution facilities.

• Even though dairying supplies 80 percent of agricultural production in the state, 90 percent of Vermont milk is shipped south to Massachusetts where it is mixed with milk from other states at dairy processing plants. Only three dairies in the State can guarantee that the milk they sell actually comes from Vermont.

Side Notes:

Even though local food costs more, when you compute all the environmental, energy and pollution costs of food shipped across the country and from around the world, the debate changes and local food looks more attractive.

Obstacles to More Local Food Continued ...

• Another obstacle to local foods is that some people view local as either elitist or eco- friendly. They don't feel comfortable at farmers' markets. They like the convenience of supermarkets where they feel the food is safer. Some people feel overwhelmed at farmers' markets with all the people, cars, and music.

• Farmers' market managers said there needs to be more advertising and education about local food. Most of the markets see the same folks every week. The typical customer is middle to upper middle class - depending on where the market is located. The more rural markets have a mix of people. Tourists come and buy a limited range of products. The question remains whether the general public supports farmers' markets.

• Farmers' market managers said that farmers need to provide more local meat, poultry, pork and eggs. There is currently not enough supply to meet demand.

• According to some distributors, technology, competition, lack of scale, and the short growing season are the challenges facing local growers. In California, they use mobile coolers that chill produce from 85 degrees, when it's picked, down to 45 degrees, within ten minutes of picking. This helps in extending the shelf life of the food. In warmer places, they can get two crops off the same field, whereas a farmer in Vermont can only get one crop. The other advantage in areas like California is that the processing plants are located next to the fields.

• Other challenges: Different products have different barriers. Grass-fed beef, for example, needs to be finished off in the summer when grass is available, so there are inherent limits on providing a year-round fresh supply. There is a lack of slaughterhouses not only for beef but also for poultry and hogs.

POTENTIAL OPPORTUNITIES

• Local food is enjoying new interest. Items in demand include flour from grain, dried beans, eggs, cider vinegar and oils. The supply of local beef is increasing as more people are demanding grass-fed beef. Cooperative slaughter and packing facilities for meat and poultry would provide an opportunity for farmers.

• There are also opportunities for processing, storage, and distribution of crops that are already raised in Vermont like root crops and fruit. These would provide local food to consumers on a year-round basis and extend the growing season for locally grown produce and fruit.

• By mid-winter in Vermont, potatoes are imported from California and carrots from Quebec. Frozen vegetables are also an opportunity, since there is an abundance during the short growing season. The technology for such a facility is simple and low risk. There needs to be better coordination of delivery systems.

• Shoppers are becoming more health conscious and concerned about the environment. This provides them with a greater incentive to buy local. Because national organic standards have led to more industrial-scale organic production, in many cases local makes more sense than organic if one knows the place where the food comes from and how it's grown. On the other hand, organic does bring a higher price to the grower.

• The opportunities for small, entrepreneurial food enterprises that serve niche markets is huge. Take for example, Vermont's history of start-up businesses like artisan cheese. There are great possibilities for a local-branded dairy bottling facility.

• Winter farmers' markets are beginning to sprout up all over the state. Holiday markets are also popular. Farms like CSAs that sell directly to consumers are growing in number and popularity. Many growers would do better with direct market sales at roadside stands and farmers' markets.

• Institutional buying by the Vermont State government, hospitals, schools and colleges, prisons, and the ski areas could provide a stable market for farmers. It's hard to pay the bills just selling at farmers' markets.

Source: This material was taken from the graduate work in 2006 of David S. Timmons at the University of Vermont in the Department of Community Development and Applied Economics. Timmons has continued graduate work at the University of Massachusetts.

THE WHEAT CHALLENGE:

The rising price of fuel and animal feed and the surging consumer demand for locally grown bread has increased the need for local wheat. More Vermont farmers are growing organic wheat, even though the number is quite small. Ben Gleason of Gleason Grains in Bridport, Vermont is the largest wheat producer but grows and sells only a small amount of the wheat he grinds into flour compared to what's needed by local bakers. Gleason plants 35 acres of wheat each year and rotates another 65 acres for a total of 100 acres. In 2007, he harvested 45 tons of wheat.

Jack Lazor of Butterfield Farm in Westfield, Vermont sells wheat flour to food co-ops and natural food stores, but again, like Ben Gleason, he can't begin to meet the demand. Jack bought his farm in 1976 and began growing grains soon after. He started with 6 acres of wheat, flint corn and barley with the goal of providing enough food for his cows and family. Now he plants 150 acres of grains and legumes including corn, soybeans, peas, barley and wheat.

Sam Sherman of Champlain Valley Milling in Westport, New York -- across Lake Champlain from Vermont -- mills organically-grown wheat and sells the flour to bakeries and flour distributors throughout the Northeast. Sherman purchases the grain from the Upper Midwest, Western U.S., Saskatchewan, and two northern New York farms.

He told me the organic grain market is growing 20 percent a year. Sherman said that there is great potential for growing wheat and other grains in the northern counties of New York and Vermont. He could use 6,000 acres of locally-grown soft and hard spring wheat and winter hard wheat to mill into flour.

USDA

Photo Courtesy of Red Hen Bakery, Middlesex

One of the greatest challenges of the "eat local" movement in Vermont, New York and other parts of New England is the demand for local, organic wheat production. Over the years, very few wheat varieties have been developed on organic farms and plant breeding of wheat has become all but a lost art in the Northeast.

An historical context might be helpful at this point in the discussion. In the mid 1800s, there were general stores in most towns and families fed themselves. Grain and corn were ground at local mills. At one time, when the United States stretched no further West than the Mississippi River, Vermont was known as "the bread basket of New England." Forty Five Thousand acres of grain were grown in the Champlain Valley in the 1850's. It was ground into flour and sent to the urban areas. The Westward Expansion began in 1846 and ended around 1912. Everything changed when farmers went west after the Civil War and found conditions ideal for growing wheat.

One of the major factors in determining the quantity and quality of the wheat harvest is the weather. Erratic rainy conditions result in fungal diseases which makes it hard to grow wheat - especially in the Northeast. If one were to go back to the turn of the century, one would find a number of wheat crop failures in Vermont due to wet weather. That's why most of the wheat is grown today in the Midwest where drier conditions make it more amenable for wheat production.

Modern wheat varieties were developed with climates, soils, and management techniques different from the ones once used in New England. Ironically, the last well-known breeder was a University of Vermont biologist, Cyrus G. Pringle, who made major contributions in wheat breeding during the mid to late 1800s.

Vermont farmers face a number of challenges in developing wheat varieties appropriate to its climate and soils. Farmers need to gain technical skills to produce their own genetic crosses of small grain varieties. This is just beginning to happen. A new wheat breeding project is

UVM Baily-Howe Collections

underway with a 2007 grant from the Northeast Sustainable Research and Education Program (NE-SARE). The grant is being managed out of the University of Vermont by Heather Darby, a farmer and Agricultural Extension agent.

The Wheat Challenge Continued ...

The purpose of the SARE grant was to grow and select improved wheat varieties for both baking and animal feed quality that are suitable for growing conditions in Vermont. The other purpose is to help rebuild farmer knowledge of plant breeding. Modern varieties were used in the trials as were heritage varieties such as Pringle's "Defiance."

Northeast Region

SARE

**Sustainable Agriculture
Research & Education Program**

In May 2007, 19 varieties of spring wheat were planted at Jack Lazor's Butterworks Farm in Westfield. Three came from Cyrus Pringle's wheat varieties, five came from the North Dakota State Wheat Breeding Program, and ten from Washington State's Wheat Breeding Program. The modern varieties were mixed with heritage varieties such as Pringle's "Defiance.

Heather Darby said the number of farmers interested in growing grains in Vermont is increasing.

Vermont grows less than one percent of the wheat it consumes for bread-making

Granite millstone installation. Meunerie Milaniase, Milan, Quebec

She points out that there are many obstacles including the high cost of combines, drying equipment and storage facilities. There are also no commercial mills in Vermont to convert the grains into flour.

In the last six years, the number of Vermont farms producing wheat has increased and more farmers are anxious to start growing wheat, barley, oats, rye and soybeans. In the spring of 2008, a statewide grain growers meeting took place. The Northern Grain Growers Association was formed, with participants from Vermont, New Hampshire and Massachusetts. One of those participants at the event was Brent Beidler, a dairy farmer from Randolph, Vermont.

In the late summer of 2007, Brent climbed onto his big red combine and harvested wheat -- something rarely seen in over a century. At an annual spring festival in Randolph, a lunchtime crowd cheered as the flour in the rolls came from wheat grown at the Beidler farm.

In February 2009, the Northern Grain Growers had their annual meeting. There were talks and workshops on grain growing and baking. An agronomist from Quebec, Elizabeth Vachon, discussed growing practices implemented by farms in Quebec to produce wheat that meets high baking standards. Master bakers spoke as did small wheat growers in Vermont and Maine. There was such an overwhelming response to the meeting that many people had to be turned away.

* For more information, go the Northern Grain Growers website and newsletter.

At Cornell Research Farm in Willsboro, New York, long-term organic trials on organic wheat are also being tested. You can review a report on 29 varieties of winter wheat and 16 varieties of spring wheat from Cornell at www.nnyagdev.org. Small grain trials have been conducted for twenty years at Cornell Baker Research Farm in Willsboro, New York on spring and winter wheat, spring and winter triticale, winter rye, spring barley and oat varieties.

MEUNERIE MILANIASE

There is a sustainable model of wheat production and milling in the Northern Townships just over the border from Vermont in Quebec. Robert Beauchemim of La Meunerie Milanese in Milan, Quebec, mentioned earlier, has been grinding wheat into flour and working with Quebec wheat growers for over 30 years to develop appropriate wheat varieties. Beauchemim has an agronomist on staff who works directly with the grain growers. * Go online to Meunerie Milanese for more information.

In October of 2008, Heather Darby and a group of Vermont's grain growers and bakers visited Meunerie Milanese. One thing was clear. It will take years of hard work to develop the right varieties of wheat along with appropriate cultivation methods, crop rotations, fertility management and milling and baking in order to produce high quality flour for Vermont artisan bakers. But this is a start.

Robert Beauchemim told me that it would make sense to have a flour mill located in Vermont one day in the future.

There are basically 3 types of wheat. Hard-winter wheat planted in the early fall, and hard and soft spring wheat planted in the spring. Timing is critical to growing grains. Take for instance hard-winter wheat. It does best on heavy and loamy soils where there is plenty of snow cover. Beauchemim told me that hard winter wheat doesn't grow that well around Montreal where there is not much snow cover whereas in the Eastern Townships west of Montreal, there is good snow cover. It all depends -- location, soil, sound fertility management and the farmer.

* **Flour Quality** depends in part on wheat protein called gluten, which gives dough its elasticity and bread its chewy quality. Flaky pastry flour has lower-gluten qualities. Animal feed comes from wheat with very low gluten quality.

GOOD COMPANION BAKERY

Eric Andrus is a farmer and baker of European-style artisan bread, who is rising to the grain challenge in a unique way. Andrus of Good Companion Bakery of Ferrisburgh grows organic grain using horses and a reaper/binder. Before he can bake the bread, he threshes, winnows, and mills the flour using Civil War-era technology, including an old-fashioned reaper-binder pulled by his powerful Percheron horses, Molly and Star.

Andrus and his wife Erica purchased 110-acre Boundbrook Farm in Ferrisburgh in 2005. After preserving the land through the Vermont Land Trust, they launched Good Companion Bakery, which provides bread to a Community Supported Agriculture (CSA) initiative and local farmers' market. They have begun baking pies and cobblers using local products. Andrus bakes about 400 loaves of bread a week. Shares are also available through Good Companion's own CSA bread program. In the bread-share program, people sign up to receive a certain number of loaves a week. In 2007, 30 families signed up and in 2008, that number was doubled.

Visit www.goodcompanionbakery.com.

Jillian Andrus, Boundbrook Farm.

Good Companion Bakery continued ...

Eric Andrus chose to plant hard red winter wheat in 2007 and it did well. However, in 2008, a solid week of rain destroyed most of the grain crop. Good Companion Bakery is one of only three Vermont bakeries that is vertically integrated -- Andrus does everything from growing the wheat, to harvesting, to baking with a lot of help from Erica and friends. .

Jeffrey Hamelman, baking director of King Arthur Flour in Norwich, Vermont, is very supportive of Good Companion Bakery. He believes Andrus is creating a truly local product - from start to finish. Hamelman is an accomplished baker and teacher who brings a variety of experience and skills to his position at King Arthur Flour. He is a driving force behind the new wheat initiative in Vermont bringing together wheat farmers and bakers.

Molly and Star

Photos Courtesy
of Good Companion Bakery

ANOTHER VERMONT BAKING MODEL

The Naga Bakehouse in Middletown Springs in the western side of Vermont bakes bread the old-fashioned way - with the support of the whole family. Two of the children, Ellis 8, and Tikko, 11, help their parents Doug Frelich and Julie Sperling, grow and harvest the grain, grind it into flour and bake bread in a wood-fired oven. Naga's received a grant from the Vermont Community Loan Fund to design and build the oven. Most of the flour used for baking is purchased even though they are growing more wheat, spelt, rye and flax.

The breads are sold at the Rutland and Middlebury Co-ops. Frelich and Sperling's naturally leavened breads are as they put it "consistently inconsistent." They bake heavy-duty, multi-grain loaves, potato knish and caraway sticks. And they are able to support their family and supplement their income by teaching baking classes.

ARTISAN BAKERS

While little wheat is grown in the Green Mountains, Vermont is home to more artisan bakers per capita than any other state, as it is with artisan cheese and beer. Chuck Conway and Carla Kevorkian founded O'Bread at Shelburne Farms in 1977 and are still baking their sourdough breads. Jules and Helen Rabin started Uplands Bakery in Plainfield a year later. They baked European-style breads in a stone and brick oven similar to ovens in France until their retirement a couple of years ago.

Today, there are dozens of other bakeries, including Bohemian Bread from East Calais, Patchwork Farm and Bakery in Hardwick, On The Rise Bakery in Richmond and John Millquist's Trukenbrod Mill and Bakery -- to name a few. Lets not forget Red Hen Bakery in Middlesex, which bakes a hearty, organic multi-grain bread - one of many breads. Two of the heaviest long-lasting European style breads are Deeter's in Northfield and the famous sourdough rye bread of Bread and Puppet Theatre in Glover.

Side Notes:

Until there are more Vermont wheat growers and mills, good quality local bread will not be available to the majority of the population. There is a lot of work to do and it will take time but it's happening.

A REALITY CHECK: FACTS AND FIGURES IN THE NORTHEAST

• The Northeast imports 95 percent of its food and energy. The region's food system is linked to the national and global food system.

• The near total dependence on energy intensive food production and distribution from other regions of the country means that most consumer food dollars leave the Northeast.

• Food produced in the U.S. travels an average of 1,500 miles from field to kitchen. It cost the consumer 25 cents in transportation fees for a head of lettuce in 2006. That figure is higher today. Imported food from Mexico and other countries travels farther.

• The national and global food system has gained greater market share in the last few years and is becoming more efficient and consolidated.

• Dietary trends toward fast food, processed food, and low- nutrition foods are having a negative impact on the health of the region's citizens.

• Access to healthy food, especially fresh foods, is particularly limited for low-income families.

Source: New England Small Farm Institute in Belchertown, Massachusetts. Call (413) 323-4531 for more information. Check out NESFI on the web.
* There are more stats on the Northeast in the Lifting the Yoke website.

B. LOCAL FOOD AND FARMING SOLUTIONS IN THE GREEN MOUNTAINS

You've heard this all before, but I'll say it again. If change is to come, we can't continue down the dependency highway called the global food system. Local markets bring farmers and people together, produce jobs, save farmland and support the local economy. Local markets also diminish agricultural impacts on the environment by reducing transportation distances, fossil fuels, reliance on intensive agricultural inputs and food waste. The consumers' food dollars need to shift from the global industrial food model to local, community-based food systems.

For positive change to occur, a concerted effort needs to take place through a spirit of cooperation. Members of the farm community, consumer groups, agricultural officials, federal and state officials, colleges, universities, non-governmental organizations, and, of course, the business community need to work together for the common good.

Farm To School Program, Vermont FEED

Brian Snyder, the director of the Pennsylvania Association for Sustainable Agriculture (PASA), sums up farming and markets in the Northeast like this: "It has become increasingly clear in recent years that if family farms are to flourish again across the American countryside, farmers must reconnect in a meaningful way with their closest neighbors and with rural communities in their region."

Snyder goes on to add, "Fortunately, at the same time that many farmers are rediscovering the enduring value of their neighbors, average consumers are showing increased interest in the quality and safety of their food supply. They are expressing a preference to buy food that is grown on nearby farms, by farmers they know and visit. Farmers and consumers, it would seem, are yearning to find each other. They are like two highway crews tunneling through a mountain from opposite sides. The mountain represents all the complexities of today's marketplace, including issues of processing, transportation, marketing, and government regulation of the food supply chain."

COOPERATION AND PARTNERSHIPS

In Vermont, people in the farm community are starting to find ways of working together with the larger community. Farmers are teaching school children where their food comes from and also providing fresh, local vegetables to school cafeterias. This was reported on extensively in Part 2, The Battle of the Bulge.

One farmer who sold food to the schools in Burlington but didn't have time to harvest his fresh basil, called the principal at Edmunds School and students plucked, cut and filled 18 large bags of basil. Then they made fresh pesto for pizza and pasta. This is just one of the many small partnerships that strengthen farming and preserves what is good about local agriculture. Here are some other examples.

Vermont Bakers' Collective: Past Tense

Baking and farming have something in common; They can be a lonely businesses. "When you're doing all the baking and delivery yourself, it's just hard," says Claire Fitts of Montpelier, owner of Butterfly Bakery and maker of cookies, scones, and granola. In 2004, Fitts and two other Montpelier bakers, Pat Powell, maker of Nana's Lemon Curd, and Stephanie Rieke, owner of Nutty Stef's Vermont Granola, started the Vermont Baker's Collective. Five other businesses joined them.

Rieke and Powell came together to create an apple granola bread baked by Powell using Rieke's granola. They used Vermont products in the bread like maple syrup and honey. Oats were almost impossible to find locally. There was some wheat available, but not much.

The eight companies that made up the collective, were small -- mostly run by individuals who did all the baking, packaging, and billing. The collective allowed individual members to consolidate ordering, distribution (delivery), and billing.

The members combined packaging, product development and marketing efforts. A local supermarket manager said the collective's streamlined delivery process made it easier to carry more of their high-quality local products. The collective had its own shelf of baked goods at the City Market/Onion River Co-op, a downtown market in Burlington.

The collective disbanded in 2007. Pat Powell of Nana's Lemon Curd went out of business. Clair Fitts of Butterfly bakery now does her own distribution. Stephanie Rieke of Nutty Steph's Vermont Granola found it easier to sell directly to her customers. (The name for the granola comes from the nuts in the mix.)

Steph's granola, trail mix and chocolate-granola "Magic Chunks" were filling shelves and bulk bins in area markets and food co-ops, but she was losing money on all the products except for the Magic Chunks. The profit margin on the oats, nuts, and maple syrup concoctions was low. She lost some control when she gave over the manufacturing end of the operation to friends. She also felt she was losing contact with customers as she spent more and more time in front of the computer screen.

Photos Courtesy of Stephanie Rieke

Allen Sirotkin, owner of Green River Chocolates in Brattleboro, who made Steph's Magic Chunks, wanted to merge their businesses. He moved his equipment to her old factory in Montpelier and eventually she bought him out - going deeper in debt.

Photo Courtesy Stephanie Rieke of Nutty Steff's Magic Chocolate Chunks

Steph decided to make a big move when she opened Nutty Steph's Chocolate Shop in Middlesex on September 9, 2008 -- sharing a building with the Red Hen Baking Company and Cafe that had moved from Duxbury. The chocolate gig has been good for the bottom line and now Steph is meeting customers again -- right in her own shop.

When some of the original business owners dropped out of the Vermont Bakers' Collective, other value-added specialty foods businesses stayed and new ones joined. The distribution part of the business evolved and eventually became part of the Vermont Foods Delivery Service (VFDS) of Duxbury. Then, VFDS went out of business and Freedom Foods of Randolph took over distribution. These food distribution models are still going through growing pains.

Freedom Foods: In May 2008, Cathy Bacon, founder and President of Hillside Lane Farms, and Molly Creelman, founder and President of Miss Molly's Provisions merged operations and founded Freedom Foods. Molly makes natural buttercream frostings. Bacon's Hillside Lane Farms produces Vermont value-added cheese spreads, vegan and organic pancake mixes. The mixes use King Arthur organic flour that's made of a blend of wheat grains and organic Vermont maple sugar.

Cathy Bacon was the President of the Vermont Specialty Food Association Board of Directors for four years.

During her tenure she participated in working up strategies to develop, promote and support the Vermont food industry. It was a period of re-focusing and educating state representatives on the specialty food industry in Vermont, as well as urging state agencies to work with one another in supporting the development of Vermont value-added products. Bacon told me she received little support from the State.

Freedom Foods' new warehouse, processing facility, retail outlet and distribution center opened in downtown Randolph in September 2008 on the site of the former Randolph Food Co-op. They have a paid staff of eight that works in the processing facility to support the production and packaging of their own creations as well as products for other Vermont specialty food companies. This is called co-packing. They also assist in ingredient sourcing, recipe refinement, storage of raw and finished goods and distribution services.

Freedom Foods serves as a local distributor to 40 specialty food companies in Vermont -- everything from jams, jellies, condiments, granolas, syrups, candles to vinegars, pickles, relishes, crackers, baking mixes and natural, allergen free foods. In 2009 Castleton Crackers signed on with Freedom Foods to produce their crackers as their home was too small to expand their business. Other small food businesses, both in and outside Vermont are showing interest in having Freedom Food co-pack their products.

Black River Produce does a portion of the trucking and distribution for Freedom Foods. This is a natural connection since Black River travels all over Vermont picking up produce, processed goods and dairy products and dropping them off at stores in Vermont and the Boston Market. According to Kathy Bacon, there is a need for more trucking and distribution within the State.

The Freedom Foods initiative is a natural progression in the production, marketing, sales and distribution of Vermont value-added products. It's a way of combining a number of steps from the fields to your pantry. Check it out on the web.

Freedom Foods has a close working relationship with the Vermont Food Venture Center. (VFVC) - a non-profit business that provides shared-use kitchen incubator space for new, small food processors who want to produce value-added food products such as jams and pickles. VFIC is not in competition with Freedom Foods. In fact, they help each other out when needed. Some value-added businesses have moved their processing to Freedom Foods when their production grows in volume.

* See more on VFVC in Part 3 on page 265.

Four Examples:

• Pickles: Let's take the fictitious case of Fred the pickle maker from the hills of Central Vermont. Fred loves growing cukes, making pickles in his kitchen and marketing them to local stores. He decided he needed to go the next step by finding a facility to process larger amounts of cukes into pickles. He went to the Vermont Food Venture Center (VFVC) in northern Vermont in Fairfax.

Fred's business increased but Fairfax was a long way to go. He decided he couldn't do it all i.e., grow, process, promote, sell, and deliver the pickles. It was clear to him that he needed a larger facility to make the pickles and a place that would distribute them instead of him tromping all over the Green Mountains. That's where Freedom Foods came in. It's closer to Fred's farm, has a large processing facility and a distribution network.

• Yogurt: Vermont is the home to the first water buffalo farm in the U.S. The company, Bufadi di Vermont of Woodstock, uses the buffalo milk to make yogurt and cheese. They contracted with United Natural Foods, Inc., to distribute their yogurt. (United is the largest publicly traded wholesale distributor to the natural and organic foods industry in the country.)

The problem was that the yogurt had to be shipped to Dayville, Connecticut -- their wholesale distribution warehouse -- before it was sent all over the country and back to Vermont. In comes Freedom Foods. They now distribute the yogurt right from their facility in

Randolph, which is close to Woodstock.

• City Market/The Onion River Co-op located in Burlington, Vermont, aggressively markets locally grown products. At a holiday event in December of 2005, Vermont Agency of Agricultural officials were flanked on one side by Christmas trees from Craftsbury decorated with pewter from Danforth in Quechee, wooden ornaments from Middlebury, and strings of cranberries from the Vermont Cranberry Company. Other items being sold were Vermont cheeses, local organic milk, apples, cider, and fresh meat. Even the snacks were Vermont-based and carried the buy-local message. The cookies were made by Vermont school children through the Vermont Food Education Every Day (FEED) program. The ingredients were Vermont-grown oats, maple syrup, and fresh local eggs.

• Valley Food and Farming: A Regional Effort
Every spring, there is an annual "Flavors of the Valley" exposition at the local high school in Hartford. (Valley Food and Farming (VFF) is part of a larger organization called Vital Communities.) One of its purposes is to foster relationships that make local agriculture a vital part of daily community life in the Upper Connecticut River Valley of Vermont and New Hampshire. Flavors of the Valley is now in its 8th season, with hundreds of booths where people meet local farmers, buy local foods, attend workshops, sample foods and receive the 40-page Valley Food and Farm Guide.

I was amazed at the large turnout and number of farm and food booths and information shared at the event. The place was jam-packed. * See the Valley Food and Farming website under RESOURCES for more information. It is packed full of activities and programs. We need more efforts like VFF in the different regions of the state. An Internet site similar to the VFF Internet site is being planned for the Champlain Valley in northwestern Vermont.

A REGIONAL FLAVOR

Like the rest of the Northeast, Vermont is dependent on different regions of the country for a good share of its food. These areas have a comparative advantage when it comes to growing certain crops. Vermont can't produce oranges like Florida, or rice like Louisiana, but it can produce dairy products, apples, hay, maple syrup, vegetables, soft fruit, herbs, flowers, beef, lamb, pork, and more for local consumption. Vermont's food and agricultural sector is enhanced by what's called the "creative economy."

The term refers largely to businesses that emphasize the arts, culture, heritage, and agriculture. The premise is that an area infused with creativity and a strong sense of community will retain businesses as well as attracting tourists. Food and agriculture are critical to a "creative economy" in the Green Mountains. Some call this "an economy with a regional flavor."

June Holley, CEO of the Appalachian Center for Economic Networks in Athens, Ohio says, "A regional flavor is when you make a "tasty soup" by combining all the interesting places, local foods and farming, the arts, recreation, lodging, and culture to express the uniqueness of your region."

Vermont's food and agricultural sector are an integral part of this regional flavor. Vermont's uniqueness is closely tied to food thanks to the State's national recognition as a food innovator. It is a leader in artisan cheeses. Ben and Jerry's ice cream is known worldwide. Food processing is the second-largest source of manufacturing in Vermont, concentrating on dairy products such as ice cream, cheese and yogurt. Few tourists return home from a vacation in Vermont without some specialty food item like maple products. Agritourism is an up-and-coming attraction on farms trying to make ends meet.

TASTE OF PLACE

On Sunday, November 9th, 2008, three countries came together at the University of Vermont to explore the culinary flavors that make their countries unique. The Taste of Place Expo workshop featured experts from France, Quebec and Vermont. The goal was to explore the development of foods that represent tastes unique to a region.

Local Vermont food author Amy Trubek said, "France's food culture long ago celebrated the importance of terroir, or taste of place, as seen in their place-based quality labels which include financial and research support for small-scale farmers, winemakers, cheesemakers and others."

Even though Vermont brands are known and respected internationally, the Green Mountain state is a relative newcomer to a "sense of place". Trubek says that Vermont is poised to create a model for the rest of the U.S.

Vermont Public Television launched a new food series called *Feast in the Making* in the summer of 2007. The show highlighted local chefs, farmers, and food. The opening show featured Doug Mack of Mary's Restaurant at Baldwin Hill in Bristol, the hoop greenhouses of Vermont Herb and Salad in Benson, and the grazing dinner during Vermont Fresh Network's Annual Forum. The purpose of the series is to show the average consumer the importance of the local food economy.

Martha Stewart's magazine, *Blueprint*, featured a slew of Vermont products in the May/June 2007 issue, including Dragonfly Sugarworks maple syrup, Woodstock-Water Buffalo yogurt, Magic Hat #9 beer, Green Mountain Granola, American Flatbread, Pop Soda and a trio of artisan cheeses from Taylor Farm, Thistle Hill Farm and Twig Farm.

A new magazine, Vermont's own *Local Banquet,* can't compete with Martha Stewart, but has begun to highlight the politics, economics and cultural values of eating locally. The publishers of Local Banquet, Meg Lucas and Barbi Schreiber, started the magazine in order to reconnect communities around the state. It's not about upscale gourmet foods, but focuses on foods that can be grown close to home. Readers of the magazine learn from farmers, producers, chefs, food artisans -- from the field to the dinner table.

Photos Courtesy of Local Banquet

Another new Vermont magazine called, *edible Green Mountains (EGM)* is a quarterly published by Deborah Shapiro. EGM is part of a family of publications collectively called Edible Communities, which already includes *edible Missoula*, *edible Iowa River Valley* and *edible Ojai* from California. The edible concept, according to the company's website, is to "transform the way communities shop for, cook, eat and relate to the food that is grown and produced in their area." And finally, *Eating Well* is a national magazine that is produced in Charlotte, Vermont.

As well as new magazines, a wide assortment of local food books have been written by local authors, such as *Cooking with Shelburne Farms* by Melissa Pasanen. Chelsea Green Publishing of White River Junction is a leader in books on sustainable living, energy and food.

Lynn Wollenberg, the past director of the University of Vermont's Center for Sustainable Agriculture, lobbied for a September statewide food celebration to be held each year. Her goal was to broaden awareness of local bounty by asking Vermonters to try two new locally grown foods. Wollenberg's motivation came from the fact that Vermont leads the nation in per capita direct sales of produce from farmers to consumers.

MORE GOOD NEWS

I stated in the preface, "Thoughts On A Cold Day In the Green Mountains" that I see Vermont as a model for the rest of the nation. Dairy farmers are converting from conventional to organic milk operations in record numbers in order to receive a stable, higher, and fairer milk price. Artisan cheese makers are winning awards throughout the country and value-added products are popping up around the state.

While the number of dairy farms in Vermont continues to decline, the overall number of farms remains fairly stable. There are currently 6,500 farms with an increasing number of small, diversified operations. The number of farms rose by six percent from 2002-2007. According to the Census of Agriculture, there were just under 6,000 farms in 1974. Overall, there are 15,000 people involved in agriculture in Vermont.

Vern Grubinger, the former director of the Center for Sustainable Agriculture at the University of Vermont, said, "Agriculture isn't dying, and it isn't going away, but it is changing." Grubinger said that in the 1970s, three-quarters of Vermont farms were dairies. Now three-quarters produce something other than dairy. Nevertheless, dairying still contributes $2 billion to the local farm economy or 80 percent of farm profits.

Grubinger said that as Vermont's dairy farms have become more productive and consolidated, they've also become fewer in number. The number of dairy farms is now a little less than 1,100. In 1980, there were 5,000. Some are now larger and others have stayed relatively small, remaining economically viable by going organic or diversifying. Many of these dairy farms grow Christmas trees or pumpkins, produce maple syrup, make cheese, or saw lumber.

More and more farms are using organic techniques and sustainable practices. These ventures include agritourism, the making of farmstead cheeses, greenhouse production, the growing of flower, vegetable, herb and floriculture crops, grass-beef production and organic milk

Cows on a Frosty Morn in Waitsfield, Vermont

production. Small farmers can make a living if they can find the right product and create a profitable niche market. This is happening across the state as farmers sell more products to local merchants, schools, and restaurants. The 2002 census reported that direct-to-consumer sales is among the fastest growing sectors of the economy.

According to Grubinger and the Vermont chapter of the Northeast Organic Farmers Association (NOFA), the most dynamic agricultural sector in Vermont is organic farming. NOFA estimates that in 2006, there were 394 certified organic producers as compared to 212 in 2000. In 2006, there were 66,827 acres in certified organic production as compared to 22,148 in 2000. The gross sales by Vermont certified organic farmers (farm income) was $32,679,051 in 2006. The gross sales of Vermont certified organic processors was $47,991,443. These totaled $80,670,494 in gross sales.

Organic dairy farms have grown between 15 and 20 percent a year for the past few years. Twenty percent of 1,100 dairy farms in the state are now organic. The average age of organic farmers in Vermont is 46 years compared to the average age of 54 years for conventional farmers.
*Source: NOFA Vermont * Vern Grubinger can be reached at the University of Vermont Extension Service in Brattleboro at (802) 257-7967, ext.13 vernon.grubinger@uvm.edu.*

C. THE ADVANTAGES OF LOCAL FOOD PRODUCTION ARE TOO NUMEROUS TO NAME

LESS TRAVEL

The Leopold Center for Sustainable Agriculture at Iowa State University published a report in 2003 called, "Checking the Food Odometer: How Far Does Your Food Travel?" Researchers analyzed the distance that 16 locally-produced food items travels from 34 different farms to conference centers, hotels, and other institutions in central Iowa. The Center found that local produce traveled an average of 56 miles, while produce from conventional sources had come nearly 1500 miles. And this study dealt only with domestic produce. Consider the fact that 39 percent of the fruit and 12 percent of the vegetables we consume comes from outside the United States.
*Source: USDA * See page 35, food graph on travel distances.*

THE MULTIPLIER EFFECT

On average, the amount of money that stays in the community for a local store is more than three times the amount for a big box store. It's not just the price of that screwdriver that counts. The added cost of higher taxes, the loss of empty downtowns, and the cost of greater government spending on social services need to be considered.

One could see farming in the same light as a local business. The farmer is just one part of the economic picture. One also needs to factor in the milk hauler, farm machinery dealer, seed company, veterinarian, food processor, restaurant, food store and yes, the consumer, who purchases local food. When these businesses are gone, the community loses both economically and socially.

The Institute for Local Self-Reliance studied the impact of independent businesses versus chains along the mid-coast of Maine. They found that locally owned businesses spend 44.6 percent of their revenue within the surrounding two counties. They spend another 8.7 percent elsewhere in Maine, mostly on wages and benefits, goods and services purchased from other local businesses, and taxes. Big box stores returned an estimated 14.1 percent, mostly as payroll. The rest leaves the state.

THE IMPLAN MODEL

A 2000 economic study using what is called the IMPLAN Economic Model shed new light on the importance of agriculture in Vermont. Data from the U.S. Census of Agriculture and the National Agricultural Statistics Service has traditionally been used to determine the value of farming in Vermont -- estimated at about half a billion dollars annually for the past several years.

However, those agencies measure only farm income and they omit many value-added enterprises and indirect economic impacts in their calculations. As a result, they have significantly underestimated the economic importance of Vermont's agriculture. The IMPLAN Model shows that Vermont's agriculture is worth $2.6 billion per year. This is significant in terms of the impact on Vermont's rural economy.

The new data includes the following:

Vermont consumer purchases:	$148 million
Products exported from Vermont:	$1.23 billion
Value of farm production:	$681 million
Value of food industry production:	$1.05 billion
Multiplier effects from wages and input purchases:	$887 million
Total:	**$2.6 Billion**

Photo Courtesy of the Vermont Farm Bureau

Using 2000 data, the IMPLAN model shows the direct value of Vermont farm products at $681 million. This is about a third higher than the census estimate, in part because the value of products that are used on the farm in lieu of purchased inputs, such as feed, animals, seeds, and seedlings, are included in the IMPLAN estimate.

Just under one-third of all Vermont farm production, or $195 million in food, is used for such products as bottled milk, apple cider, ice cream, meats, and yogurt, by Vermont's farm-related industry which produced $1.05 billion worth of products in 2000. It is clear that the farm-related food industry is closely tied to the farm economy.

The value of the secondary economic impact of agricultural equipment, fuel, supplies, wages, calculated by IMPLAN, was $391 million in 2000. The value of the secondary impact of the farm-related food industry was $496 million. These indirect economic impacts do not include such activities as tourism, hunting, and recreation. Also, agritourism is not always included as a revenue source for farms when cash receipts are calculated.

Source: The IMPLAN research study was done by two University of Vermont graduate students in the Applied Economics and

Community Development Department.
This report was commissioned by the Vermont Sustainable Agricultural Council. It is called "Vermont's Agriculture: Generating Wealth from the Land"

IMPLAN modeling software is based on input-output methods frequently used by planners and economists to assess impacts of economic development and is distributed by the Minnesota IMPLAN Group at www.implan.com.

OTHER ECONOMIC INDICATORS

According to the Vermont Job Gap Study's "Leaky Bucket" report in 2000, "If Vermont substituted local production for 10 percent of the imported food (10 percent of $1,808 billion = $181 million), it would result in $376 million in new economic output, including $69 million in personal earnings from 3,616 jobs."

Vermont's Agency of Agriculture, Food and Markets has been beating the economic drum since 2003 with its "Buy Local: The 10 Percent Difference Campaign." If Vermonters shifted just 10 percent of their food purchases to locally grown food products, it would add more than $100 million to Vermont's economy.

The Efficiency of the Family Farm: Numerous studies have shown that the family farm is more efficient than factory farming, and that regional solutions, such as farmers' markets, natural food co-ops, food stores and restaurants that provide local food contribute more to the community in terms of a clean environment, healthy social and economic relationships and food quality.
See study "Efficiency: Family Farms and Factory Farms - Land Stewardship Project Faribault, Minnesota."

Consumers Demanding Change: A number of land grant universities produced a study of American attitudes about food and how it is produced. Here are some of the results: 71 percent said they would be willing to pay more for locally-produced food and food that was grown in ways to protect the environment; 92 percent said that genetically-modified foods should be labeled; 77 percent said that government policies should focus on helping the family farm.

Communities and the Land: Besides the production of healthy food, local food production helps ensure that land will be kept open and our communities will stay vibrant. Those of us who live in Vermont and other rural parts of the country are aware of how much the rural landscape is being stressed. Many Vermont farms have gone out of business and the land is reverting back to scrub. Some farms have been sold for development. The farms that remain are precious. They provide open land and pastoral scenery and benefit the regional economy. People long for an open working landscape.

It doesn't take long for a pasture to revert back to golden rod, briars, saplings and then grow into young trees. By then, it's hard to bring the land back to farm.

Many urban and suburban dwellers love the aesthetics of farmland scenes with barns, fields of animals, and acres of green corn. There is a strong spiritual need for people to commune with nature and the land. There is something to be said about rural scenes and how they fill what I call our "spirit gaps." This is one of the reasons agritourism has taken off like wildfire.

Buying local is a pleasure, especially when it means stopping at a rural farm stand. Driving along a scenic country road or spending an afternoon at a pick-your-own apple orchard on a crisp autumn day is a joy.

Sprawl is not inevitable. Great efforts are being made in Vermont and other states to support and strengthen the food and farming connections between our communities and the working landscape, so we all can prosper. In the long run, when the cow pasture down the road turns into rows of identical houses, we all lose. Yes, we need affordable housing but it doesn't need to be where the cows munch on grass. U.S. Census data for 2000 show that rural communities are absorbing 40 percent of Vermont's population growth, resulting in the loss of valuable farmland, forest and wildlife habitat.
An organization called Smart Growth Vermont is focused on issues of sprawl, growth, and the connection between how we use the land and the implications for jobs, housing, economic opportunity and environmental protection. Stay informed with the Smart Growth E-newsletter. (They used to be called the Vermont Forum on Sprawl.)

Smart Growth Vermont
170 Main Street
Burlington, Vermont 05401
(802) 864-6310
www.smartgrowthvermont.org

9 Reasons to Buy Local

-- Vermont Agency of Agriculture

1. Locally grown food tastes better.
2. Local food is better for you.
3. With all the issues related to food safety, there's an assurance that comes from knowing who grows your food.
4. Buying food supports local farm families.
5. Local foods build community.
6. Local food preserves open space.
7. Local food keeps taxes down. (Farms contribute more in taxes than they require in services, whereas most residential developments contribute less in taxes than the cost of required services.)
8. Local food benefits the environment and wildlife.
9. Local food is an investment in the future.

Leopold Center for Sustainable Agriculture
Average distance by truck to Chicago Terminal Market

The objective of the Leopold Center is to reduce the negative impact of industrial agriculture on our natural resources and rural communities and to develop profitable sustainable farming systems.

	Distance	# States supplying this item	% Total from Mexico
Grapes	2,143 miles	1	7
Broccoli	2,095 miles	3	3
Asparagus	1,671 miles	5	37
Apples	1,555 miles	8	0
Sweet Corn	813 miles	16	7
Squash	781 miles	12	43
Pumpkins	233 miles	5	0

Each truck represents about 500 miles of distance traveled

Why Buy Local? Five Other Advantages in a Nutshell:

1. Local businesses and farms produce more income, jobs, and tax receipts for local communities than big box stores.
2. Local businesses and farms are more likely to use local advertising, banks, and other services.
3. Local businesses donate more money to non-profits and are more accountable to their communities.
4. Supporting local businesses preserves the economic diversity of our communities and the unique character of our neighborhoods.
5. Supporting local businesses and farmers is good for the environment because it cuts down on fuel consumption. Buying locally produced goods reduces the need to ship goods from thousands of miles away and also cuts down on the distances shoppers travel.

Source: Organic Consumers Association

A Tale of Two Carrots:
California Carrots vs. Vermont Carrots Grown in the Intervale

Photo Courtesy of the Capital City Farmers' Market

Travel: A California carrot travels thousands of miles by refrigerated truck or plane to the grocery store.

A Vermont carrot grown in the Intervale, a rich floodplain located within the City of Burlington, travels less than 1.5 miles to the Burlington Farmers' Market.

Taste & Nutritional Value: A California carrot has been sitting in a refrigerated warehouse for a week or two before being shipped across the country. The starch content of carrots increases during storage as the plant cells dry out. A local carrot can be eaten within days of being picked -- all fresh and crisp.

Environment: Eating local carrots from the Intervale greatly reduces fuel emissions resulting in less global warming and pollution.

Local Economy: If each Vermonter bought 10 percent of their food locally, about $100 million would be added to the Vermont economy.

Community: You won't know where the California carrot is grown or the farmer who grows it. You can visit the farm and the farmer where the carrot is grown in the Intervale.

Tip to the Consumer

* A 25 POUND BAG OF OATS:
Why not start with a 25 pound bag of organic oats purchased from a local food co-op or buying club? Look at all the oatmeal porridge, granola, and delicious cookies that can come from that bag of oats. Kids love to make cookies and if those oats are grown locally, that's even better.

I would like to throw a curve ball into the discussion on buying local. A team of researchers at the University of California, Davis, are asking questions about the carbon footprint of food. (A carbon footprint is a measure of the impact of human activities on the environment in terms of the amount of greenhouse gases produced.) They stated that the fact that something is local doesn't necessarily mean that it is better for the environment. The distance that food travels from farm to plate is important, but so is how the food is packaged, grown, processed and transported to market.

Consider strawberries. If mass producers of strawberries ship their product to Chicago by truck, the fuel cost of transporting each pint of strawberries is relatively small, when one considers the thousands of containers of berries. When a local farmer carts a small amount of berries in a pick-up truck to different farmers' markets, is the farmer using less energy? Not according to one strawberry distributor, but that conclusion could be questioned. What is clear is that transporting food by ship or rail is relatively inexpensive as compared to air travel.

The researchers raised other questions. Are canned tomatoes a better environmental choice in winter than fresh tomatoes from abroad? And what about those folks that drive to a local market in their SUV to pick up one or two items for supper when they could do all their shopping once a week at the supermarket?

Photo Courtesy of Capital City Farmers' Market, Montpelier

D. DIRECT MARKET ALTERNATIVES: PAST, PRESENT AND FUTURE

One way to counter industrial agriculture and its food marketing system is to develop direct market alternatives. In the past, farm stands provided consumers with fresh fruits and vegetables. They still do, but today there are a number of other alternatives, including farmers' markets and an old-new form of market initiative - year-round enclosed public markets. Some markets are called food sheds. In general, they are larger than farmers' markets. Food sheds are closer to the size of a public market.

FARMERS' MARKETS

According to the USDA, the number of farmers' markets has doubled nationally in the past decade, to more than 3,700. In Massachusetts alone, the number has grown from seven in the late 1970s to more than 90 today.

Farmers' markets are the largest growing sector of the food industry. The farmers' market in Madison, Wisconsin has 20,000 customers each week. The growing popularity is attributed to a number of factors: more demand for freshness and the higher nutritional value of locally grown food, less tolerance for factory-raised meat; increased awareness about supporting local economies; and environmental concerns about the use of chemical fertilizers, pesticides, and antibiotics.

Sociologists estimate that people have ten times as many conversations at farmers' markets than at supermarkets. Take Lincoln, Nebraska. During the summer, thousands of residents flock to the Haymarket Farmers' Market, staged weekly on a street adjacent to the train depot. It hosts 50 growers who are located within 150 miles of the city. The open-air market buzzes with conversation, music, and talk about food.

Paul Rohrbaugh, a farmer who sells at the Haymarket, is also the executive director of the Nebraska Sustainable Agricultural Society, a coalition of farmers, gardeners, educators and city folk. He says, "Farmers' markets are springing up in small towns throughout the state for the first time in 30 to 40 years." In the poorer neighborhoods of Lincoln, where fast food joints flourish, local farmers are offering fresh fruits and vegetables to 2,000 families four times a week at the community soup kitchen.

Amish Farmer, Redding Terminal Market, Philadelphia

Rolling soft pretzels, Redding Terminal Market, Philadelphia

HISTORY OF MARKETS

The practice of farmers bringing their produce to town is as ancient as agriculture itself. Farmers' markets represent a form of commerce and social interaction.

For thousands of years, farmers have been hauling their goods into town squares, where food and gossip are exchanged along with beans and turnips, potatoes and other vegetables, apples, other fruits, baked bread, and livestock.

Just look at Les Halles in Paris, which ran for more than eight centuries, from 1137 to 1971. The Rialto in Venice has been going strong since 1097. Philadelphia has the famous old Reading Terminal Market. New York has many open air and enclosed markets as do most major cities. There is a new public market in Portland, Maine, and three large in-door four-season markets in Montreal.

Washington, D.C., has the old, historic Eastern Market with its long brick building of the 1800s. Seattle's Pike Place Market, with its famous seafood and produce, has neon "Public Market," "Farmers' Market," and "Meet the Producer" signs.

In the U.S., some public markets have become landmarks and tourist destinations. Take, for example, Faneuil Hall Marketplace in Boston. What was once a market where farmers brought their produce by horse and wagon from the surrounding towns of Lexington and Concord, was transformed in the late 1970s into a trendy shopping area offering gifts and clothing, and pricy food. In response, small farmers' and green markets have sprung up near Faneuil Hall to provide "real" food to the masses. A new movement is beginning to take place for an old idea as well: a permanent, year-round Boston Public Market.

* Faneuil Hall was built in 1742 by Peter Faneuil, a wealthy Boston merchant, and presented as a gift to the city as a marketplace for fisherman, produce and meat vendors, as well as a public meeting place. The public meeting space was upstairs in the hall where great political debates took place on the foundation of democracy in the country. In the early 1800s, the Quincy Market building was added next to Faneuil Hall, and the complex remained a center of commerce.

FOUR VERMONT FARMERS' MARKETS PLUS ONE FROM THE BIG APPLE

All over the Green Mountain State, Vermonters flock to the many farmers' markets, from Newport in northeastern Vermont near the Canadian border to Brattleboro in southeastern Vermont close to Massachusetts border. In 2008, there were 75 farmers markets including ten winter farmers' markets.

Lots of change has been taking place in markets over the last few years in Vermont. No longer are they just operating on Saturdays; one can find them open for business in the middle of the week. Many markets now offer a greater variety of foods including eggs, beef, pork, cheeses, farm-raised fish, breads and ethnic foods.

It used to be that farmers' markets were started by earth crunchy folks like me but that's all changed now. In Milton, the local Grange organization sponsored a market. The New England Federal Credit Union is supporting two new markets in Williston. In Hinesburg,, the Lions Club founded a market four years ago to raise money to help those with reduced eyesight and hearing problems. Markets have become a venue for communities to pool their resources and serve their neighbors. In Richmond, you can donate your hair for wigs to those with cancer. Markets have become musical events along with face painting, puppet shows and farm animal exhibits.

2007 marked the 20th anniversary of the Vermont Farm-to-Family program, administered by the Vermont office of Economic Opportunity. The program provides $150,000 worth of coupons annually to income-qualified households to be used towards the purchase of locally grown fruits and vegetables at farmers' markets across the state. In 2007 a pilot project at three markets enabled low-income families to use their EBT plastic cards to purchase food-stamp eligible foods at farmers' markets.

Photo Courtesy of Capital City Farmers' Market

MONTPELIER: CAPITAL CITY MARKET THE STATE'S GRAND-DADDY MARKET

The first Montpelier Farmer's Market was set up behind City Hall in 1900. This local tradition dwindled out after half a century, then was rekindled in 1977 through the combined efforts of farmers, local and state officials, and Vermont NOFA.

At today's Capital City Market, you can buy everything from zucchini to wool yarn, from lamb to blown glass. You can find 20 apple varieties, as compared to 5 in most supermarkets. Musical performances and hot food of many ethnic traditions add to the festive atmosphere of the market. "It's a gathering place for the community, with space for people to hang out and talk," says market manager Jessie Schmidt.

Owners of Montpelier businesses have noted increased foot traffic on market days from both locals and tourists. One can hear comments like, "It's a gathering place and the market strengthens the town."

Photos Courtesy of the Capital City Farmers' Market
Photographer: Jamie Cope

Shopper

Samosaman Food Stand

Grian Herbs

Gold Train Limited

THE BRATTLEBORO FARMERS' MARKET

I begin to feel nostalgic when reading about new farmers' markets being developed, especially when I look back to the early 1970s when I founded one of the first farmers' markets in Vermont in the town of Brattleboro. It was simple back then. I organized my farmer friends and we found a place to sell our produce. There were no grants, bureaucrats and government officials that helped the market get off the ground.

There were a number of barriers like finding a good site, marketing and advertising, and bringing in a mix of farmers and vendors. There was also a problem with a few members of the business community. They felt the market would be too competitive and take away business. We tried to explain to them that just the opposite would occur; we would bring more business to town. One telephone caller told me to beware of slippery banana peels. Those were the days.

In the beginning, there was a general reluctance on the part of the greater community to support such a venture. They couldn't conceive of the concept. The community had to get used to the idea of a farmers' market, especially when it was being driven by a number of young upstarts and hippies like me, or what the locals called "flatlanders." But in life, things change.

First, the market had to move three miles from Elliot Street in the center of downtown Brattleboro some 4 miles away to the Old Skunk Farm in West Brattleboro. We didn't want to move from the downtown, but the site was being developed and we had no choice. And then we had to recruit more vendors.

I remember going to a meeting at the local Brattleboro Senior Center to suggest the idea of the center having a crafts booth. I explained the idea, and they were very open to it. Their experience at the farmers' market made them feel valued and brought in some extra cash, but the main benefit was social. The seniors loved getting out, talking to others and sharing their crafts.

Once people arrived at the Old Skunk Farm and saw the booths filled with fresh vegetables and fruits, crafts, as well as homemade pies and other baked items, herbs, and flowers, the market took off like wildfire.

Every Friday evening, I would pick vegetables and soft fruit, fill up bushel baskets with produce, get my signs and tarps out, and load up the truck to the hilt. I made sure my 1951 dark green Chevy truck with bucket seats and a 12-volt battery would start by parking it up on the hill, so I could jump-start it, if necessary.

One serious challenge came with the territory. A local grower was transporting vegetables up from Massachusetts, some 35 miles south of Brattleboro down Interstate 91. This was against the rules of the market. Most of the farmers knew what he was doing, but couldn't prove it. One Saturday morning before the market opened, an older apple grower took the young man into the woods behind the market and told him how it was going to be in the future. I don't know what he said, but it worked. The local grower never went down to Massachusetts again and all was well.

Peter Gould's Pies: Peter Gould and his other hippie friends lived at one of the local communes, called Packer's Corners. Peter made these great pies and sold them at the market, and he always went home without any pies. I have to admit I was a little jealous because he made more money than I did and I was working in the fields all week and Peter's pies were made the day and night before the market. Such is life.

By the end of the market day, I had traded for frozen rabbit and two pies plus cash in my pocket from selling vegetables. I felt like a rich man. I would offer poorer families good deals at the end of the day. I dropped off vegetables at the Common Ground Restaurant. By that time I had little left in the truck save some spent vegetables for my pigs.

Now the Brattleboro Farmers' Market is the place to go on Saturday mornings. It has become institutionalized in a good way except it's a little pricey for some folks.

* Dwight Miller of Miller Orchards in Dummerston was the first apple grower to join the market. Dwight provided legitimacy to the market and was a friend to many farmers in the area. He passed on in August of 2008.

THE OLD NORTH END WALK-TO-MARKET

For the past eight years, on Tuesday afternoons, from June through October, you'll find a market across the road from the H.O. Wheeler School in Burlington's Old North End. Ninety percent of the customers live within three miles of the site and up to 60 percent are first-generation immigrants. Farmers offer produce oriented to the eating interests and habits of the neighborhood. A typical selection at the market might include Vietnamese greens and chilies and Asian basil, popular with many Vietnamese families that make their home in the Old North End, along with traditional vegetables like corn, green beans, cucumbers, tomatoes, and potatoes.

The Vermont Campaign to Aid Childhood Hunger started this market in 1997 to address the community's need, and NOFA-VT contributed grant money to the project. The Champlain Office of Economic Opportunity supports the market's mission of bringing good-quality locally grown food to this economically disadvantaged area by holding cooking and nutrition classes right on site.

Farmers' Market Photo Courtesy of Vermont NOFA

ALBURGH: THE NEW KID ON THE BLOCK

In 2001, area farmers, town officials, businesses, and non-profits came together to create the Alburgh Farmers' Market in the northwest corner of Vermont. The project began with a new priority: support local agriculture, as part of the town plan. The town planning commission struck up a partnership with the University of Vermont to provide technical assistance and grant writing. NOFA chipped in to fund promotional materials and "Shop with the Chef" events, in which a local restaurant chef gave cooking demonstrations at the market using local produce.

After four years of operation, sales at the market supported more than 40 acres of local land. Customers were drawn to booths filled with produce, flowers, eggs, cheese, artisan-baked goods, preserves, syrups, and crafts. Fifty random interviews conducted in 2003 showed that 40 percent of the customers were community residents, 37 percent were tourists and 23 percent had pulled off the highway -- often en route to New York or Canada -- just to shop at the market. Unfortunately, the Alburgh Farmers' Market closed down at the start of the 2006 season. Too few vendors was the reason given by the folks I spoke to in the community.

Chester Farmers' Market logo

Photo Courtesy of Vermont NOFA

SPROUTING A WINTER FARMER'S MARKET

Vermont's newest initiatives are full-season markets that open their doors during the winter months. Ten communities now have winter markets and many towns hold special Christmas holiday market fairs.

Greg Cox, a market organizer, told me about the winter farmers' market in the old Strand Theater in Rutland. In order to enter the market, consumers must walk through the Rutland Area Natural Food Co-op. The winter market is open Saturdays and offers greens, frozen rabbit, chicken, pork and lamb along with root vegetables, squash, homemade cheese, maple syrup, apples, cider and baked goods. Seventy percent of the vendors are farmers.

The Montpelier Winter Farmers' Market at Vermont College is doing business on the first Saturday of each month, starting in early December and running until April. Jessie Schmidt, the market manager, said the concept of a winter market was spurred on by the recent demand for local food.

The Norwich Winter Farmers' Market began on Saturdays in the fall of 2006. Besides vegetables like carrots, beets, turnips, squash and potatoes, less usual varieties appear like Jerusalem artichokes, celeriac, garlic, kale and sprouts. Vendors also bring dried flower arrangements, dried and frozen meats, jams and jellies, knitted hats, jewelry, scarves, woven rugs, wooden bowls, note cards and birdhouses.

It took a lot of organizing to put the Norwich Winter Market together with vendors from Vermont and New Hampshire. Grants were received from Mascoma Bank and the Byrne Foundation, which promotes healthy lifestyles. The money helped with advertising and promotion costs, which were not covered by vendor fees. Securing an indoor venue large enough to hold the winter market was a challenge. Market rules stipulate that 70 percent of participants must be selling goods produced in Windsor and Orange counties in Vermont and in Grafton and Sullivan counties in New Hampshire.

The remaining vendor spaces are allocated as such: 15 percent to producers of prepared foods and 15 percent to crafts.

Farmers Suzanne Long and Tim Sanford of Luna Bleu Farm in South Royalton, grow six acres of vegetables as well as winter vegetables. Long and Sanford have been selling at the Norwich Market since 1988. They also run a CSA for 80 families in the summer and 30 families in the winter. Luna Bleu brings carrots, celeriac, fingerling potatoes, Napa cabbage, Delicata and spaghetti squash, and spinach and kale from their unheated greenhouse to the winter market.

The Internet: In 2008, Addison County launched a new option, an Internet/farmers' market hybrid called "Addison County Locally Grown" that allows members to order biweekly from an online list of goods for pick up. Customers pay online. The food is picked up at a central farmers' market location. Two of the advantages of this system are that there are no unsold products and growers have full access and control of the presentation they make online. The Addison County Locally Grown network is a pioneer in this type of online market. To learn more, go to Addison County Locally Grown on the web.

Some Vermont groups are hoping to increase Internet possibilities even further. The Vermont Fresh Network, which connects local farmers and restaurants, is working on a statewide online system that could pull together a grand list of available Vermont products and give large scale buyers like chefs the ability to purchase local ingredients on the web.

A MARKET IN THE BIG APPLE

Two hours north of New York City, a Brown Swiss calf is munching on grass at the Hawthorne Valley Farm. In two years, the calf, fed on a diet of hay in winter and grass in summer, will turn into a 900-pound steer. Its manure will be composted and placed back on the land for vegetables and apples. The meat will eventually become dinner for shoppers at the Greenmarket at Union Square in New York City.

Stephen Schneider, the farm manager at Hawthorne Valley says, "One of the crimes of industrial agriculture is that we've moved all of the animals off the land." The number of beef cattle raised in pasture is less than one percent of the 33 million animals slaughtered in the United States each year, according to Jo Robinson, an author who runs eatwild.com, devoted to the grass-fed movement.

At Flying Pigs Farm in the Battenkill River Valley, Michael Yezzi and Jennifer Small work with three breeds of pigs -- Tamworths, Gloucestershire Old Spots and Large Black -- that they sell at Union Square.

Vegetables and fruits have been the staples of the Greenmarket for 30 years, but now they're sharing the plate with eggs, pork, beef, and lamb from local pastures near the city and of course, those Jersey tomatoes.

Since 2000 the number of Greenmarket farmers selling pasture-raised protein -- eggs, beef, lamb, pork -- has grown from nine to 25. All the animals are raised no more than a half-day from the market.

Most of the farmers who sell at the Greenmarket say they can't compete with the large industrial farms on the supermarket level, but they can make a buck at Union Square.

Alyssa Bonilla, a 45-year-old woman from Queens, New York, buys her stew beef and liver from the Hawthorne Valley farm stand at the Greenmarket. She says, "These are decent people, and they aren't abusing their animals or their land, and I want to express my gratitude to them."

Source: Severson Kim "Give'em a Chance: Steers Will Eat Grass." New York Times 1 June, 2005.

THE 2006 NYC FARMERS' MARKET DILEMMA

Greenmarket runs most of New York City's farmers' markets. It is the largest farm-to-city system in the country and is run by the New York City Council on the Environment. Greenmarket's rules are strict. Farm staff must attend the market and sell their products. Elsewhere in the country, markets usually include independent "food artisans" selling products like tomato sauce, breads, fresh pasta, home-cured olives, cheeses, and sausages. Greenmarket allows only bakers, market gardeners, and, farmers who make cheese from their own herds.

A new outdoor market initiative developed by Nina Planck runs counter to the Greenmarket concept. She offers more diverse products than a strictly defined farmers' market. Planck was dismissed as the director of the New York City Greenmarkets after a short stint. She says, "I think the farmers' market movement has failed consumers in not making it possible to buy everything they need for Saturday night dinner. It's time to be more inclusive."

Planck's Real Food Markets include farm co-ops, local artisans (people who make food from ingredients they've bought), and farmer-purveyors (farmers who sell produce grown by other farmers in the region). Market rules stipulate that if a product can be grown locally, it must be, but other products like avocados and lemons can be used in processed products.

Many in the alternative food movement were surprised to hear that Planck, a defender of the family farm, would be running markets that could sell guacamole made from Costco avocados. Could a local food producer make jam from her neighbor's plums, and sell it at the market? Could she make jam from fruit trucked in from outside the region? Many markets call this the no-marmalade rule. What about corn husk dolls and dried flowers? You be the judge.

And what does this mean for shoppers as they have more and more food choices? "For a long time it seemed simple," said Rena Mikulski of Brooklyn, a shopper at the Union Square Greenmarket. "Organic food was good. Farmers' markets were good. Everything else was not good. Now I don't know how to choose anything. Is it local? Is it sustainable? Is it organic? Which is better? I don't know."

According to Gina Walker, a small organic grower of salad greens, who lives and works north of NYC in Columbia County, farmers' markets are not for everyone. Sparing staff and vehicles to send to farmers' markets is impossible for her. She said, "The weekend is the only time I get to see my kids. There is no way I'm going to leave for the city at 4 A.M. and come back at 8 P.M."
Source: Julia Moskin, "Perhaps It Is Time Greenmarket Itself Has Some Competition." New York Times 24 May, 2006.

Side Notes:

When I was the coordinator of the Brattleboro Farmers' Market, we allowed fresh fruits and vegetables from anywhere in Vermont, but not out-of-state. Many prepared foods were sold in booths at the market, but we didn't check as to where the raw materials came from to produce those foods. Crafts were also part of the market, but only so many crafts people were allowed, as we didn't want them to outnumber farmers. We didn't want to create a flea market atmosphere. The keys to success were diversity and competition.🌿

Eugenie Doyle sells strawberries at the Capitol City Farmers' Market in Montpelier

SUGGESTIONS FOR SHOPPERS AT FARMERS' MARKETS

- Request a particular vegetable a year in advance.
- Return clean bags, pint and quart berry baskets, and egg cartons, or bring your own canvas bags.
- Bring a large container with a wet paper towel in the bottom for flowers.
- Have change and dollar bills.
- Try a new vegetable like kohlrabi, parsnips, or kale.

As interest in local foods begins to catch on and more farmers raise crops for local markets, it becomes easier for school cafeterias, restaurants, nursing homes, hospitals, and prisons to incorporate local foods into their cuisine. The presence of a farmers' market often inspires people to start up their own food related businesses such as bakeries, butcher shops, produce stands, and small canneries -- which multiply with the growing availability of local foods.

When you walk into a grocery store, can you tell whether the potatoes were grown nearby? Do you know what farming practices were used to grow the tomatoes? Can you say for sure that your food dollars support local farmers? For most people the answer to these questions is no. In a farmers' market, food shed or public market, the answer in most cases is easy; it's local. In the wintertime, some imported foods would probably be introduced, especially in the colder climates, but these need to be marked as imported.

It's not easy to distinguish between seasonal markets called farmers' markets, year-round enclosed markets called public markets, and foodsheds. It's just a matter of degree but there are differences even though it's a little confusing. A food shed is generally seen as larger than a farmers' market.

Most farmers' markets have some type of temporary enclosure and are generally open one or two days a week; public markets are enclosed structures open 6 to 7 days a week, and are year-round operations whereas farmers' markets traditionally take place during late spring, summer and early fall and are more open to the elements. The vendors supplying the market bring their own tarps or stands. This is changing as winter markets are starting to spring up as an extension of summer farmers' markets and need to be enclosed in town halls and protected structures. In warmer climates, farmers' markets happen most of the year.

Sometimes, farmers' markets may grow in into larger markets and they are called public markets or food sheds. On the other hand, some folks still call a larger market a farmers' market. It's just a question of what one wants to call something. For example, which one of the three names would you give to the Centerville Market in Lincoln, Nebraska -- farmers' market, public market or food shed?

John Ellis was a farmer from Nebraska who sold most of his farm equipment and land to invest in what he calls a "sustainable market business." The Centerville Market was created with the help of Ellis and some of his fellow farmers in the revitalized Haymarket district of downtown Lincoln. What makes the store unique is that it is stocked with food items that haven't traveled thousands of miles. You'll find jars of corncob jelly and blueberry jam, organic flax flakes, cut flowers, dried herbs, fresh rhubarb and asparagus. The coolers are filled with ground beef, bacon and other butcher standards along with ostrich meat and duck eggs -- all of it raised by family farmers. Ellis now helps other farmers become part of the Centerville Market.

This venture was not initiated by Ellis and others for idealistic motives. Ellis is a drop-out from conventional agriculture. For decades his family farm raised corn and soybeans in York County, but they made less and less each year. As is true for so many farmers these days, expenses went up and crop prices went down. If you were to drive along Interstate 80, a highway that runs through the heart of America, you will see abandoned farms along with corn silos, barns, dairies, canneries, and farmhouses no longer being used.

At the Centerville Market, you'll find farmers like Kay Emrich, whose Emrich Family Creamery sells milk and ice cream produced at her 30-cow dairy from the neighboring state of Kansas. Jim Knopnik represents North Star Neighbors, a farm cooperative of seven families who raise beef in Fullerton, Nebraska. Rich and Lila Brock of Bumblebee Farms in Platte Center sell tomatoes and cucumbers raised in greenhouses pollinated by bees.

Ellis says, "We want to be able to feed our own people," noting that people in Lincoln (population 225,000) spend a half-billion dollars on food each year. In contrast to Wal-Mart, which sells more food than any other supermarket in the country, Ellis says, "We can come in with heart, with the original food, not some replica."

On the west side of Lincoln, there is a Super Wal-Mart store that probably does more business in a few hours than Centerville will do in a year. It is nearly impossible to find anything grown nearby. One of the store's most popular items is a Salisbury Steak TV dinner from Banquet on sale for $.79. The company that makes the frozen dinner is no other than ConAgra, headquartered in Omaha. The ingredient list on the package is 165 words long. It's impossible to tell where any of the ingredients originated. Most likely it comes from one of the airport hangar-sized warehouses (860,000 square feet) in North Platte, where fruit, vegetables, meat, milk and other foods destined for kitchen tables sit in mammoth refrigerators.◐

ROADSIDE STANDS

Before there were farmers' markets in rural areas of the country, traditional roadside stands dotted the countryside and they still do. Roadside stands serve as direct marketing tools that link communities. They benefit neighbors by providing an outlet for fresh vegetables and fruits, honey, maple syrup, bread, jams and jellies and other value- added products from local farms and processors.

There are thousands of roadside stands that operate today even though other market solutions are now available such as farmers' markets. A recent survey of roadside stands in Vermont reveal some results that may help them continue to maintain their stature as a rural marketing outlet. It was found that successful roadside stands have greater diversity and availability of farm fresh produce and value added products like pickles and jams along with a convenient location. * For more information on the findings, go to the Lifting The Yoke website.

Elizabeth's Farm Stand

A VISION FOR THE FUTURE: THE YEAR-ROUND WATERFRONT PUBLIC MARKET

There are many varieties of public markets located in the major cities in the U.S. like the Reading Terminal Market in Philadelphia, and Pike's Place in Seattle. In the fall of 1996, I had an idea that would take the concept of a local farmers' markets one step further into the future with an enclosed wholesale and retail market on Burlington, Vermont's waterfront. The new market would be called the Waterfront Public Market. It would serve consumers, restaurants, food service companies, schools, senior centers and catering businesses - all year long.

The Burlington Waterfront sits on one of the most lovely and expansive lakes in the country, Lake Champlain. To the west are the grand old mountains of the Adirondacks in New York and to the east are the lovely Green Mountains of Vermont. In between are the flat and rolling hills of the Champlain Valley, where one-third of the population of Vermont lives.

The Waterfont Market continued...

Thousands of people visit the waterfront in the summer including tourists -- mostly from Canada. Many use the bike path, walk the boardwalk, take the ferries around the lake, sail, kayak, canoe, and boat on the lake. There are condominiums, upscale shops and a theater close to Union Station with a number of artist studios. A new science museum ECHO-Sceince Museum was completed in 2003. There is a skate board park and the old Moran energy plant is being converted into a multi-use facility. One day, full-train service will again arrive in Burlington at Union Station from NYC.

The Burlington waterfront is well on its way to becoming the recreation and cultural hub for the city. What's lacking is a full-scale, year-round, enclosed market that offers a wide variety of local fresh foods, crafts, and features small food concessions, bakeries, and other micro-business enterprises.

The Waterfront Market would include a wholesale and retail component. Larger-scale anchor businesses like a restaurant, natural-foods market, greenhouse, and floral shop would provide stability for the market. Small farmers, crafts people and artisans would provide fresh garden vegetables and fruit, cheese, poultry, eggs, baked goods, prepared foods, fresh and dried flowers and herbs, clothes, quilts, jewelry, wood products, shoe and clothing repair, crafts, and an array of other Vermont products year-round.

Small fish and meat markets would be included, along with affordable food concessions, and senior citizens' craft booths. Add to this a micro-brewery and a not-so-upscale restaurant, as well as an upscale restaurant run by the New England Culinary Institute. This would provide a mix of stores and shops, large and small, that would serve the entire community.   Successful public markets thrive when there is diversity and competition. Some folks would go to "Frank's Meat Market" and others would shop at "Gail's Fine Meats."

An effort would be made to use as many Vermont food products as possible. During the growing season, much of the food sold at the market would come from local farmers and food processors. Flower shops, restaurants and bakeries would feature Vermont food products when available. This would give the market a particular appeal as a place to find "Vermont grown and produced products."

The market would be open for retail trade six days a week and on the weekend. Two mornings a week would for wholesale trade. On Tuesday mornings, the wholesale floriculture business would operate with sales of green and potted plants, cut flowers, bedding plants, and perennials for local garden stores, grocery stores and florists. Another day would be set aside for wholesale vegetables and fruits for restaurants and food service businesses.

There would be special days for Christmas fairs, Easter, Mother's Day, the annual Vermont Flower Show, and other horticultural exhibits.. A large greenhouse would be an integral part of the market. It would be a real draw to the people who live and work in Burlington, along with tourists coming in on the trains and boats. Local musicians, story tellers and actors would be perform throughout the year.

Affordability and accessibility would be critical to the markets success. Parking would be necessary even though the public would also need to learn new ways of accessing the market. We don't always have to drive right up to the store. Alternatives could be found, such as bus service, light rail and shuttles from parking areas outside the waterfront market. Ingrained patterns of behavior can change with time and practice especially with the on-going energy crisis . At first people resisted the concept of recycling -- now it's embraced.

To be able to sit in a greenhouse with the smell of flowers, drinking hot coffee or tea, and eating pastries would give the Waterfront a touch of warmth on a cold winter's day. And after you've had a hot drink, you could go skating on the ice rink next to the market or go out onto the lake.

Side Notes:

As of the spring of 2009, the Waterfront Market was still only an idea. Back in 1996, there were meetings and discussions but I'm afraid little action. The way I saw it was that once the politicians, government planners, and bureaucrats got involved, the process slowed down. I believe the mistake was in not letting the "entrepreneurial spirit" take hold. The anchor businesses and smaller vendors were willing to take the economic risks in setting up the market. I still hope it happens. ✺

E. THE NEW KID ON THE BLOCK: COMMUNITY SUPPORTED AGRICULTURE

The newest and fastest growing movement bringing farmers and consumers together is the community supported agriculture initiative (CSA). A CSA is a partnership between farmers and consumers whereby consumers buy a "share" in the farm and assume the risks and costs associated with the farm. The typical CSA is where the farmer provides a wide variety of fresh, local produce through the growing season and the consumer agrees to purchase a "share" of the harvest, at a set price before the summer growing season begins. It's a contract. There are no middlemen. For example, for between $15 to $30 a week, a family picks up produce from the farm in cardboard and wooden crates filled with fresh salad greens, tomatoes, corn and other vegetables.

Chris Siegriest and Dana Dwinell-Yardley
Wellspring CSA Harvesting Greens

The CSA movement has grown from a few pioneers in the late-mid 1980s to more than 2,116 CSA farms that feed about 340,000 families a week, according to Local Harvest, a Santa Cruz, California website that tracks CSAs and farmers' markets. The number of CSA operations is only a tiny fraction of the 2.1 million U.S. farms counted in the 2002 Census of Agriculture, but it's real and growing and represents a new way of keeping farmers on the land in this era of massive consolidation.

In Chittenden County, the largest county in Vermont, the number of farm shares increased 70 percent from 2007 to 2008 season for a total of 1,700 shares. THe main reason for this change is the desire to eat local and food born diseases and higher fuel costs. The number of CSAs in Vermont is now higher the number of farmers' markets.

According to the late Robyn Van En, the former director of the Center for Community Supported Agriculture at Wilson College in Chambersburg, Pennsylvania, CSA farms vary, but most follow the model of a small, organic farm or group of farms. Some CSAs contract with other food producers to bring in specialty items like bread, honey, eggs, berries, chickens and cheese. Others offer a newsletter with recipes. In some cases, the members provide help with the harvest.

CSAs' continued...

CSA Budget: The grower draws up a budget that reflects production costs for the year -- wages, seeds, soil amendments, equipment, supplies, land cost, insurance, etc. The total is divided by the number of people the farm site can support. This determines the price of a "share." Share prices vary from farm to farm, ranging between $350 to $500 for a season-long supply of mixed, fresh vegetables.

Members pay in advance to provide the grower with spring start-up costs. Some farms offer installment plans that allow for three or four payments during the season. Others offer subsidized shares to low-income families or accept food stamps. CSAs often provide shares to local food banks, soup kitchens and community pantries. Many CSAs have "work shares," by which they exchange labor for part of the cost of the produce.

Associative Economics: One aspect of CSAs that's rarely discussed is the concept of "Associative Economics." It's what the original CSAs were based upon. Here's how it works. The true price of a crop is when the farmer receives enough to satisfy his or her economic needs until it is time again to produce another crop.

Some interesting dynamics unfold in this scenario, First, food and labor are taken out of the equation as the community provides the necessary economic support for the farmer. To some, farmers have no business being in the market economy, where excess production causes problems. When farmers can make decisions based on the needs of the farm, rather than monetary concerns, farms thrive.

Marketing is not the farmers gift just as farming is not for most people. When a group of people cover the farm's annual budget, as they do with CSAs, the farmer is able to put all their attention towards nourishing the soil, caring for the livestock in a humane way, handling manure safely and supporting the total "farm organism."

Source: Jeff Poppen, "Associative Economics," Biodynamics, Spring, 2008.

The foundation of Poppen's article comes from the work of Rudolf Steiner, who wrote about Associative Economics under the name - "Three-Fold Social Economic Order" back in the 1920s. In addition, Steiner gave a series of farm lectures in 1924. From these talks, emerged the start of the Biodynamic farming movement, which survives today. In the 1950s, Trauger Groh, a biodynamic farmer from Germany, took Steiner's social and economic ideas and helped to start the CSA movement in Germany, which eventually came to the shores of America. .

GENERIC CSA NOTES

• The number of acres in production on a typical CSA farm varies but tends to be less than ten.

• Membership varies from 500 members on the larger farms to 15 to 30 on the smaller ones. In either case, good organization and management are essential for success.

• Members share the risk of production with the farmer. A hailstorm may reduce their share of lettuce for a few weeks.

• Some CSAs offer discounts to members who help with the work on the farms.

• CSAs have programs that invite members to take part in life on the farm through tours, potluck dinners, cooking classes and workdays. In the process, members learn how to eat locally and seasonally, and develop a relationship with the grower and the land the food comes from. As one person said, a carrot actually tastes like a carrot when it's picked from the earth one day and picked up by the member the next.

• Customers generally pay a little less for produce through CSA subscription programs than they would at the supermarket or organic food stores because there is no middleman and many members say they cut their food bills. However, the selection can be limited at times depending on a particular farm. Some customers complain that they receive more produce than they can consume.

• CSA farmers say that of all ways they make money, the CSA shares pull in revenue with the highest profit margin and with the least hassle.

While CSAs have many advantages as a farm production model, they aren't for every producer. They require a significant amount of time in finding new shareholders and educating them about why a CSA model works. The large percentage of time spent wooing customers instead of growing food can be frustrating at times. And the relationship building doesn't stop after a customer joins. CSA members expect is a deeper connection to the farm than with a farmers' market or farm stand

STORIES OF VERMONT CSAs
PLUS ONE FROM NEW YORK STATE

Golden Russet: Will and Judy Stevens run the Golden Russet Farm in Shoreham, Vermont close to the shores of Lake Champlain, providing vegetables and fruits to their shareholders. The shares that customers purchase range in cost from $120 for a fall share -- enough vegetables a week from October through December for two hungry adults -- to $275-$420 for a full-season share (June through October). An additional $50-$70 per season buys delivery.

GOLDEN RUSSET FARM

The shares Will and Judy sell each year add stability to their business. The CSA money allows them to concentrate on growing the crop, which results in better yields of higher quality, as well as reduced risk and less waste of unsold food. CSA shares account for only one-fifth of overall revenue at Golden Russet Farm. The rest comes from farmers' markets, food co-ops, restaurant sales, and Judy Steven's greenhouse plant business.

Wellspring: In mid-September on a Sunday afternoon, the Wellspring Farm in Marshfield, Vermont celebrates its harvest festival. Bright orange carrots are painted on children's faces and there is a squash carving competition. Sweet corn is roasted on the grill along with potatoes and other vegetables. Pasta salads feature cherry tomatoes, cucumbers and peppers grown on the farm. There are local meats, cheeses and apples. Most of the folks who attend the harvest festival at Mimi Arnstein's farm are among its CSAs 125 members. (Arnstein apprenticed for two years at CSA farms in Burlington's Intervale.)

In 2004, one of Mimi's biggest shareholders was the New England Culinary Institute (NECI), which bought three full shares for its flagship Montpelier restaurant. NECI also presented a number of cooking demonstrations at the farm. Sarah Klein, a NECI student from Arizona, put it well when she said, "I love the food. I love being on the land where the food came from. I've been here four times and people are coming and saying hello. It's like having an instant community."

Wellspring CSA Farm Photos

Harvesting Vegetables at Wellspring

Mimi Arnstein in the Greenhouse.

Friends of Wellspring

Shareholder Shopping at Wellspring

Harvesting Greens

THE VERMONT FARM VIABILITY PROJECT

Mimi Arnstein of Wellspring worked with the Vermont Farm Viability Program (VFVP), to develop a business plan that would help expand her CSA program. She is one of 200 farmers who has worked on a business plan that analyzes business opportunities and thinks through such activities as adding on a new barn, transferring the farm to new owners, investing in energy conservation, dairy equipment and season extenders.

Mark and Gari Fisher, who operate the Woodcock Farm Cheese Company, a sheep dairy in Weston, Vermont, enrolled in VFVP to investigate greater market and sales opportunities for their cheeses. Dexter and Alice Randall of Troy, Vermont worked on a business plan to map out the transition of their 432-acre dairy farm to organic, and to plan for the transfer of their farm to the next generation.

The three farms mentioned above were all awarded implementation grants to help them complete the projects outlined in their business plans. Their business plans helped Mimi Arnstein, the Fishers and Randalls secure financing, apply for grants, lay out business goals, objectives, and financial statements for use in making management decisions.

Mimi Arnstein was awarded a grant to help with the costs of installing tile drainage to improve her fields and increase vegetable production. Her business has expanded since enrolling in the Farm Viability Program in 2003 when she had 40 members; she now has over 100 shareholders at Wellspring CSA.

When the Randalls applied for an implementation grant through VFVP they were shipping organic milk to the Organic Valley Co-op. They were awarded a grant to help them purchase new milking equipment, which has helped them with their bottom line. The Fishers applied for a grant in order to expand their cheese-making operation by helping them purchase a cheese-making vat and install a new boiler and heat exchanger -- allowing them to make pasteurized cheeses.

All of these grants required a one-on-one match for the projects.

The VFVP is free to farmers and enrolls farms year-round, on a first-come, first serve basis. Farmers must meet eligibility requirements to be enrolled; they must be full-time Vermont residents, own or lease farmland, have an active farm business and have gross farm sales of $10,00 in the previous year.

Over the past three years, the Farm Viability Program has awarded small grants of $10,000 to 35 farmers. Funding came from the Argosy Foundation, and will continue from the Castanea Foundation. These grants have helped farmers construct new greenhouses and hoop houses for season extenders; make improvements to old barns, fencing and other facilities; construct refrigeration and root cellars; and purchase equipment for on-farm dairy processing.

The Vermont Farm Viability Program is administered by the Center for Sustainable Agriculture at the University of Vermont.

Mimi Arnstein, Parker Nichols, Chris Siegriest
Photo Courtesy of Wellspring CSA

CSAs Continued …

There are many advantages to CSAs like Wellspring. Some of the shareholders help with the harvest. In general, the prices are lower than farmers' markets as customers agree to buy up-front and take what is available. Like many CSAs, Wellspring is now a fixture in the community. CSAs keep barns in good shape, fields in operation and support regional farm suppliers.

The Common Ground CSA is a non-profit group at the University of Vermont (UVM) dedicated to sustainable farming. The workers are students eager to learn about organic gardening practices. This student-run educational farm is a place to learn, but also a place to give back to the community and foster a positive stewardship with the land. The three-acre CSA site is part of the 97 acre Horticultural Research Farm at the University of Vermont, purchased in the early 1950s and used for agricultural research and instruction.

The season begins in June and runs till mid-September. A regular share feeds 2 to 3 people. A share provides support for hands-on farming by students at UVM, provides healthy, fresh and locally grown produce to the shareholders; supports organic agriculture, and creates a positive relationship between UVM and local hunger relief organizations. The CSA donates more than half of its produce to the local food shelf. If you don't want a share, you can donate a share to the local food shelf. For more information, contact commonground@uvm.edu.

Every spring, a draft horse workshop is held at the UVM Horticulture Farm, where the three-acre CSA plot is plowed with two teams of draft horses. I can't wait to hear the quiet sounds of the Percherons moving steadily and slowly through the earth.

Pete's Greens: Pete Johnson of Craftsbury offers a year-round CSA. Some of his offerings include green Savoy cabbage, purple Kohlrabi, dark blue/black fingerling potatoes and pink and white chioggia beets. These are just some of the 70 tons of storage crops that he and his crew harvest from 22 cultivated acres. Johnson has started up an online picture gallery to help customers navigate the less-recognizable weekly items.

In addition to fresh, stored vegetables, Pete Johnson also provides some frozen produce and has built a commercial-scale kitchen and walk-in freezer for processing and preserving. Besides serving the CSA, Pete sells vegetables to local restaurants, grocery stores and food co-ops and provides free food to the local food kitchens. Recently, he began a winter CSA, where members can purchase vegetables 12 months of the year. He delivers as far as Burlington some 90 minutes away.

Judy Geer of Morrisville, a member of the CSA made some comments about eating Pete's vegetables on a seasonable basis. She said, "It's a great challenge, and it ties us more closely to the land, and gives us just a small sense of how our forbearers lived in the years before mass-produced, mass-preserved and mass-transported food."

Pete Johnson made the following comments on food security. He said, "Our times are becoming a little more uncertain. Food security could be life security. Vermont has the ability to feed itself although we will have to rebuild our infrastructure. We need root cellars and slaughterhouses. We need mills. We need creameries. It's all been done before. There's nothing revolutionary about any of this."

Source: Some of the information on Pete Johnson's CSA came from Pasanen, Melissa. "The Root of Fresh Flavor." Burlington Free Press, 13 Feb. 2007.

Bloomfield Farm in Charlotte, Vermont is managed in part by Matt Burke and Tanya Srolovitz. This small farm is unique as it is part of a 125 acre co-housing community – a privately owned development of 22 families. Most of the land is in fields and forestland. The housing units are built in clusters to maximize green space. Matt and Tanya raise vegetables and laying hens on an acre of land. They sell CSA shares to 30 families, 10 of which come from the co-housing community. They also sell at the Shelburne Farmers' Market, a senior residential community and local stores.

ESSEX FARM: A FULL-SERVICE NEW YORK CSA

This is the most diversified CSA I'm aware of. And believe it or not - most of its done with draft horses. Mark and Kristin Kimball, along with four other farmers, manage the five year-old organic/biodynamic CSA that provides not only vegetables but also milk, cheese, bread, yogurt and along with eggs, beef, pork and lard, and naturally-fermented sauerkraut. If you visited Essex Farm in the spring you'd see the farmers milking cows, milling grain, and boiling maple sap. In the root cellar would be crates of milk, eggs, carrots, beets, garlic, and flour. And in a nearby meat trailer, you'd find ground pork.

Essex Farm is located close to Vermont -- ten minutes across Lake Champlain by ferry from Charlotte, Vermont to Essex County, New York. Each share costs $2,800. A couple pays $3,200; kids under 13 eat for free. Twelve members of the 75 member CSA pay on a sliding fee scale. There were 59 members in 2006. The shareholders take as much produce, milk, meat and other farm produce as they need. They need 20 new members in 2009.

Mark Kimball would rather give produce away than feed it to the pigs. I understand what he means. When I was a commercial vegetable grower, I wanted to make sure nothing was left in my truck when I got back to my farm from the Brattleboro Farmers' Market. Mark told me that he would like to call the CSA something else --

more like "Essex Farm Serves the Community." He wants to grow and produce a full complement of healthy food and he wants the community to participate and share in the bounty. When Julie Ward, one of the members of Essex Farm was asked how much her family purchases in local stores, she said that they pick up odds and ends at the grocery store, but for the most part, all of their food needs come from the farm. That is the goal of Essex Farm.

ESSEX FARM NOTES:

• Belgium work horses are used for plowing and harrowing the vegetable and grain crops and tractors are used for the haying. The goal is to sell the mechanized farm equipment.

• All the slaughtering is done on site.

• The farmers log, tap the sugar bush, and hay on about 350 acres. There are ten acres of grains, 10 acres of vegetables and some fallow land totaling about 504 acres. A local propery owner recently sold them 80 acres for $105,000.

• They milk 6 Jersey cows.

* Kristen Kimball is completing a book called *From The Dirty Life*. It will be out in 2010. I've only seen one passage, but if what I read was any indication, *From The Dirty Life* will be a real testament to the author's ability to describe life on the farm as it really is. It's rich like the mud in spring. Kristen has a gift for bringing the written word down to earth.

Sugaring With The Kimball Family at The Essex Farm,
Photo By Dan Suyayasu

Today, many CSAs are getting more bang for their buck by diversifying and offering local meat, cheese, honey, maple syrup, bread, flowers and other value-added agricultural products as well as offering food products all winter long. In order to do this, they are working with other farms. For example, Burlington's Intervale Community Farm, established in 1990 - the first and oldest CSA in Vermont - provides goat's milk to its members from a farm in East Fairfield.

Most CSA shareholders go to the farms to pick up their produce, but some CSAs provide weekly pickups at central locations, such as schools and natural food stores. Full Moon Farm delivers to three central locations in the Burlington area. A couple of CSAs deliver right to people's homes.

David Zuckerman and Rachel Nevitt own and manage Full Moon Farm where they raise vegetables. The CSA has grown to over 250 shares. In 2009, David and Rachel moved their CSA farm from the Intervale to a rural area close to the town of Hinesburg where Zuckerman grows vegetable. He will add strawberries, fruit trees and beef cattle in the future.

Zuckerman is a member of the Vermont House of Representatives and was former chair of the Agricultural Committee. He has been a key spokesperson for the eat local movement in Vermont. He attributes the growth of the CSA movement to three main factors: food scares and meat recalls; peak oil and energy consumption; and healthy eating trends. He says an awareness of the rural character of the state and the need to preserve it have motivated people to join CSAs in Vermont more than other parts of the country. The idea of a CSA operating as a local food store was first advanced by Pete's Greens in Craftsbury.

AN UNLIKELY MARRIAGE

A unique CSA initiative was developed by the Massachusetts-based nonprofit, Community Involved in Sustaining Agriculture. Fifty employees from MassMutual purchase shares in a local CSA at Red Fire Farm in Granby, Massachusetts. MassMutual Insurance Company is located in Springfield.

Richard Goldstein of the insurance company says, "Our employees take a step toward a healthier lifestyle by having access to fresh, local, organic produce delivered right to the workplace." This is a win-win for both the company and the local farm.

CSA History: There is some disagreement as to where the CSA movement began. Some say it started in Japan in the 1960s with a group of woman interested in building direct relationships between farmers and consumers to provide healthy, locally grown food at a fair price. They called it "Teikei," or "partnership and cooperation" in Japanese.

Others believe the CSA movement started in Germany where over 50 years ago, an experiment began with the CSA concept in mind on a number of Biodynamic farms in Germany. Farmers provided vegetables, dairy products and bread at a farm store and consumers bought shares. Trauger Groh was involved in this early CSA initiative in Germany. He now lives in Temple, New Hampshire where he started one of the first CSAs in the U.S. in 1984. Jans Vander Tuin and Robyn Van En started a CSA in South Egremont, Massachusetts about the same time as Groh. Both initiatives grew out of the Biodynamic farm and garden movement, the Camphill initiative and the philosophy of Rudolf Steiner.

There is a book on CSAs by Trauger Groh and Steve McFadden of Arizona, called Farms of Tomorrow which traces the early history of CSAs in Germany and across the world. When McFadden and Groh wrote about CSAs in the 1990s, there were about 60 CSAs in the U.S. In 2004, that number had climbed to 1,700. An updated version of the book was completed a few years ago.

CSAs are spreading around the world - from Brazil, Argentina, France, Denmark and in Japan, where it has matured into a movement with thousands of members.

Challenges: Communication, Change and Questions for the Future The CSA movement comes at a time when corporate growers have moved into the fast-growing organic industry, forcing some family farmers to shift to direct-marketing strategies. CSAs are helping to change America's relationship with food and farming by forging personal ties between environmentally conscious growers and consumers, something corporate farms will never be able to do.

While CSA numbers have climbed over the years, there have been some failures. These include situations where farmers did not ask enough money for shares, where farmers did not have the necessary farming skills and where farmers were growing food on rented land that was not secure from year to year. Some CSAs failed because the farmer was not skilled at community building and in some cases, the farmers and the shareholders could not get along. That's life.

One way CSAs work is when families share in the planting and the harvesting, so that everyone appreciates where the food comes from. One way CSAs work is when families share in the planting and the harvesting, so everyone appreciates where the food comes from. To run a successful CSA farm, there has to be a spirit of cooperation and commitment between the farmers and shareholders. Farmers and shareholders need to be able to sit down and communicate their needs to one another.

Some of the questions that have been raised of late are: What's going to happen when questions of sustainability arise without a shared set of values? What happens when tough economic times catch up with subscription farms, like when the energy crisis really hits home? Is a community necessary to support a CSA, or do you just need a group of consumers?

Trends: One trend that is happening is cooperation and collaboration among farms. CSAs are looking for ways to work together, especially in urban areas.

Bakeries, orchards, vegetable farms, and food co-ops are forming networks of support. A number of CSAs are working out arrangements with land trusts, by which communities can permanently set aside land for farming.

Another change is where the community purchases the farm under a land trust agreement. This happened in the Wilton/Temple New Hampshire area many years ago. In this scenario, if the farmer leaves the farm, another farmer could take over and grow food for the community. There are several CSAs where a nonprofit owns the land, but the farmer owns the CSA business and has a low-cost, long-term lease.

* For more information on CSAs, go to :
  www.csacenter.org and www.biodynamics.com
* For a Vermont CSA list, go to
  www.vermontagriculture.com/csalist.htm.
  or visit the Vermont NOFA website at www.nofavt.

Robin Van En, Indian Line CSA Farm,
South Egremont, Massachusetts.
Photo by Clemens Kalischer

F. NATURAL FOOD CO-OPS: WHERE ARE THEY GOING?

In Vermont, there are 13 natural food co-ops with lots of diversity and brown rice. They range in size from 1000 square feet with just over 100,000 in sales to 16,000 square feet and $20 million in sales. The Adamant Co-op in Calais, one of the oldest co-ops in the country, begun in 1939, is also one of the smallest at only 800 square feet. The co-op sponsors the infamous Black Fly Festival and just added a modern bathroom.

The Buffalo Mountain Food Co-op in Hardwick is small by comparison to the much larger Hunger Mountain Co-op in Montpelier. The narrow aisles at Buffalo Mountain are filled with cans of beans and bins of grains. It's the kind of old-time co-op where you can leave notes for friends. Meats are stored in regular home-freezers.

Most food co-ops in Vermont have generally stuck by the principal of providing natural/wholesome foods. Some stores are strict in what they offer while others provide conventional brands, and beer and wine along with natural brands. The goal of many co-ops in Vermont is to provide a living wage along with quality health care for their workers. Let's begin the co-op story with a history of the cooperative movement.

A HISTORY OF COOPERATIVES: HOW DID THEY START?

The modern cooperative movement dates back to the 1840s, when a group of cotton and wool weavers in the depressed town of Rochdale, England, decided to fight back after being cheated by shopkeepers who sold them flour mixed with plaster, used tea leaves dyed to look new, and rancid butter under a layer of fresh butter.

In 1844, at the height of the Industrial Revolution, 28 members of the Rochdale Equitable Pioneers Society formed a cooperative to purchase necessities. The society opened a small retail store on Toad Lane, based on a set of principles and practices that would become the foundation for the modern cooperative movement. They sold unadulterated goods at fair prices, and profits were distributed to the members. In 1895, the principles of that store formed the basis for the International Cooperative Alliance (ICA) which today represents more than 200 cooperative organizations in 92 countries.

In September 1995, on its 100th anniversary, the ICA summarized its mission, stating, "The test of our values is to translate social theory into social fact and to make them effective in daily life." In other words, social justice must be translated into economic justice.

Filling Bulk Bins at a Food Co-op

Photos Courtesy of the Hunger Mountain Food Co-op.

Fair Trade

Montpelier High School Cooking Class Cooking with Whole Foods
(photographer: Herbalist and Food Educator Sandra Lory, School Kale Harvest)

Old and New Strategies: A Counterweight

Cooperatives are one way to combine resources in the world of corporate giants. There are many kinds of cooperatives. A producer-owned cooperative is owned by those who manufacture, grow, create, or produce a product, including farmers, factories, and artists. They work together to produce and market their goods and provide credit, equipment and production supplies to their members.

A worker-or employee-owned cooperative is owned and controlled by the employees. Worker-owned co-ops can be found in almost any industry, including food stores, processing companies, and energy businesses. A consumer-owned cooperative, such as a food-coop, enables consumers to secure a wide array of goods and services.

Other examples include health and childcare co-ops, housing co-ops and credit unions. Consumer-owned cooperatives like food co-ops offer an alternative form of business in which the prime purpose is not to make money for shareholders, but to provide the foods the member-owners wish to buy, at a reasonable cost. What makes a cooperative business different from profit-driven business is that the goal is to build a sustainable economy in which everyone can participate. In cooperatives, profit is a resource that can be redistributed to the member-owners or invested in new services for the membership.

• Over 100 million people are members of the 47,000 cooperatives in the United States.

THE ANITA GROCERY COOPERATIVE

In rural areas across the country, some communities are forming food co-ops out of necessity, like the one in Anita, Iowa. The town was about to lose its only grocery store. The food market was so important that its closure motivated the town residents to buy shares and create the Anita Grocery Cooperative. They formed a board, sold about 300 shares at $200 each, and took out $150,000 in public and private loans. On December 1, 2006, the doors opened.

The townspeople of Anita felt they had no choice. The loss of the 90-year-old Main Street Market would have meant a virtual end to downtown traffic and trouble for the remaining businesses. It was clear that without the store, the town would become just another place to buy gas and pick up milk. Residents wondered what would become of their town without a gathering spot and a community store. Chris Karns, an Anita native who owns an insurance company, said his business couldn't survive without the traffic the local grocery brings to town.

Farm co-ops are old hat for most Midwest farmers but the concept of a community grocery is a new phenomenon. The hope is that the idea will spread to other rural areas beset by the same problem as Anita, Iowa.

Food Co-ops: Co-ops were originally formed as a way of reducing food costs through bulk purchasing. A 1995 International Cooperative Alliance statement addresses the issue: "By taking ownership over portions of the economy, cooperative members are saying we can meet our needs better than they are currently being met. Because the effort is a mutual one, cooperative members understand that to provide for any member is to provide for all members."

The core values of food co-ops have basically remained the same for the last 160 years. A cooperative is a member-driven organization with a structure of shared responsibility, ownership, risks and benefits. The goal is to provide whole and natural foods, although there are a lot of questions today about just what is natural and whole. Many co-op stores also carry conventional foods like Coca-Cola and Kraft Macaroni & Cheese. Another change in the last 15 years is that many consumers who shop at food co-ops are no longer required to participate in stocking shelves or filling up bags of raisins.

Nationwide, there has been a decline in natural food co-ops, from a peak of 800 to 300 today.

FROM THE ONION RIVER CO-OP TO CITY MARKET

After the City of Burlington lost its last supermarket a few years ago, there was no place to shop for groceries. Many citizens, especially those without transportation, low-income shoppers and people with disabilities, were left in the lurch.

There were a number of large mega-supermarkets in the Burlington area, but they were located on the outskirts of the city. A hot debate ensued in the City as to what type of food market should be located in the downtown.

The Burlington City Council sent out requests for proposals (RFPs) for a market competition. The three finalists were Shaw's, a national chain, Mac's, a local Vermont grocer with a number of small stores; the local Onion River Food Co-op. Mac's dropped out of the competition, citing too much politics. Shaw's wanted to build a store, but it was considered much too large for the site by some members of the city council. Concern was raised as to whether the Onion River Co-op would be able to provide lower-priced conventional foods, as it was basically a natural-foods store. In other words, would the co-op just sell garbanzo beans and brown rice, not Wonder Bread, Coke and Mr. Clean? The co-op agreed to carry conventional brands.

In the end, the Onion River Co-op, which added the name City Market to its title, won the battle by a wide margin on the Burlington City Council. Some complained that the selection was marred by cronyism on the part of the powerful Progressive element on the council who shopped at the co-op. (The Progressive Party is a left-of-center third party in Vermont.)

Co-op Member Pulling a Lever for Bulk Honey at the Onion River Co-op

Photo Courtesy of City Market/Onion River Coop

THE CLASS ISSUE
AND FOOD SHOPPING PREFERENCES

Consumers shop where they feel most comfortable. This is true everywhere shoppers have a choice. Putney, a village in south eastern Vermont, offers a good example of class shopping preferences. You have the flatlander/hippie/liberal types -- what I call the "Crunchy Granolas," who shop at the Putney Food Co-op, which features natural foods and an upscale deli/snack bar. At one time, when the Putney Food Co-op was a smaller store run by local people, many people shopped there. (The co-op started in 1941.) There was a butcher, as was common in smaller grocery stores. Natural and health foods were just coming onto the market then.

Much has changed in the last 15 years. The Putney Co-op moved to a different location and built a larger new store filled with natural foods. Today, the native people, whom I call "Fluffer Nutters," go to Mountain Paul's for milk, Skippy peanut butter, juice, and the newspaper and drive to Hannaford's Supermarket eight miles south in Brattleboro for their big time shopping.

The Putney General Store serves everyone in the community with a variety of items, but it's not a large food-market. The store burnt down in the spring of 2008 and the community is working with the owner to rebuild.

Side Notes:

This is my own take on the class issue. Some might disagree with the terms I used in regards to why shoppers shop where they do. I find them useful in describing class differences. The fact is that there are class differences.

GRADUATE DISSERTATION
ON FOOD SHOPPING PREFERENCE

To further pursue the topic of food shopping preferences, I asked Linda Berlin, a faculty member at the University of Vermont, why consumers shop where they do. Berlin completed her dissertation on the topic of consumer views about organic food at Tufts University. The following summary is a portion of her findings.

RESULTS OF TWO FOCUS GROUPS
IN BURLINGTON, VERMONT

• The non-organic group in general focused more on price, convenience, familiarity with the store, and time. The organic group focused on similar themes and added food quality in balance with price. They also mentioned that the atmosphere and culture of the store was what brought them there to shop, along with the availability of specific food items like free-range chicken eggs.

• Many people who purchased organic foods and shopped at the local food co-op described the co-op as a community-gathering place, a place that had meaning for them beyond food. However, a number of shoppers expressed less enthusiasm for the newer, larger co-ops.

• Some "organic" shoppers expressed their sense of isolation at the larger supermarkets and described how no one was available to serve them. They found the stores to be impersonal, too bright and crowded.

• In contrast, the "non-organic shoppers" discussed their discomfort with food co-ops and health food stores, describing them as "intimidating." They indicated that the culture was unfamiliar, as was the process of shopping there. One consumer commented that people in co-ops were like a family and said she did not feel comfortable in that situation.

• For those people who were considered frequent organic buyers, there tended to be a strong association with food cooperatives, small health food stores, and whole food stores. They said these stores were intimate, friendlier, with a shared outlook.

• Some shoppers at organic stores felt uncomfortable because they weren't as conscious of health issues. Another respondent said she and her family shopped at the co-op for health reasons but said her friends made fun of her for shopping there.

• One shopper at a mainstream supermarket said that there is a guilt-free atmosphere there because the shopper doesn't have to think about bigger food issues.

• Other non-organic buyers commented that organic co-ops aren't very friendly or helpful, but the food is healthy; that farmers' markets are elitist and full of aging hippies; and that these places are full of those "granola" kinds of people and one feels out of place.

• Another respondent put a more positive spin on food co-ops by saying that organic folks are more conscious about nutrition and not as concerned about show. Other respondents said that people at larger supermarkets are from all walks of life, and there is more diversity of people and foods.

HISTORY AND GROWING PAINS
AT THE ONION RIVER CO-OP

Let's go back in time to understand the changes that have taken place in the co-op culture. The Onion River Co-op began in 1971 as a small buying club and evolved into a food co-op. This was true of many co-ops. In the early 1980s, I was a commercial organic truck farmer who sold organic vegetables to Onion River on Archibald Street in the Old North End of Burlington. In those early days, the co-op was a hole in the wall with a friendly spirit where all the crunchy types shopped alongside the new immigrants, locals, professionals and low-income people.

When the co-op moved to a larger facility, a lot changed. The prices began to rise, as many new organic processed foods came onto the shelves. Conventional foods were still on the shelves but they were fewer in number. The other result was that the down-home feel was no longer there.

Many Vermont food co-ops have gone through similar growing pains, evolving from small operations into larger stores with many offerings. The bins of grains and tofu that once stood center stage have been pushed to the side as a great selection of organic products have come into being -- everything from hummus and tahini spreads to homemade breads, wines, and beer, jams, upscale organic processed food and a deli to boot. For the most part, the food co-op culture has changed from a grassroots, feel-good kind of place into larger stores with many more food products.

One advantage of co-ops is that the consumer can buy in bulk and save money with items like grains, pasta, herbs, spices, maple syrup, dried fruit, and honey. Co-op members can also save money by signing up for jobs, such as stocking shelves and filling up bags of dried fruit. For each hour members work, they receive a discount on food purchases. Most co-ops provide seniors and low-income people with discounts. They are like credit unions in that they are owned by their members/shoppers. .

Since the opening of the downtown City Market, Price Chopper, Shaw's, Hannaford's and other regional supermarket chains have added organic and natural food sections and begun to offer bulk items such as grains. This is happening nationwide.

From the **Onion Skin Newsletter**,
Onion River/City Market Co-op

Side Notes:

I believe that the most healthy, sustainable food is organic and locally grown. But at what cost? Many families simply can't afford organic free-range chicken and grass-fed beef or organic tomato sauce.

A couple of years ago, the Hunger Mountain Food Co-op in Montpelier decided not to sell organic turkeys at $4 a pound as the price was too high, They sold the less-expensive Misty Knoll turkeys from New Haven, Vermont, that aren't certified organic but fed vegetarian feed with no animal by-products and kept in a large airy barn when they access to open pasture. And they are fresh, not frozen.

Side Notes:

I don't want to wax nostalgic for the "good old days." The food co-ops have gone through many transformations. The Onion River Co-op/City Market is working on being a place that welcomes the entire community -- a store that is both accessible and affordable. Some has been done and mucg more needs to happen. Most co-op managers I've spoken to struggle with the high cost of how organic foods and how organic foods have been taken over by mega-food corporations. They do their best to buy local vegetables, breads, cheeses, dairy products, free-range chicken and beef and specialty items, and to offer the lowest prices they can for organic foods, but it is tough going. For example, Near East brand natural foods are sold at the larger supermarkets at a price the co-ops can't compete with. Near East used to be owned by a small company; then it was bought out by Quaker Oats, which was taken over by Pepsi. And so it goes.

HUNGER MOUNTAIN FOOD CO-OP

The Hunger Mountain Food Co-op in downtown Montpelier, the capital city of Vermont, built a new facility in the last few years. Hunger Mountain does not need to cater to everyone in the community, as there is a supermarket in downtown Montpelier. The co-op for the most part provides organic food to a middle and upperclass clientele. That's clear from walking down the aisles in the store and identifying the types of shoppers reaching for the organic sauces, choosing among the local baked breads, or having a cup of tea and a muffin. The store has a good feeling with an attractive atmosphere and a professional staff. The co-op does over $14 million in business each year.

Early on, the workers at the new Hunger Mountain Food Co-op had to learn how to run a store the hard way, by way of burnout and a large turn over in personnel. From what I've seen, there is now a core of committed and responsible staff. The co-op continues to grow and prosper each year. In 2007, the membership voted to renovate and enlarge the store.

Earth Day at Hunger Mountain

Photos Courtesy of Hunger Mountain Food Co-op

THE BRATTLEBORO FOOD CO-OP

The Brattleboro Food Co-op took over a downtown supermarket in a low income area of Brattleboro many years ago. In 2007, the co-op decided to expand at its present location rather than move to a shopping center on the outskirts of town. This was a healthy decision, as it kept an anchor grocery store in the city and at the same time lessened the effects of suburban sprawl. Some co-op members are now raising questions regarding the $6 million dollar expansion which they consider much too costly and inappropriate.

THE RANDOLPH FOOD CO-OP: PAST TENSE

The Randolph Food Coop, located in rural town in the White River Valley, was smaller in size than the 1600 square foot Brattleboro Food Co-op. The co-op was basically a natural and organic food store that had few conventional foods, not even a Pepsi cooler.

There's a Shaw's supermarket less than a mile from town. Years ago, the Price Chopper supermarket in Randolph closed its doors. In response, the Randolph Food Co-op brought in conventional foods in order to meet the needs of the entire community. According to the co-op staff, the local townspeople were not familiar with the co-op culture. And because it didn't offer a large number of food items, many local folks didn't feel comfortable shopping there. Add on the fact that some co-op members did not want conventional foods in the store. Eventually, the co-op went back to being an organic/ natural-foods store. Unfortunately, the co-op built up a large debt and had to close its doors in 2006. Not all co-ops make it.

Many of the Randolph Co-op members now travel to Vermont's newest co-op in South Royalton created by two people frustrated because there was no grocery store within 20 miles of their town. According to Peggy Grote, one of the owners, the South Royalton Market Co-op store is thriving, having doubled in size in the last couple of years. The store provides both conventional and organic foods. Grote said that the grocery store could not survive with just natural foods.

Some rural co-ops are still small and exude that down-home crunchy feeling -- like the Adamant Co-op in Calais mentioned earlier. The 800-square-foot space includes the town post office and a pot-bellied stove. Janet MacLeod is the board president of the Adamant Co-op. She is a third-generation of MacLeod's; her grandparents were among the eleven families that each contributed five dollars to get the store going in 1939. They were farmers, carpenters and teachers who wanted a local place to buy groceries.

Monument Farms and Food Co-ops

Representatives of three of Vermont's largest food co-ops collaborated with Monument Farms Dairy to produce a new milk brand called "Vermont Co-op Milk." Monument Farms is a 78-year-old dairy in Weybridge, Vermont. Millicent Rooney, the daughter of the founder of the family-owned dairy, kicked off a tour of the facility in 2006. There was a picture of her as a young women helping to deliver milk from the back of a pickup truck full of ice. Today, Monument Farms has 1,600 acres along with 375 milkers and is one of only three Vermont dairies still bottling milk from its own cows.

The three Vermont food co-ops have demonstrated their commitment to local family farms by agreeing to pay a fair and fixed price to Monument Farms to help even out seasonal fluctuations in the milk market. The new label guarantees co-op customers a Vermont hormone-free milk.

Have the Co-ops Been Co-op-ted? Northeast Cooperatives was once the dominant food co-op distributor in New England. In 2002, its member-owners voted to merge with United Natural Food, Inc., a large private distributor. They had been told by the general manager they were facing bankruptcy. The question was how, despite rapid growth, yearly sales exceeding $130 million, a new physical plant, and a strong network of more than 1,200 buying clubs, retail co-ops, and private health-food stores, could Northeast have lost so much money?

United, which included Stowe Mills and Cornucopia, had ten times the sales and eighty times the equity of Northeast. Now only three organic food distributors are left, out of 28 from 1982. The same thing happened in the wholesale seed industry. Seed giant Seminis was created from a number of mergers. The company eventually doubled its prices and shrank its selections. Seminis was recently bought out by none other than Monsanto.

In the world of business, consolidation brings change, and this means that consumer prices generally increase and choices decline. This was confirmed by a number of food co-ops in the Northeast, including the Buffalo Mountain Co-op in Hardwick, Vermont, the Belfast Maine Co-op, and the Willimantic, Connecticut Co-op. It's the same old story: prices went up, selections went down. Programs were also dropped, like the project to train co-op managers. The number of local buying clubs has also diminished in number, as has the number of smaller producers.

More and more northeastern co-ops are turning to the small Associated Buyers warehouse in New Hampshire for their goods. Associated chose a different path than Northeast.

They decided not to accept the "get big or get out" mentality. Content with its niche and flexible about case lots, Associated Buyers seems to be succeeding. So folks, bigger is not necessarily better.

Source: The information from "Where Have All the Co-ops Gone," comes from the 2004 FEDCO seed catalog. FEDCO always has interesting articles to share with their readers, besides being an informative seed catalog. FEDCO is also one of the few seed companies organized as a cooperative. Consumers own 60 percent of the co-op, and worker members own 40 percent.

Butterworks Farm

Jack and Ann Lazor

Ann Lazor with calf

Butterworks Farm Supplies Yogurt to Food Co-ops.

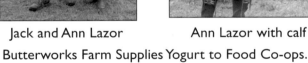

WHEREVER THERE IS COMPETITION, PRICES GO DOWN; WHEREVER THERE IS CONSOLIDATION, PRICES GO UP

G. GREEN MOUNTAIN RESTAURANTS, DINERS, AND COUNTRY STORES

What are the advantages of supporting local diners and restaurants with food from local farmers and food processors? The obvious one is keeping food dollars at home. Others include preserving open land for farming, reducing energy costs, supporting farm machinery dealers, and having an overall positive economic effect on the community.

More local foods are appearing in restaurant menus because consumers are demanding them. They want to look at a menu and know that the food is locally grown and who the farmer is. Farmers benefit by having their foods prepared and presented by chefs who desire local, fresh food.

Michael Bosia Photograph

SEVEN TASTY MODELS
Community Investment Eateries

Claire's Restaurant and Bar of Hardwick, Vermont hit the Green Mountains running on Memorial Day, 2008. It's located in the historic Bemis block next to the Buffalo Mountain Food Co-op. A fire did substantial damage to the Bemis Block of buildings a couple of years ago. By the spring of 2008, all the structures had been rehabilitated through the support of organizations such as Housing Vermont, The Vermont Preservation Trust and the local land trust.

Claire's is not your typical food establishment. It's being supported by a group of what some call "angel" investors. The Hardwick Restaurant Group, LLC made up of 4 local partners, a restaurateur, book store owner, attorney, and professor, provided the initial start-up costs and raised capital for furnishing and equipping the restaurant space. They will also fund the lease for 5 years.

The Preservation Trust of Vermont paid the first year's lease of $15,000. The Trust believes in the "community investment model," where everyone in the community has a vested interest in the project and stake in the future of the downtown.

Side Notes:

When I was growing up in Louisville, Kentucky, close to the banks of the Ohio River, my folks would take my brother, sister and me out to the country in our big gas-guzzling Chrysler to eat home-cooked meals at the Old Stone Inn and The Colonel's Lady, of Colonel Sanders fame, before the fame. All the food came from the local farms. You cannot compare the taste of a fresh farm-raised chicken or a freshly picked tomato, all juicy and flavorful, to its plastic counterpart. The Colonel's Lady was the restaurant started by Colonel's Sanders wife, long before KFC went global. Amen!

CLAIRE'S

Local Ingredients / Open to the World

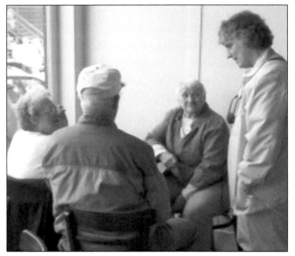

Patrons at Open House

Staff at Claire's

Heather Gray Photographs.

The Preservation Trust of Vermont has supported other Vermont downtown communities since 1980. They worked in Putney to resurrect the local bookstore, helped the village of Starksboro bring back the general store and supported the revitalization of Latchis Hotel in Brattleboro.

Another form of support for Claire's came from a group of community members, who purchased coupons called "Community Supported Restaurant Coupons." Each one is worth $1,000 and provides discounts of $25 one time per month, for ten months of every year, during the first four years of operation. Overall, 200 community members pledged money to help start Claire's.

Also supporting the venture are local food and farm operations, such as Pete's Greens, Bohemian Bread, North Hardwick Dairy, Vermont Milk Company, Vermont Soy Company, Jasper Hill Cheese, Hazendale Farm and others. Coupon holders Kristin and Neil Urie of Bonniview Farm in South Albany arranged to deliver their first $1,000 of cheese to the kitchen at Claire's with no charge as their community-supported restaurant coupon.

The impetus for Claire's came from Robert Fuller, the owner of the Bobcat Cafe and Pub model, which started up in 2002 in Bristol. Residents there asked restaurateur Fuller to open a local eatery using mostly local foods. Fuller owns two other up-scale restaurants and is a partner in other eateries. He agreed to proceed with the project if 12 local people came forward to demonstrate their commitment by lending $5,000 each. In a week, their were eighteen commitments and soon the number grew to thirty two. Each one of the investors gets 25 percent off dinners for themselves and a friend. In five years, Fuller plans to pay back the sponsors in full, plus interest. Brewing local beers is part of the cafe's operation. The spent grain is sent to Laplatte River Farm to feed its beef cattle and in return supplies the cafe with naturally-raised beef.

IT TAKES A VILLAGE

As you can see, the impetus behind Claire's and Bobcat Cafe came from friends and businesses in the community. Banks say that restaurants have a high rate of failure. in many case, they won't lend them the money. The Bee's Knees, a 5-year-old Morrisville restaurant recently raised $75,000 from dozens of customers for renovations. Sharon Deitz, the owner, said, "You're not only raising capital, you're building community." She went on to say, "It's changed my energy level around, ... I don't feel like I'm alone in this crazy construction project."

It's not only Bee's Knees and Claire's that have received community support. Other restaurants and small natural and specialty food markets such as Mountain Greens Market in Bristol, Fat Hen Market in Vergennes, Sweet Clover Market in Essex Junction, Nunyuns Café and Bakery in Burlington and Vermont Green Grocer in Richmond -- have received community support.

Bill McKibben, Ripton author and activist said in 2007 in his book, *Deep Ecology,* there are many benefits to what he called, "the economics of neighborliness." A community funding network builds value that cannot be measured simply in dollars. In many ways these community funding networks are similar to what happens on Community Supported Agriculture (CSA) farms, where members of the community buy shares in the farm.

LET US NOW PRAISE FAMOUS DINERS
-- PAST TENSE

In 2002, the Farmers Diner opened its doors in Barre, a working class city and granite capital of Vermont. The diner itself was so old it was radically new. Whats made it special was the food, where it came from and the man who started it all: Tod Murphy. Murphy founded the 50-seat diner in 2002 with the help of some investors. His goal was to support nearby farms and to demonstrate that local, organic, sustainable agriculture is viable and that taste and tradition matter. Seventy percent of the food came from 35 local suppliers and producers.

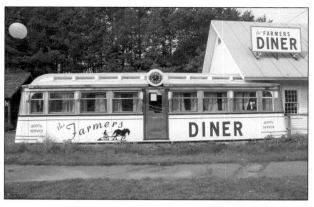

The diner was probably the only business that both Gourmet magazine and the World Watch Institute devoted attention to in 2004. Even Ben & Jerry offered advice. At the Farmer's Diner, you could have a cup of chili for $2.75, or a grilled cheese sandwich for $3.50 and a philosophy, to boot. A 16-ounce glass of organic milk cost $1.95, compared to $1.49 at the Friendly's down the street, but the customers were willing to pay modest premiums in exchange for the high quality of local food.

Some of the potatoes and vegetables were grown on the farm of Will Allen and Kate Duesterberg in the hills above the Connecticut River; the bread came from Northfield; the milk, butter and ice cream from Earl Ransom and Amy Huyffer and their Guernseys at the Strafford Dairy.

Just down the road from the diner in South Barre was a small, corrugated metal building with a few small rooms, one hot and smoky, another cold and bloody.

It's the former home of an old Shell gas station. Vermont Smoke & Cure Smokehouse is one of the smallest USDA-inspected meat processing plants in the country, and one of the few not controlled by a large food company. Every diner needs a good supply of bacon, pork sausage, turkey and ham from local farmers.

The New York Times magazine said the smokehouse has "the finest bacon on the planet." Murphy bought the smokehouse and started operating it before he opened the Farmers Diner in Barre. The smokehouse produces meat from about 400 Vermont farms a year -- some small and some smaller. The Farmers Diner line of smoked products is also sold to food co-ops and independent natural food markets in Vermont and New Hampshire, supermarket chains and in New York City at Zabar's, Balducci's and the small Food Emporium chain. About 50 percent of the pork comes from Vermont and the other meat comes from Quebec. The pigs are raised free of antibiotics, fed no animal byproducts and have access to open pasture in season.

Photo Courtesy of Vermont NOFA

Oops, I forgot to mention that the cheese in the grilled cheese sandwiches came from John and Janine Putnam's farm. Janine told Tod Murphy they were having trouble discarding the whey, a waste byproduct of the cheese-making process. Murphy knew that the Putnam's 15-year-old son, Andrew, was looking for a part-time job, so he suggested that Andrew raise hogs by way of the whey, and he would buy them. It worked, and that's where some of the bacon came from at the Farmer's Diner.

The Farmers Diner was competing with diners that get their chickens from Sysco and Tyson -- chickens that are cheaper and that are shipped from who-knows-where and pumped up with antibiotics. In an era in which ten companies supply more than half the food and drink sold in the U.S., Tod Murphy was bucking the trend. The goal at the diner was to be the first of many in the development of a Farmers Diner franchise.

The next phase for Murphy and his investors was to develop other diners and a central food-processing plant where animals from area farms would be slaughtered and local organic tomatoes would be turned into vats of salsa and pasta sauce.

You may have noticed I've been writing in the past tense. The Farmers Diner in Barre closed its doors in 2005, as it was not large enough to make it financially. There were just 50 seats and a small kitchen with no room for even an automatic potato peeler. Given the regulatory issues and other costs of doing business, a small family-priced diner is difficult to operate at a profit, given the amount of labor needed to prepare local food in the tiny kitchen. Every time I was at the diner it was packed but again, it was a small space.

JUMP-START TO 2006: THE FARMERS DINER MAKES A COMEBACK

The second Farmers Diner opened in the fall of 2006 in the upscale tourist town of Quechee. The new site has a combination barn and diner with 110 seats and a large kitchen. Murphy is convinced that his dream of a diner and a line of smokehouse products will succeed this time. According to Murphy, the diner in Quechee is large enough to do the volume necessary to make a profit. The smoked and cured meats, continue to be produced by Vermont Smoke & Cure in South Barre.

Murphy said, "Our goal of spending 70 cents of every food dollar within 50 to 75 miles is radical for a business in a global economy where greed, a.k.a. maximizing profit and externalizing costs, is commonplace. But to regular citizens, I don't think we are radical. Great tasting food and a good cause, but not radical."

The real challenge according to Murphy is to find local farmers to grow more cucumbers and tomatoes. If the diner is going to sell homemade dill pickles, they need a reliable supplier of cucumbers and someone either in-house to make the pickles or a local pickle-maker. The and the same could be said for tomatoes. A local grower could raise tomatoes and the diner or local sauce maker could process them into salsa and tomato sauce for the Farmers Diner customers in the winter. By the way, the diner did make some dill pickles last year and they were a great success.

The Farmers' Diner

The business in Quechee was busy during foliage season in October of 2006 but then it slowed down over the winter. Murphy said they're starting to build up the business within the local community -- putting together author readings, going to the local Chamber of Commerce functions and providing catering services to businesses. He said, "Because we opened at the end of summer, we scrambled to find enough local produce, so we are putting together a meeting with farmers to plan out production for 2007."

Murphy shared some final thoughts. He said, "I've certainly learned a great deal about what is required and what is possible for a robust independent food economy in Vermont. Wendell Berry has outlined the principles for a thriving local economy. Step one is to meet your own need to the maximum degree from your own resources. ... We know that Vermont can produce all of its own dairy needs and then ship the excess to regional markets. We could do the same with grains, legumes, storage vegetables, fresh and canned vegetables and protein, both meat and soy-based. What's needed is the infrastructure: canneries, slaughterhouses, and creameries. The other issues are land costs, the cost of capital, and most of all, where are we going to find the farmers."

Along the same line, Murphy told me in March of 2007 that the real challenge is to have enough density of farmers and food producers within a region like the Upper Connecticut River Valley and Central Vermont area where he's located. Without that density, it's difficult to have the necessary production, infrastructure and distribution networks.

O'Naturals - Gary Hirshberg, the CEO of Stonyfield Farm in New Hampshire, started a new venture called O'Naturals. O'Naturals has four organic quick take-out and sit-down restaurants in Maine and Massachusetts. They feature flatbread sandwiches, tossed salads, Asian noodles, fruit shakes and more.

O'Naturals was created to provide delicious, quick, natural foods to the public. The menu includes words like free-range, grass fed, organic and free of additives. The food is fresh and free of additives. Recently, O'Naturals opened itself to franchising. For more information, go to ONaturals.com

SCRUMPTIOUS NEIGHBORHOOD CAFE & BAKERY - THE PAST

This next model is as different from the Farmers Diner as cats are to dogs. If you recall, I mentioned the Old North End Farmers' Market in Burlington a few pages back. In that same neighborhood was a busy cafe called Scrumptious where you could find a pot of carrot-ginger soup on the stove and a tray of raspberry pastries coming out of the oven. The cost was a little more than a fast-food lunch, but the meal came with slices of fresh, warm bread.

Barbara Cook, the owner of Scrumptious, said that even though it cost her more to buy fresh local food, her net expenses were actually less because there was less "shrinkage" -- the portion of food that must be discarded because of poor quality or spoilage. As much as a third of a shipment of non-local produce can fall victim to shrinkage as compared to fresh, local vegetables. According to Barbara, the other advantage of buying fresh ingredients is that the food tastes better. Her repeat customers were a testament to that fact.

When Barbara opened her cafe, she bought local produce from Digger's Mirth, a farm collective close by in Burlington's Intervale. She also purchased produce from the Old North End Farmers' Market, the downtown Burlington Farmers' Market and area farms.

She further expanded her sources by joining the Vermont Fresh Network, which connects farmers to restaurants and vice-versa. In contrast to other restaurants that are part of the Vermont Fresh Network, Scrumptious didn't display the Vermont Fresh Network logo on its signs or menus. Barbara Cook wanted everyone to know that the food was fresh but she didn't want to sound too upscale or organic/vegan-like, because that would scare off the regular Joes. Scrumptious was located in a relatively poor, working-class neighborhood.

Scrumptious went up for sale a few years ago due to a lack of business. Nunyuns Bakery and Cafe took over Scrumptious in the summer of 2008.

SUGARSNAP

Sugarsnap is also a unique model. Not only is it a natural foods take-out eatery and caterer, it is the only restaurant in the area whose staff is proficient in cooking and also in growing vegetables and herbs on their two-acre organic farm in the Intervale, less than a quarter of a mile from Sugarsnap. This is the seventh growing season for the restaurant. Abbey Duke is the farmer in the ownership trio. During the growing season, she spends most of her time outside, although she still puts in hours in the kitchen, which is governed by her business partners, Katie and Kirk Fiore, both graduates of the New England Culinary Institute. Sugarsnap's unique approach even landed them on a PBS television show, "Smart Gardening."

The farm produces 20 kinds of greens, 10 varieties of basil, 20 different tomatoes, 15 types of carrots, many corn varieties, heirloom beans, and much more. This makes for interesting and simple ingredients.

Why not a fresh-off-the-farm tomato and basil salad? During the summer, tomatoes are canned, peppers are pickled and garlic sits in jars of oil. Many unique varieties of fresh herbs and vegetables would be too expensive to purchase on the open market. A typical main course at the restaurant could be BBQ chicken with roasted fingerling potatoes and zucchini, garnished with fresh, tender pea shoots.

There are 13 organic farms in the Intervale along with the Intervale Compost Project, all with the support and guidance of the Intervale Center. Three of the farms are CSAs. The three-acre, 165 plot Tommy Thompson Community Garden is also located in the Intervale as is Gardener's Supply, the largest mail-order gardening business in the U.S.

☕ COFFEE CORNER ☕
DINER

Photos Courtesy of Sugarsnap

In 1994, Brian Mitofsky took over the Coffee Corner, a traditional working-class diner, complete with counter stools, wisecracking waitresses, and busy fry cooks, which had been serving food for over 20 years at the corner of State and Main streets, a busy intersection in Montpelier, the Vermont state capital.

When Brian started the business, he was interested in using local food, but was far from starry eyed about it. He said, "I'm a capitalist. My main reason to go local is that it's better for business. When I use commercial products I have 25 percent shrinkage, but with local food it's only 5 percent. So, I get a higher yield for my money." Also, he adds, "With local products, my food is fresher. It's a better product to pass on to my customer."

The Coffee Corner serves customers milk, cheese, eggs, and meat from local sources year-round. In season, nearly all of its fruits and vegetables are locally grown. Mitofsky buys directly from farmers at the Farmers' Market every Saturday.

Brian offers a plain turkey sandwich with turkey from Misty Knoll Farm in New Haven, Vermont, which produces naturally raised poultry. He calls the sandwich the Hot Misty and says, "I'm afraid if I put `free-range organic' on the menu, people won't even look down to see the price, which is only $5.45 with no extras. My big emphasis is that this food is available to everyone at reasonable prices."

Helen Jordan, who works at the Vermont Agency of Agriculture, once told me of the time she went to the Coffee Corner and shared a table with a couple from Hawaii who were carting with them roasted coffee beans from plants in their backyard. The Coffee Corner brewed them up for everyone to sample. This is the first time Jordan had tasted home-grown coffee.

Brattleboro, Vermont

THE COMMON GROUND RESTAURANT: GONE, REOPENED, GONE AND RENAMED

In the early 1970s, about the same time as the opening of the Brattleboro Farmers' Market, another counterculture initiative was taking place in Brattleboro, the "River City" along the Connecticut River. The Common Ground Restaurant was born. It was the first natural-foods restaurant of its kind in Vermont.

I remember the night a group of us alternative-types were driving from Brattleboro to Keene, New Hampshire to catch a flick and we began talking about starting a natural foods restaurant. Within a year, it happened

under the leadership of Norm Kuebler. I can't tell you how many rice-and-vegetable dishes and homemade soy-burgers were served at the Common Ground, but I know it would number in the thousands. Tuesday evening was "all you could eat night," which usually meant vegetable stew, bread, and salad for $1.75. Many of those organic vegetables were grown on my farm.

The Common Ground was a real pioneer in its day. It was a worker collective, and decisions were made by the group. We all washed dishes, cleaned vegetables, cooked, waited on tables and cashed out. Community members bought shares in the non-profit operation, similar in nature to Claire's Restaurant and Pub, mentioned earlier. The restaurant went through many changes, including hiring a manager, as consensus doesn't always work. The importance of buying from local farmers was at the top of the list of priorities when the restaurant began and continued through the years.

The Common Ground thrived in the counter-culture atmosphere of the times and beyond, but in the 1990s, it declined and closed in 1999. You gotta pay your taxes if you want to run a business. It reopened in early November of 2006 when a new board of directors made up of local business people, artisans and alternative types infused new life into the restaurant.

David Hiler, the new board president was a youngster in the 1970s. I took care of him and his sister, Andrea, when their mom went out on the town. A lot has changed since the counterculture days of the early 1970s; my beard turned grey and the flower children grew up.

The Common Ground was resurrected because it was not only a restaurant, but also a community gathering place and a music venue. Unfortunately, the restaurant closed again because of strong competition. It was sold in 2008 to the The Common Loaf Bakery of the Twelve Tribes communities located in Westminster. The bakery features breads and soups made from farm fresh ingredients. The farm grows, mills and bakes with their own Basin Farm spelt flour. The restaurant never re-opened.

Hank Dimuzio of Ledgend Farm and Doug Mack,
Chef of Mary's Restaurant at Baldwin Hill

THE VERMONT FRESH NETWORK: CONNECTING FARMERS TO RESTAURANTS

In the early 1990s, Brian Mitofsky, now the owner of the Coffee Corner in Montpelier, was working for Marriot Food Services. One fall he was asked to organize a 1,200 person fund-raising dinner. Mitofsky decided that an all-Vermont menu would suit the occasion, but he found that even during harvest season, it would be difficult to stock the banquet with local Vermont foods.

It was clear back then to Mitofsky and others that there were alternatives to relying on the complex food supply chain where everything from tomatoes to lettuce to strawberries went through countless middlemen -- to eventually arrive in our homes and restaurants, devoid of any connection to the farm where it was grown -- and where farmers received a pittance of the profits from their hard work and investment.

Mitofsky decided to help organize a governor's commission to coordinate and build relationships between local farmers, restaurants and distributors. There was strong support for this effort from the New England Culinary Institute and the Vermont Agency of Agriculture.

This was the beginning of the birthing process for the Vermont Fresh Network (VFN).

Today, VFN links 230 chefs and restaurants with 120 farmers and food producers of Vermont. It celebrated its 11th year of operation in 2008 with over 300 members. The mission remains the same: to build innovative partnerships among Vermont farmers, chefs, and consumers in order to strengthen Vermont agriculture. The goal is to connect the state's farmers and producers with chefs in an effort to see more locally grown food served at Vermont restaurant's. Membership is based on direct participation. This arrangement insures that farmers are working directly with restaurants, and that chefs are actively communicating and cultivating their relationships with farmers and producers.

Restaurants in VFN print the names of the local farms they use and a description of the farms products on their menus. This is more than just waxing poetic about agriculture. It brings the customers' attention to the fact that the ingredients are local. For example, they can taste the quality of the chicken from Misty Knoll Farm in New Haven and the salad greens from Lilac Ridge Farm in W. Brattleboro.

Vermont Fresh Network Farmers and Cheesemakers

When the VFN first started, the only chefs interested in using local ingredients tended to be those upscale white tablecloth establishments. These chefs recognized the way to get the best ingredients was to go to the source.

A new move by VFN to reach out to more consumers, chefs, waitstaff and farmers began in the last couple of years with what's called Farmers' Dinners (no connection to the Farmers Diner). Having farmers come into the restaurant and share their stories with the waitstaff and diners has had a lasting impact on everyone involved. Local family restaurants started seeking out local food as a way to represent their commitment to their communities. VFN was the catalyst for this new relationship.

One of the dinners took place at the Ground Round, a chain restaurant. This is not the kind of establishment that would normally turn its menu over to local offerings. However, today the burgers come from Chip Morgan of Wood Creek Farm, the cheese from Shelburne Farms, and the bacon in the bacon burger from Vermont Smoke and Cure.

POTATOES, GREENS AND CHEESE

Left: Don Heleba, potato farm in Rutland; above, Half-Pint Farm, Mario and Spencer Wilton, Intervale in Burlington; Below, Emmett Dunbar, Anglai Farms, Londonderry, Vermont.

Vermont Fresh Network Continued...

Cracking the doors of the large, corporate franchises remains a great task but there have been some openings. When Bob Scott, the general manager of the Ground Round decided he wanted to purchase locally grown food, he had to be able to convince upper management that it would be a smart business decision.

Every year now, VFN schedules Farmers' Dinners at member restaurants across the state from March through December to educate consumers and educate successful farm-chef partnerships. The menu highlights produce from local farms, but what makes the events special is that the farmers themselves show up to talk with the diners about their farms. At one of the dinners, Hank Bissell of Lewis Creek Farm in Starksboro spoke about the 50 acres of vegetables he grows and the reality of being a small farmer supplying local restaurants.

VFN STORIES

Chefs: Tristan Toleno, owner and chef at the Riverview Cafe in Brattleboro says, "I buy all my chicken from Misty Knoll and the salad greens I get from Lilac Ridge are fresher than I could buy wholesale. But the truth is that purchasing this way costs me a little bit more, so it's important that my customers recognize and appreciate the use of local products." Toleno gives customers a choice when it comes to burgers. You can buy a local burger from grass-fed beef for a little more gelt or a conventional hamburger.

Riverview Cafe is not an upscale eatery. It serves the local population. At first, folks weren't' sold on eating local but after time and some education by Toleno and the staff, they came around to the idea. Toleno has seen a lot of change in the last five years. He believes there has been a strong cultural shift towards eating local food.

One of the question he's asked is what happens in February when folks want all the fixings in a salad. Tristan's answer is simple. Riverview won't have as many local ingredients in the salad as they do in summer. In winter, they buy tomatoes and lettuce from a local hydroponic greenhouse.

When Steven and Lara Atkins came home to Vermont after five years in California, they were thrilled to find a network that made it easy to find the small, hands-on food producers they could showcase at their Richmond restaurant, the Kitchen Table Bistro. They have had many farmers' dinners at their establishment.

A Farmer: When Hank Demuzio was establishing his farm in Middlebury, raising fallow deer and marketing venison, he needed help starting out in a niche market. He said, "I can raise good deer, but it was a learning curve talking to chefs about what they want." Chefs prefer particular cuts of venison.

Riverview Café

Photo of Tristan Toleno, Chef and Owner of Riverview Cafe.

NEW ENGLAND CULINARY INSTITUTE™

A Chef's Perspective: Jamie Eisenberg was once a chef at the New England Culinary Institute (NECI) based in Central and Northwestern Vermont. Her first awareness about the importance of buying local came from a guest speaker at an annual forum of the Vermont Fresh Network. The speaker, Michael Ableman, a writer and organic vegetable and fruit farmer from California, said that the cost of buying locally and seasonally should be measured not in dollars spent, but in the ultimate health of the planet and the people. His message was inspiring to Eisenberg and gave her the impetus to make sure that each graduate of NECI heard about the issues of sustainability and buying local. She said, "The choices made by them will bring our `sustainability' back in balance, one chef at a time."

At the time (1995), Jamie Eisenberg had just taken on the job of director of purchasing for NECI and was responsible for holding the bottom line on a huge food budget. Eisenberg went on to teach the culinary arts at NECI where she was a very popular teacher. She now works at a restaurant in Burlington. Ableman's latest book is *Fields of Plenty* (Chronicle Books, 2005).

Photo Courtesy of the
New England Culinary Institute

Other books include *The Good Earth*, (1993) and *On Good Land* (1998). Ableman is the subject of the award-winning PBS broadcast Beyond Organic, narrated by Meryl Streep.

All over Vermont, chefs are looking to small farm producers for everything from specialty meats, like venison and emu, to baby vegetables and fresh-picked berries. Most Vermont Fresh Network (VFN) farmers who sell to restaurants must also direct their marketing efforts to farmers' markets, food co-ops and direct off-farm sales. Meghan Sheridan, the Executive Director of VFN, says, "It is all about relationships -- whether it's the chef, the produce buyer or the neighbor. The most compelling and long lasting selling point of local foods is that its all about people in your community."

It's clear that VFN has made incremental steps to nourish the buy-local movement and to welcome all kinds of eateries into the mix. Sheridan put it well when she said, "Local food is for everyone: diners, pizza joints, white tablecloth, dining services and yes, even franchises." She went on to say, "If the local (fast-food joint) could buy locally and meet a farmer's sustainable price point, wouldn't you want them to?"

*For more information on VFN, go online to their website. or contact Meghan Sheridan, Vermont Fresh Network
P.O. Box 895, Richmond, VT 05477
(802) 434-2000*

LACE:
LOCAL AGRICULTURAL COMMUNITY EXCHANGE 2007

When the Farmers Diner, previously mentioned, left the city of Barre for the town of Quechee a couple of years ago, it created a wide gap in the downtown. A new initiative called LACE has begun to fill the void. LACE is a local-produce-oriented grocery store, a cafe and an educational center run as a nonprofit. The founder, Ariel Zevon, made it her mission to help the Barre community reconnect with local farmers and provide healthy food to the people of Central Vermont.

Photo Courtesy of
New England Culinary Institute

She put it well when she said, "It seems illogical to rely on mega-industrial food suppliers from thousands of miles away, when there are family farms all around us struggling to make ends meet. By using local resources our community will become more self-reliant; by learning more about the food we eat everyday we will become healthier in mind and body; by channeling our money back into the land that feeds us we will boost the local economy and preserve our rural farming landscape."

Ariel Zevon is the daughter of the late singer and songwriter Warren Zevon and god-daughter to close family friend Jackson Browne, the popular guitarist and singer. Jackson Browne gave a concert on June 13th 2007 at the Barre Opera House raising $60,000 to support LACE. The audience was treated to great music and produce from Vermont farmers, including potatoes which one person in the audience called Vermont gold.

Buy Fresh/Buy Local

The Pennsylvania Association of Sustainable Agriculture (PASA) joined with the Philadelphia Fair Food and Farm to City Projects to unveil a marketing campaign called the "Buy Fresh Buy Local." It aims to connect farmers and consumers through a network of farmers' markets, CSAs, restaurants, caterers, and other market venues, focusing specifically on Philadelphia for the first stage.

The campaign uses an online "Local Foods Guide," plus traditional advertising, to get the word out to consumers on where they can connect with local markets and farmers. Some Philadelphia restaurants will feature locally raised ingredients. Farmers' markets in the City of Brotherly Love will sell everything from strawberries and tomatoes to naturally raised beef, aged cheeses, locally made breads and BBQ chicken and ribs cooked right on the spot.

The campaign's eventual aim is to make sure consumers throughout Pennsylvania have a reliable method of identifying farm-fresh products grown in their region.

The Buy Fresh - Buy Local campaign is part of an even larger, nationwide initiative organized by the FoodRoutes Network of Millheim, Pennsylvania, which provides technical support to community-based groups working to strengthen regional markets for locally grown foods. FoodRoutes provides communication tools, networking opportunities and information resources to organizations that are trying to rebuild local food systems across the country.

Lace, Continued ...

The bread and butter of LACE is a restaurant and store which sells Vermont made and produced natural foods and supplies. Photos and descriptions of local farmers are posted throughout the market and once a month, the community has the opportunity to meet a farmer. The restaurant serves healthy locally grown foods. Additional space has been added, including a section dedicated to Vermont-crafted non-food items, handmade soaps, books, and cleaners.

LACE has a farm-to-community kitchen where residents can process local food, develop value-added products and attend a variety of food, cultural and agricultural classes for adults and children.

Zevon told me that local librarian Heather Herzig comes to LACE and reads stories to children related to food. They then go into the kitchen and prepare the food. It's called Cook-A-Book story time. That's what I call community.

Affordability is often a challenge for natural food stores and food co-ops that sell locally grown produce and processed goods. Because LACE is a non-profit, it is meant to serve the whole community. Zevon said, "One of my goals is to reach across the gamut from gourmet foodie types to low-income families and to make sure that everyone feels welcome ... One new initiative has been to provide nutritious left-over food to the needy after lunch and at the end of the day. Currently, some food deliveries are made to those in need."

A stick of pepperoni from Vermont Smoke & Cure in Barre costs $3.59 and a 16-ounce tub of yogurt from the Vermont Milk Company in Hardwick is $1.50 -- both fair prices. The fresh vegetable section is stocked with produce from Vermont farmers. The vegetables aren't marked as organic or conventional. Zevon said, "All of our produce is grown naturally; not all of it is certified organic." She explained that LACE did not want to exclude growers who were not certified organic.

Ariel Zevon told me that LACE has been well received by the Barre community. I found it refreshing to walk into the former Homer-Fitts Department Store and experience all the activities of LACE. The space is large and can accommodate additional growth -- even perhaps a small food shelf. We will see how this new food model works out in the marketplace. It wasn't that long ago that community supported agricultural initiatives spread across Vermont. Time will test LACE financially and its grand vision.

* LACE received a sizable grant from the Vermont Department of Health through Central Vermont Community Action for a community enterprise kitchen where families and individuals can process food and create value-added products.

Photos Courtesy of LACE

Jackson Browne, Arial Zevon and Senator Patrick Leahy at the Grand Opening of LACE

OTHER VERMONT MARKETS

There are many types of country and general stores in Vermont. Some large-scale operations like Dakin Farms and the Vermont Country Store cater to tourists and the native population. They are well-known nationally. Both have strong sales of mail order food items.

On the other side of the coin is Vermont Green Grocer, a small natural-food store in Richmond that provides a host of local fresh produce, and processed goods. It's more like a small grocery store with lots of health foods. Vermont Green Grocer shut its doors in the spring of 2009 from lack of sales.

Healthy Living in South Burlington is the largest of the large when it comes to health food stores. It's new store has 30,000 square feet of space, much larger than the largest natural food store or food co-op in Vermont.

There are also many country and general stores that carry just about everything, including Vermont value-added food products.

The Taftville Country Store is located close to the wealthy towns of Quechee and Woodstock. The store has long served as the village's social and political center. Two-thirds of the store's revenue comes from tourism and mail-order sales of Vermont-made gift products.

Charlie Wilson, the proprietor, says, "Our main promotional angle is that we are a country store specializing in gourmet Vermont products." There has been an explosion in the specialty foods industry in the last ten years. Carrying so many Vermont products has just been the natural evolution of the store.

In 1957 the store's catalog was selling Vermont cheese, syrup, and honey to New Yorkers. Now its web site sells more than a ton of Cabot cheese every year, along with Fox mustard by Phyllis Fox of Woodstock, Muffaletta by Karen's Food Co. of Rutland, pancake mixes made under the store's label, and lots more.

Sixty percent of the store's sales come from Vermont-made products.

The Richmond Corner Market in Richmond carries some of the same Vermont products as the Taftsville store, but it's not an upscale market with a catalog of Vermont products; it's more like a typical grocery store. The Richmond Corner Market works with local farmers to supply its clientele with local cheese, meats and produce -- and the response has been positive. That wasn't the case ten years ago when people simply didn't expect to find Vermont products in local stores.

Photos Courtesy of the Barnard General Store

Photo Courtesy of FH Gillingham, Woodstock, VT, Still in Operation

H. FROM THE FARM TO THE UNIVERSITY

Gaining access to locally grown foods is a growing movement in colleges and universities across the country as students are demanding the use of local food in their cafeterias. In recent years, members of farm organizations, food-service personnel, farmers and processors have collaborated on bringing local foods to the campus.

THE UNIVERSITY OF VERMONT

The University of Vermont (UVM) spends $5 million a year on food. Eighty percent comes from out-of-state food vendors and twenty percent from local farmers and food processors. More than 40 Vermont producers supply the University with local food -- everything from baked goods to dairy products, chicken, fruits and vegetables.

The food program at UVM is run by Sodexo, a multinational food-service corporation that operates on 600 U.S. campuses and 80 countries around the world. It's the largest food-service business on the globe having reported $17.7 billion in revenues in 2007.

Sodexo's name use to be a bad word in Vermont's fresh-food circles. The French food-service multinational has had a reputation for alleged human rights violations and ownership of private prisons. Though Sodexo Alliance, the Paris-based parent company, sold all its stock in Corrections Corporation of America in 2001, their involvement with overseas prisons comes up periodically.

Another concern has to do with labor practices. Fewer than 10,000 of Sodexo's 120,000 employees currently belong to a union. In 2007, a group of students at UVM protested the low wages paid to campus workers, including the 250 Sodexo employees at the University.

Sodexo prepares an average of 8,000 meals a day during the academic year at UVM. Black River Produce, a Vermont distributor, has a network of 60-some Vermont growers that provides local food to UVM's 15 dining facilities. Vermont artisan cheeses, Vermont Soy products, Champlain Orchards apples and cider, Misty Knoll chicken, and vegetables from Arethusa Collective Farm in the Intervale are sold to UVM. Booth Bros. Dairy in Barre, owned by HP Hood, supplied 38,000 gallons of milk in 2007. In 2007, UVM sent 208 tons of food waste to the Intervale, where it was composted and used on the land at Arethusa and other vegetable farms. Quite a loop, hey!

THE HISTORY OF SODEXO AT UVM: JUMPING THROUGH THE HOOPS

In the spring of 2005, farmers, and cheese-makers and Vermont's Deputy Secretary of Agriculture met with Sodexo and the UVM dining staff, the first step in a long process of working out a way to bring more local food into the cafeteria system. The University represented a large untapped revenue source for Vermont producers, but getting into the market required all parties to change the way they did business.

One of the key issues was how to deal with all the University eateries. Having 100 farm trucks drive up to one of the main cafeterias on campus was unworkable. Josef Quirinale, formerly of Sodexo told me that the key was to have a Vermont food distributor like Black River Produce work out a way to pick up the farmers' products and deliver them to the University. In September of 2005, Sodexo certified Black River Produce as one of its distributors. Burlington Food Service is another certified distributor.

The distributors clean, prepare and clearly label the foods, in case a food-borne illness requires a product recall. Sodexo requires the distributors to have $5 million in liability insurance. If a student got sick from the food, someone would have to be held responsible.

That's why third-party inspection is needed to check on the safety of the food.

According to Quirinale, the real issue is one of safety and liability. Black River Produce must be able to store the food properly and deliver it on time. For example, any seafood must be stored in a separate container. The liability insurance requirement is all but impossible for Vermont's small farmers to meet, so they've rarely been part of the system. Today, Vermont producers and farmers get their products picked up by Black River and distributed to the University without paying for the insurance themselves.

As you can see, there have been a number of hurdles to jump. This is a complicated business. For the University of Vermont to be "buying fresh Vermont produce" that had been shipped to a New Bedford, Massachusetts, distributor and then back to the University struck David Miskell, owner of Miskell's Vermont Organic Tomatoes, as nonsense. However, Miskell was more upbeat when he learned that Black River was in the process of being certified by Sodexo.

Photos Courtesy of Middlebury College Dining Service

257

THE PRESENT CHALLENGES

Increasingly, quantities of Vermont-made honey, maple syrup, vegetables and fruits, chicken and cheese and other dairy products are served at the University of Vermont. The reality, however, is that Sodexo cannot limit itself to Vermont-grown products as the supply is limited at this time. Romaine lettuce and citrus fruits still arrive from far away places.

While mesclun mix, carrots, corn and other vegetables grown within a 50 mile radius serve the campus in summer, winter squash, apples and cider are the favorites in the fall. There is still not enough produce year round. Sodexo would give Misty Knoll Farms of New Haven, Vermont their entire poultry business, but they don't have the capacity. Preserving root crops during the long winter months is another challenge for farmers as they do not have the needed storage capacity.

When the new $61 million Dudley H. Davis student center opened in August of 2007, students had a slew of food options including several local food vendors and eateries. Instead of tapping nationally known restaurants to fill vendor slots, several Vermont restaurants opened locations in the Davis Center. The Farmers Diner of Quechee was selected to be a local vendor. They examined the possibility, but decided not to participate because of the financial risk.

Michael Moser, from the Center for Rural Studies at the University, opened the "Growing Vermont" store at the Davis Center. The store is student run and features Vermont products, including my book, The Woodchuck's Guide to Gardening.

OTHER FOOD CONTRACTS

Champlain College in Burlington and Saint Michael's College in Colchester also have food contracts with Sodexo. In 2007, St. Michaels college began composting food waste. The compost was spread on flower beds and new areas to be planted into grass.

About 30 percent of the food under the heat lamps in the Green Mountain Dining Room at St. Michaels comes from Vermont producers and vendors.

Side Notes:

In the mid-1970s when I was a commercial vegetable producer in southeastern Vermont, I had to jump through all kinds of hoops in order to sell to a supermarket chain. I sold organic lettuce in wire and wooden crates to a supermarket chain called OK Fairbanks. The challenge was to supply enough crates each week and make sure the quality was high. The local managers loved the lettuce once they tasted it, but the higher-ups didn't want to deal with a small farmer. It was easier for them to work with the large distributors who purchased iceberg lettuce by the truckload from California.

MIDDLEBURY COLLEGE

Middlebury College is located in the heart of Addison County, one of Vermont's prime agricultural regions. There are 2,500 students at the school. The college has its own independent food service and according to the manager, their top priorities are quality and buying local. For example, the college purchases all its Thanksgiving turkeys -- fresh, not frozen -- from the local Stonewood Farms.

According to the Vermont Fresh Network, more than 20 percent of all purchases at Middlebury's Dining Services come from Vermont. The college has developed partnerships with a number of local farms, including Lewis Creek Farm (vegetables), Wilcox Dairy (ice cream), Happy Valley Orchard (apples and cider), Maple Meadow Farm (eggs), Misty Knoll Farm (chickens), Hillsboro Sugarworks (maple), Vermont Butter and Cheese Company (cow and goat cheese), Cabot Creamery (cheddar and cottage cheese) and Monument Farms (milk). For the past fifty years, the college has been buying milk from Monument Dairy Farms in nearby Weybridge.

Maple Meadow Egg Farm is located ten miles away from the college. The owners, George and Jackie Devoid, support their family on the farm that George's father began in 1946 with 400 chickens and a bike delivery route around Lake Dunsmore. This is the farm's 56th year of service to the college.

Middlebury College is also interesting because it has more flexibility than schools like the University of Vermont to invest labor in local foods. For example, a local business provided granola to the college, but it had gotten too expensive. Instead of giving up, Middlebury College looked for a local source of oats and made the granola themselves.

Fish and seafood come from the Boston market via Black River Produce. Black River also delivers vegetables and fruit to the college. The other main food supplier and distributor is Burlington Foodservice Company, which was recently bought out by a mega-large food service company from Chicago. Squash Valley is a smaller Vermont producer.

DARTMOUTH COLLEGE

Dartmouth College in Hanover, New Hampshire, has been successful at getting local food on the menu. They have received support from a regional group called Valley Food and Farm (VFF), a program of Vital Communities in the Upper Valley region of New Hampshire and Vermont. A couple of years ago, VFF received a grant from the Northeast Sustainable Agriculture Research (NE-SARE) program to coordinate a profitable relationship with local farmers and the college.

A VFF food/farm task force included Upper Valley farmers, the Dartmouth College Organic Farm, Dartmouth College Dining Services, wholesaler representatives, Dartmouth students and faculty. They all partnered together to create strategies for providing healthy, locally grown food on campus.

Some of the activities included working with local produce farms to figure out the best delivery system, as well as which vegetables to include and on-campus taste testing.

Boiling Maple Sap, Middlebury College Dining Service

THE VERMONT FRESH NETWORK EXPANDS ITS MISSION

In a new move, Vermont Fresh has begun to take steps to connect farmers to college campuses by providing vending machines with local milk.

A second step was to get more local Vermont foods offered in the catering menu by providing high quality ingredients. Part of the key here was to include healthy, non-fast-food options on the menu. Farmers had to plan ahead with greater production capacity.

BLACK RIVER PRODUCE: A LOCAL DISTRIBUTOR

In 2006, Black River Produce started shipping food to Sodexo. They pick up Vermont food products from farmers and food processors and deliver them to schools, colleges, food stores and restaurants in Vermont and New Hampshire.

Since 1978, Black River has been providing Vermont and New England chefs and customers with fresh fruit, dairy products, vegetables, seafood and flowers. The company is committed to distributing local foods such as Grafton Cheese, Cold Valley Apples, and Vermont Butter and Cheese. Co-owner Steve Birge told me, "We work with small time local growers. We find out what our customers want. The retail part of our business, like a country store, carries local produce."

The other owner of Black River, Mark Curran, is a member of Vermont Fresh Network. Curran said that in 2006 Black River moved about $24 million in produce.

Of that amount, $1.65 million went to local farmers and food processors in Vermont -- including Pete's Greens of Hardwick, Deep Roots, a vegetable farmers' collective in the Northeast Kingdom of Vermont; and Lewis Creek Farm in Starksboro. Black River is also able to purchase excess produce that would otherwise go to waste -- everything from fruits, vegetables and bread -- and distribute it to local restaurants. The quantity increases every year.

Black River also picks up produce at Vermont farms and transports it directly to Boston markets and Whole Foods stores. Its purchase of organic products is increasing; conventional foods are staying about the same. After dropping off Vermont products like vegetables, apples, cider, maple syrup, and cheeses to the Boston market, they pick up produce and return to Vermont saving on energy costs.

During the summer months, Black River averages three tractor-trailer loads a week to Beantown. The company also works with Thomas Dairy/Creamery of Rutland to distribute its milk products in Vermont. Some farmers deliver directly to Black River like Jack Lazor of Butterworks Farm, who drops off organic yogurt at the North Springfield facility, the best yogurt in Vermont.

Black River Produce moved to North Springfield, Vermont in 2005 and is one of the two largest food distributors in Vermont. It has 28 refrigerated trucks and 35 trucks running everyday, purchasing food from the Boston market. Black River receives direct deliveries from as far away as California, Washington state, Mexico, and Florida.

Steve Birge and Mark Curran, Co-owners Black River Produce

I. VERMONT'S VALUE-ADDED PRODUCTS: MYTH OR REALITY?

A REGIONAL FLAVOR

Like the rest of the Northeast, Vermont is dependent on outside food sources for most of its food. Other areas of the country have a comparative advantage when it comes to growing certain crops. Vermont, for example, can't produce oranges like Florida, or rice like Louisiana, but it can produce dairy products, apples, maple syrup, vegetables, soft fruit, herbs, flowers, beef, lamb, pork, and many value-added products for local consumption. Or how about water buffaloes, yaks and organic, kosher maple syrup! They're all here in the Green Mountains.

Vermont's food and agricultural sector is enhanced by what some call the "creative economy." This refers to businesses that emphasize the arts, culture, heritage, and agriculture. The premise is that an area infused with creativity and a strong sense of community will retain businesses as well as attracting tourists. Food and agriculture are critical to a "creative economy" in the Green Mountains. Some call this an economy with a regional flavor.

June Holley, CEO of the Appalachian Center for Economic Networks, says regional flavor is like making a tasty soup by combining all the interesting places, local foods and farming, the arts, recreation, lodging, and culture to express the uniqueness of your region.

Vermont's food and agricultural sector are a integral part of this "regional flavor" concept. The Vermont brand is closely tied to food, due to the state's national recognition in food innovation, especially in the area of artisan cheese. The Cheese Trail, a journey of artisan cheesemakers through the Green Mountains, is described in detail in a few pages.

Ben and Jerry's ice cream is known all over the world. Food processing is the second-largest source of manufacturing in Vermont, concentrated on dairy products such as ice cream, cream cheese and yogurt. The New England Culinary Institute, based in Vermont, has an international reputation. Few tourists return home from a vacation in Vermont without some specialty food item like maple products. Agritourism is an up-and-coming occupation on farms trying to make ends meet.

Amy Trubek, a University of Vermont professor and former instructor at the New England Culinary Institute, has written a book, *A Taste of Place: A Cultural Journey Into Terroir*, on the connection between food and place. The French have a term for the flavor of certain locales: le gout de terroir.

Trubek, the former Executive Director of the Vermont Fresh Network, says that what has taken place in the U.S. is the increasing homogenization and industrialization of our food supply, but this is changing as more people are interested in local food and how it is grown and prepared.

Amy Trubeck believes that Vermont is ahead of the curve with regards to understanding the importance of "Terroir." She uses the Vermont Fresh Network as a model for connecting farmers with chefs. When chefs incorporate local foods into their menus they're creating a cultural change.

A Taste of Place isn't about the agricultural ways of the past or fringe food. It focuses on what could be the future of food and farming in Vermont. Trubek says we can grow much of what we need. The challenge is in having the infrastructure to support this effort.

Amy Trubeck

THE VERMONT BUY LOCAL LOGO

FARMERS AND ACTIVISTS INVOLVED WITH VERMONT NOFA HELPED TO INITIATE THE "BUY LOCAL" MOVEMENT IN VERMONT IN THE 1970S. IN 2003, THE AGENCY OF AGRICULTURE TOOK A MORE ACTIVE ROLE, EVEN THOUGH MANY CRITICS FEEL MORE NEEDS TO BE DONE.

Vermont Seal of Approval: As far back as 1975, the Vermont legislature authorized the Secretary of Agriculture to establish an identity label, which would be applied to agricultural products produced in the state as long as they met standards of quality. The legislation led to the establishment of the Vermont Seal of Quality (VSQ).

During its first 25 years, the VSQ was a regulatory-based program, serving primarily as a means of identifying Vermont farm products that met or exceeded federal standards. Through 1999, sugarmakers represented approximately two-thirds of program participants while the dairy industry dominated the program in sales.

By the mid 1980's, there was a limit to the number of inspections the agency could perform as many new products and commodities like Christmas trees, nursery stock, and processed food came onto the market. There was a lack of personnel to regulate the program. Within a ten year period, the program was shuffled among three different agencies and now it's back under the Agency of Agriculture.

It was not until 2003 that other more

permanent changes were made to the system. The "Buy Local" initiative was instituted to promote the purchase and promotion of Vermont farm products. However, there has never been enough money to support the program. For twenty years, value-added products have struggled with erratic marketing efforts. It's been like trying to keep the old tractor working with wire and old parts.

What's clear is that the Vermont Seal of Quality should be maintained and strengthened as should the "Buy Local" initiative. The ideal program would include both marketing and regulatory support. While the "Buy Local" marketing program has been well received in the state, many of the major markets for Vermont products lie outside the state, where the "Buy Local" message is lost.

Source: Justis, Steve. "History of Vermont Seal of Quality." Vermont Agency of Agriculture, Agriview, February, 2007.

The Good News: The Green Mountains have for years been in the enviable position of featuring strong value-added business settings with a homespun ambiance, like apple orchards, and dairy farms. When folks think about Vermont, they conjure up images of black-and-white Holsteins munching on green grass in a bucolic pastoral setting, and a red barn in the background, or a family picking apples in an orchard, or maple trees being tapped for their sweet syrup in late winter, snow still on the ground.

By one estimate, the value of the state's farm-related food production topped $1 billion in 2000. Much of that revenue went to Ben & Jerry's ice cream and Cabot cheese, which makes 14 million pounds of cheese a year.

On-farm entrepreneurs can capitalize not just on organic and natural products, but on locally produced products. Farmers and producers can get a better price by marketing a product's freshness, the importance of family farms and the working landscape. This type of "niche" marketing can increase Vermont's national appeal and enhance the possibilities for a dynamic farm economy.

HOW'S BOUT THEM APPLES

The apple industry in Vermont has declined 40 percent in the last 15 years as a number of orchards went out of business and others reduced apple production. The changes that took place were due in part to higher labor costs and the erosion of the Vermont utility apple market. Utility apples are the ones that go into products such as pies and juices. Apple juice that used to be shipped from Vermont to various markets dried up when China started exporting apple juice puree to New York and New England markets.

Besides rising labor costs and the loss of utility apples, a new technology and marketing tool helped to seal the fate of some apple orchards. Apple growers were required by supermarket chains to have stickers placed on eating apples. Many apple growers couldn't afford the machinery to place the stickers on their apples.

Green Mountain Orchard in Putney was transporting bins of apples down to southern New England to have the labels put on. It was expensive and did not prove to be economical for the farm. Even though the orchard sells some wholesale apples, they are now focused on selling apples and apple products right from the farm. They have also diversified their operation with blueberries and other fruits. The orchard makes and sells cider, doughnuts, pies and other value-added Vermont products like maple syrup.

After years of losing apple sales to national and international markets, Vermont's apple market has begun to stabilize. Many orchards have changed over to pick-your-own operations in order to cut back on labor costs.

Photo By Jessica Lavallee Remmey

Many orchards now focus on bringing the community to the orchard for fall harvest festivals and other events. A number of orchards have diversified into CSAs operations.

Over 75 percent of the income from Nick Cowles's Shelburne Orchards is now pick-your-own. Nick is famous for his homemade apples pies and ginger cider drink.

Nick Cowles, owner of Shelburne Orchards

* In 2006, there were 40 commercial apple producers in Vermont, and sales of the fruit generated more than $12 million, plus another $7 million in products such as cider and pies. Apple prices were stronger in 2006.

Ezekial Goodband of Scott Farm in Dummerston has created a niche market with some unique apples and new marketing strategies. His name sounds like one of the old-fashioned varieties he cultivates. Goodband is becoming Vermont's heirloom apple expert with 70 varieties of rare apples.

You can find bushels of Newtown Pippin, Belle de Boskoop, Esopus Spitzenburg, Pitmason Pine Apple, D'Arcy Spice and many more apples at Scott Farm.

Goodband sells apples directly from Scott farm to the natural food co-ops throughout the state. The fruit is distributed by Black River Produce. Goodband has also created the first fruit CSA, whereby families receive a peck of peaches and apples per week for six weeks beginning in September through October.

Apple Picker

Ezekial Goodband Courtesy Hunger Mountain Co-op

Photos and Logos Courtesy Shelburne Orchards

THE VERMONT FOOD VENTURE CENTER (VFVC): A REAL ALTERNATIVE

On any given day, the aromas of garlic, maple, tomato, and honey waft out the windows of the Vermont Food Venture Center. Jeff Mitchell of Vermont Pepper Works is cooking up a batch of Hempin' Jalapeño Pepper Sauce. By the end of the day, he'll have capped, sealed and labeled 1,000 bottles, ready to be shipped all over the country.

VFVC has a 3,000-square-foot facility. The kitchen uses Blodgett ovens, pasta cookers, fruit processors, walk-in-coolers and freezers, and Hobart mixers that provide food processing facilities to the state's six northernmost counties.

Much of the space (10,000 square feet) is used for walkways, shipping, storage and handling. The costs are minimal at $25 an hour along with some consultation.

Thirty-five specialty food businesses use the center each year to test, chop, bake, freeze, fill, and store, such products as mapled nuts, green-tomato chutneys, chocolate-filled pastries, Indian sauces, apple sauces, maple dressings, and, of course, Hempin' Jalapeño Sauce. There's was even a wild blueberry farmer from Maine who came over in the fall to make jams and jellies from his wild blueberries.

The businesses range from full-time clients that use the facility several times a week to new start-ups that use it less frequently. One continuing trend is increased value-added food processing of Vermont origin: maple, apples, cheeses, honeys, and berries, to name a few.

VFVC was founded in 1996 in Fairfax. According to Brian Norder, the project director, food processing is the second-largest source of manufacturing in Vermont behind electronics. This is because of the many cheese, yogurt and dairy processing plants throughout the state.

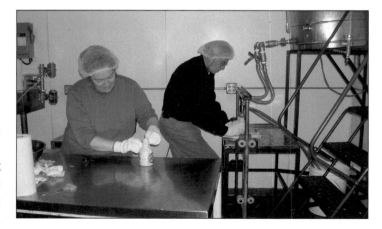

Maple Syrup Being Bottled at VFVC as a Fund-raiser for the Lamoille County Food Shelf.

VFVC Continued...

Norder said 60 to 65 percent of the Center's clients are still in business since they began, and 63 percent of the processors use Vermont products such as honey, maple syrup, apples and dairy products. He said that if the center helped to create 100 specialty food operations, that would give you a good-sized manufacturing plant.

Tomato Research: What would it take to process Vermont-grown tomatoes into a tomato puree to be used for sauces? When it comes to producing and processing tomatoes, it's a vastly different ball game than making value-added pickles or jams. When VFVC researched the matter, it found that it would cost between $2.75 and $3.50 to process local tomatoes into a pound of tomato puree.

Arethusa Farm Canning Tomatoes.

Compare this cost to those large institutional cans of tomatoes which come out to be somewhere around $.50 a pound. Sure, you could sell fresh tomatoes from your farm stand or to a school in the fall. Or you could produce a high-end, boutique tomato sauce that might be too expensive for some folks. On the other hand, if the processing center was close to a group of vegetable farms that raised tomatoes, the processor might have a better chance of competing in the marketplace.

VFVC recently chose a new site with a larger facility in Hardwick because of increased farm activity in dairying, soy processing, seed businesses, and vegetable production. The farming community around Hardwick has a lot of energy and activity. The new facility will be 10,000 square feet.

Norder said, "The new facility will allow us to expand our work with fruit, vegetable and maple producers." We plan to also expand into artisan cheese making and meat processing.

The facility would be used for cutting, packaging, and wrapping meat. Foods like soups, stews and Shepherd's pie could be processed at the plant. Another advantage is that there is a slaughterhouse nearby in Troy. There could be some affinity through research and development projects with the Vermont Milk Company (VMC). VMC is a new venture that produces cheese curds and yogurt from local dairy farmers in an industrial park in Hardwick.

When I asked Norder how Vermont stacked up with other states in regards to food/ag business, he said that Vermont was ahead of the curve but other states were catching up. Norder said, "Vermont has a number of great initiatives -- the Women's Ag Network, Vermont Land Trust, the Intervale, farm-to-school programs, and other projects. Overall food entrepreneurship is now seen as viable economic development as it matures."

Funding for the new VFVC facility have come from the 2008 Farm Bill and Federal Economic Development Funds. VFVC must still raise more money before breaking ground.

* *Vermont's Senator Patrick Leahy said, "Small businesses are a driving force in the Vermont economy and specialty food production is an important and growing part of the market. The Vermont Food Venture Center gives small specialty food entrepreneurs the opportunity to grow beyond their kitchens."*
* *For more information on the project, contact Brian Norder at (802) 849-2000 or go to the Vermont Food Venture Center site on the web at www.vfvc.org*
* *There are some twenty facilities in the country similar to the Vermont Food Venture Center. The Vermont center is considered one of the top three in terms of culinary and food science knowledge. They work closely with Cornell University in Ithaca, New York, as well as with the University of Vermont (UVM) with the Northeast Center for Food Entrepreneurship. Sorry to say, the grant at UVM ran out in 2004.*

VFVC EXAMPLES:
VALENTINE'S KITCHEN INC.

Maria Jakobeit made fresh salad dressings at VFVC. She grew up creating dressings in her hometown of Tegucigalpa, Honduras, learning everything from her mother, who not only ran a busy home kitchen, but also had a restaurant called Fernando's. Maria's two products, Caesar dressing and strawberry hazelnut dressing, are a memorial to her mother.

During the last ten years of her life, Maria's mother developed Alzheimer's disease. While taking care of her mother, Maria began to write down her mother's recipes and created them in her home kitchen. Maria then asked for help from VFVC, which provided a kitchen and processing center. Maria decided that she wanted to support Alzheimer's research efforts with some of the profits from the sale of her dressings. She contributed $.25 from the sale of each bottle.

Maria's main challenge was in finding Vermont grown products for her dressings. There are many ingredients in her dressings that aren't grown in Vermont. She used local maple syrup but couldn't find anyone who produced organic apple cider. Maria picked strawberries at local farms, pureed and froze them. All of her accounts were with local food stores, and she gave demonstrations at the stores and food shows.

VERMONT MYSTIC PIE COMPANY

How come some people just seem to know what others love to eat?

David Barash, former business colleague of Ben Cohen and Jerry Greenfield, of Ben & Jerry's fame, came up with Vermont Mystic Pies with a little help from his friends and the Barred Rock Fund, a socially progressive venture capital fund. David remembers baking pies from scratch with his mom in the 1960s. He's found that the smell and taste of fresh-baked apple pies still has the allure it once had.

The company's all-natural bake-and-serve apple pies appeared in freezer chests in September of 2004. They're made from King Arthur organic flour and Cabot Creamery butter, both Vermont businesses. The pies were originally baked at the Vermont Food Venture Center, but the company outgrew the space.

Pies Continued...

The pies are now baked at a facility in Massachusetts and distributed to 85 stores in New England, New York, and New Jersey by United National Foods.

David Barash had to come up with the right kind of apples for the pies. He worked with Steve Justis, the senior agricultural development specialist at the Vermont Agency of Agriculture. Together they found a supply of Empire, Cortland, and Northern Spy apples from Bill Suhr's Champlain Orchards in Shoreham. Barash chose Northern Spy for the majority of the pie filling.

Spy's are my favorite apple as they have a tart-sweet taste and are great for storage.

The pies are freshly made and frozen, so that the customer can bake them at home. Mystic extends the season with blueberry pies in late summer and strawberries and rhubarb in early summer. They use other soft fruits in their pies including red and black currants from Cherry Hill Farm in Springfield.

Barash told me that the apples are sliced, frozen, and shipped out within 36 hours. They are sent from Champlain Orchards to the distribution center at Black River Produce in Springfield, Vermont where they are trucked down to the bakery in Massachusetts. There, the pies are baked, frozen, and shipped out to stores. Barash only buys Vermont apples from local growers. He believes that by creating a value-added market for Vermont utility apples, it will contribute to rebuilding the Vermont apple industry.

CHAMPLAIN ORCHARDS: A DIVERSIFIED OPERATION

The Vermont Mystic Pie Company works closely with Champlain Orchards, owned and managed by Bill Suhr. Mystic Pies received a grant from the Vermont Community Loan Fund to purchase the equipment for peeling, coring, and slicing apples. The equipment is housed at one end of the barn at Champlain Orchards, which provides sliced apples to Mystic Pies and to other bakers. Four workers run the coring machine that peels and slices 100,000 pounds of apples a year for Vermont Mystic Pie Co. and other pie makers including Suhr's own fresh baked apple pies.

Bill Suhr began growing apples on 50 acres in the Champlain Valley in 1998. He increased his revenue by selling apples directly to Vermont supermarkets rather than selling them to a wholesaler; he also markets apples for neighboring orchards and has a pick-your-own operation. Suhr is trying to figure out other ways of turning apples into marketable products. He has a cider press in the barn that produces 70,000 gallons of sweet cider a year along with the newest cider drink called Cranberry Apple. It has a mild cider and cranberry taste. The cranberries are grown in Vermont.

The bakery at Champlain Orchards supplies many stores in the area with pies. Champlain Orchards also has a farm stand that sells cider, dilly beans, apple butter, fruits and vegetables, pies, honey, maple syrup and meat.

Side Notes:

Freezing Soft Fruits

The Vermont Agency of Agriculture recently purchased a mobile freezing unit which can go from farm to farm freezing berries.

Utility fruits like apples and berries need to be frozen immediately in order to be preserved for later use.

The freezing unit gives farmers an incentive to plant more fruit and plan for the future. This will help Barash and others who want to use more apples, blueberries, raspberries, blackberries, currants, and other soft fruits in pies, jams and value-added products.

Growers would rather sell the fruit directly to the customer but what happens when you have a surplus of fruit or a hard rain is coming and the pick-your-owners stay home. The reality is that fruit needs to be picked when it's ready. If apple and berry producers can pick the surplus utility grade fruit and have it frozen, it can be used later for jams and pies and ...

Apple Orchard Crew and Farmstand,
Photos Courtesy Champlain Orchards

ANOTHER PIECE OF THE PIE:
MARKETING AND DISTRIBUTION

One challenge Vermont producers face is the distribution of farm products. Let me share a story with you about a young Vermont baker and a new distribution business. It's a small but tasty example of how Vermonters are gaining a foothold in the world of niche marketing.

Past and Present Tense: Krin Barbeiri of Krin's Bakery of Huntington was a pie maker. She baked apple and apple-crumb, strawberry-rhubarb and triple-berry pies as well as an assortment of chocolate/peanut butter and macaroon cookies. She also makes coconut cupcakes using local apples, rhubarb, and berries, Cabot butter, and King Arthur organic flour.

About a third of Krin's business came from sales at the Burlington Farmers' Market; the remainder from co-ops and natural-food stores. The problem she faced when she began was high transportation and fuel costs, distribution, and marketing.

Krin turned to Vermont Foods Delivery Service (VFDS) to pickup and deliver her freshly baked products at a cost of about 15 percent wholesale. VFDS delivered her baked goods on the same day, and collected the money and provided new outlets for Krin's products.

Most small bakers like Krin need distributors like VFDS to reach more markets and increase volume. Unfortunatly VFDS is no longer in business.

After a number of years of baking pies and cookies, Krin found that macaroons were the solution. She still bakes pies, which she sells at the Burlington Farmers' Market. Her "bread and butter" are macaroon cookies.

Vermont Roots: Vermont Roots is a different type of wholesale delivery company for Vermont specialty foods. Its' run out of Rutland, Vermont, and sells non-perishable Vermont processed food products, such as salsas, chips, cheeses, pickles, mustards, maple products, and chocolate. Many of the items come from the Vermont Food Venture Center. Vermont Roots carries over 300 different items from 76 Vermont companies. The business sells most of its goods in-state and uses UPS to ship out-of-state.

Vermont Specialty Food Association (VSFA) is made up of small and large businesses. Since it began 25 years ago, the trade organization now has 120 members and includes 1,500 food products including cookbooks, chocolates, and cheese and dairy products. Its goals are to support family farms and agritourism and to sustain

the working landscape. VSFA is the oldest organization of its kind in the country. It has been written up in Gourmet, Bon Appetit, the New York Times, Vermont Life and Yankee Magazine.

VSFA is located in Rutland, Vermont. For more information go to their website. .

OTHER NICHE MARKETING SOLUTIONS: WINDING BROOK FARM

Art Meade has found a niche by selling goats and lambs to Vermont's Muslim immigrants. Most Americans don't eat goat meat, which presents a problem for goat dairies that have a surplus of newborn male goats. Art Meade found a solution by selling meat to the local Muslim community. The key to Meade's success is an on-farm custom slaughterhouse.

Families from Bosnia, Somalia and the Middle East can buy goats and lambs from Meade, then butcher them according to the rituals of their religion. Abdullahi Adam Hussan, a Bantu refugee from Somalia described the process know as halal slaughter, in which the animal to be killed is faced toward Mecca and its throat is cut in a particular way to drain the blood. According to Meade, his problem is not sales but raising enough animals for sale.

WHAT'S IN A NAME:
A DAY OF CONCERN ON BLISS POND

A friend and I were having lunch on her porch overlooking Bliss Pond in Calais, a most peaceful setting. She had just set down two jars of salsa on the table. I looked at one of the jars and it read "Green Mountain Gringo Salsa." At one time the salsa company was located on Mountain Road in Stowe, Vermont. Today, it's owned by TW Garner Food Co. of Winston Salem, North Carolina. Nothing has changed except where it is processed. The ingredients have stayed the same. None of them were grown in Vermont.

The other jar said, "Fire in the Mountains from Mountain Road in Stowe." The company which produced the salsa was Catamount Specialties of Vermont. It was the same company that had owned Green Mountain Gringo Salsa.

A number of value-added food companies have left the state. One of the big ones was Annie's Naturals, a very popular salad dressing business, once located in Calais. It was bought and sold to a California company a couple years ago. Check out the label.

Check out the LiftingTheYoke.com website on the confusion over the labeling of Vermont products.

USDA photo

Todd Hardie, Smoking Beehives. Photo Courtesy of Honey Gardens

HONEY GARDENS APIARY

Todd Hardie, the owner of Honey Gardens Apiary in Ferrisburgh, has been a beekeeper for over 26 years. He once was a client of the Vermont Food Venture Center where he used to sell honey in bulk before he decided to create value-added honey medicinal products such as lozenges, tonics, cherry bark syrup, salves and an apiary throat spray.

Honey Gardens Apiary has also gone into the business of creating Melissa's Sparkling Mead. They join a tiny but growing group of beverage makers in the U.S. who are producing mead drinks. There are about 80 to 90 meaderies in the country and 30 or so wineries where mead is produced.

Honey Gardens has been fine-tuning the business of meadmaking. They want the community to know that Honey Gardens' Mead is an agricultural product made from regional ingredients that support the local farm economy. Melissa's Sparkling Mead is delivered to a handful of natural food stores. The idea was to start small and grow locally. For more information, go to www.honeygardens.com .

BEES POLLINATE VEGETABLES, BERRIES, APPLES AND OTHER FRUITS.

Nitty Gritty Grain Company

Top to bottom: Logo; Field of Grain; Pancake and Muffin Mix, from Nitty Gritty Grain Company. Photos Courtesy Nitty Gritty Grain Company, Charlotte, Vermont

VERMONT-GROWN CORNMEAL PANCAKES AND BAKING MIXES

One of Vermont's newest food businesses has an interesting twist. Two neighbors in Charlotte, Jane Kirby and Tom Kenyon, decided to run a joint corn product business, with Kenyon growing the organic corn on his farm and Kirby packaging and selling the corn products.

One day Kirby and Kenyon were chatting along the fence row and the idea occurred to Kirby to ask Kenyon why couldn't she use some of the corn from his fields. From there it's history and that's how the Nitty Gritty Grain Company began.

The organic cornmeal, made from the Wapsie Valley variety of corn, can be used for a number of cooking purposes including pancakes and muffins. Wheat flour and other ingredients are added to the mixes.

Kenyon cultivates up to 350 acres of organic oats, soy beans, soft white winter wheat, and corn. He ships most of it across Lake Champlain to Champlain Milling Company in Westport, New York.

Kirby is a former magazine food editor, cookbook author, and registered dietician.

VERMONT SWEETWATER BOTTLING COMPANY

During March, when the maple sap is running hard, Bob and Rich Munch can be found at Vermont Sweetwater Company in Poultney bottling carbonated maple sap around the clock. "When the sap comes," Rich says, "you have to drop everything to do the bottling." Even their mother, Grammie, gets in on the operation. Their maple seltzer, sold in a green bottle with a classic sketch of maple trees and buckets on the label, is unique in the world of carbonated beverages.

The ingredients aren't hard to figure out: 100 percent pure filtered and carbonated maple sap. If you consider that 40 gallons of sap boiled down makes one gallon of syrup, it's easy to see how the sap is about 1/40th that of the syrup. The maple flavor is rather subtle.

Over the years, Bob and Rich have created other soda flavors, all 100 percent natural; the maple seltzer remains their most unusual product. The Vermont Sweetwater products are sold all over the Northeast, from the Dean & Deluca specialty store in the Big Apple to local hardware stores.

VERMONT'S BEER INDUSTRY IS "HOPPIN"

Vermont beer breweries contribute to the state's economy by purchasing some of their ingredients locally. Morgan Wolaver, president and owner of Otter Creek Brewery in Middlebury said, "If we can get our grains and our hops locally, that would be great on both sides: reduction in the requirement for energy for shipping, but also added income to the state."

Wolaver moved from California to Vermont a decade ago. He purchased Otter Creek Brewing, Inc., in Middlebury. Wolaver's Certified Organic Ales are part of Otter Creek Brewing. Wolaver said, "Presently we're purchasing from a local farmer a quantity of organically grown wheat, and not too far out in the horizon, we'll be able to produce barleys." Sales of his organic ales have risen around 20 percent a year.

Wolaver went on to say. "You have a state of individuals or residents that truly support local products like beer, cheese, and maple syrup. Also, the people in the state have a good work ethic as well and respect for their jobs and their employers." Gail Daha, general manager of Otter Creek Brewing and president of the Vermont Brewer's Association said, "I think Vermonters are a little more committed to the quality of our environment, sustainability, and helping organic producers."

Magic Hat Brewing Co. of South Burlington is the newest Vermont brewery to produce organic beers in Vermont. They are a large brewery by Vermont standards.

Magic Hat launched a new line in 2007 called Orlio Common Ale, Orlio IPA and Orlio Black Lager. These names are subdued compared with the conventional Magic Hat beers like Hocus Pocus, Fat Angel and Jinx. It's clear they're trying to appeal to a more family oriented/outdoorsy audience as well as the younger, more hip Magic Hatters.

Beer Facts: In 2005 brewing in Vermont contributed 558 brewing and wholesaling jobs in to the State's economy; forty percent of the beer is sold in Vermont. The Green Mountains have the largest number of artisan brewers in the country per capita.

Nationally, organic beer sales were $19 million in 2005, up 40 percent from 2004 according to the Organic Trade Association of Greenfield, Massachusetts. In 2003, sales were $9 million. Certified organic beer must be made from 95 percent organic ingredients. The craft-brewing industry brings in $3.8 billion in sales each year. In September of 2006, Anheuser-Busch launched two organic beers. There are 1,378 craft brewers and 20 organic craft brewers in the country.

* Vermont State Brewers Association: www.vermont.brewers. com
* In 2007, the price of hops rose substantially -- from 100 to 400 percent -- and the price of barley made into malt went up from 25 to 50 percent. This was in part due to an increase in corn production for ethanol, or for export to China, which decreased the amount of land used for growing hops and barley. Vermont brewers believe the key is to preserve quality even it means higher prices. Some brewers are experimenting with beers using fewer hops.

1. Lake's End Cheeses
2. Green Mountain Blue Cheese
3. Doe's Leap
4. Willow Hill Farm
5. Shelburne Farms
6. Franklin Foods
7. Cabot Creamery
8. Vermont Milk Co.
9. Jasper Hill Farm
10. Bonnieview Farm
11. Lazy Lady Farm
12. Hope Farm Sheep Cheese
14. Blythedale Farm
15. Vermont Butter & Cheese Co.
16. Three Owls Sheep Dairy
17. Neighborly Farm
18. Champlain Valley Creamery
19. Orb Weaver Farm
20. Twig Farm
21. Danicing Cow Farm
22. Blue Ledge Farm
23. Crawford Family Farm
24. Consider Bardwell Farm
25. Maplebrook Farm
26. Thistle Hill Farm
27. Vermont Water Buffalo
28. Jericho Hill Farm
29. Cobb Hill Cheese
30. Frog City Cheese
31. Crowley Cheese
32. Woodcock Farm
33. West River Creamery
34. Taylor Farm
35. Grafton Village Cheese
36. Peaked Mountain Farm
37. Vermont Shepherd

THE CHEESE TRAIL

Ice cream, cream cheese, cheese curds, yogurt and artisan cheese bring in more money from value-added products than any other type of food in Vermont. Let's take cheese and follow it along the cheese trail from its early history to the present day.

Vermont has a long history of cheese making. In the mid-1800s, the backbone of Vermont agriculture shifted from sheep's wool to cow's milk, and as dairy farming increased, so did the surplus of milk. Because of this excess, more farmers became interested in cheesemaking.

Railroads expanded into Vermont in 1850; and it wasn't long before cold-storage rail cars were sending dairy products like cheese to Boston and New York. Many farming communities had a cheese factory. In 1885, there were 58 cheese factories. Three of them are still making cheese: Crowley, Grafton Village and Plymouth. With the rise in industrialization and the growth of cheese making mega-factories, the artisan cheese making tradition ended, that is, until recently, when a resurgence began to take place.

THE BORSH BELT OF ARTISAN CHEESE

Many Vermont farmers are diversifying into artisan cheese making. As of 2007, there were 37 cheesemakers. And they're doing it right on the farm. It's clear that there are innovative ways of making money from Vermont milk and cheese products, but it takes smart entrepreneurial skills and sound financial backing to be successful.

Over the past two decades, Vermont and its artisan cheesemakers are gaining national recognition churning out hand-crafted cheddars, goudas, chevres, blues, and even buffalo mozzarella. Many of these farms are open for tours, tastings and direct sales. Some are small, and others are smaller. Even though none are large by national standards, Vermont per capita has more artisan cheese makers than any other state. And now on to the "Cheese Trail."

Woodcock Farm: There are the hard-to-find farms like sheep cheesemaker Mark Fisher, who sells cheese at the local farmers' markets, gourmet stores and directly from the farm. He and wife Gari do everything from milking, making cheese and playing tour guides at the Woodcock Farm in out-of-the-way Weston. They have a flock of East Friesian sheep and graze them on 45 acres of pastureland. When the Vermont winter buries the grassland under snow, the sheep are no longer milked.

Taylor Farm Cheeses

Taylor Farm: The 180 year-old Taylor Farm in Londonderry is run by farmer-turned cheesemaker Job Wright, who makes 1,200 pounds of gouda once a week and opens the farm to tourists in search of, "life on the farm" and good cheese. Wright finds it's a lot easier to make a living making artisan cheese than milking 100 cows twice a day. The herd consists of 40 Holstein and Jersey milk cows. Wright has added lodging, a farm stand, sleigh rides and educational activities on the farm.

Frog City Cheese: Plymouth Cheese Farm sits close to the boyhood home of Calvin Coolidge in Plymouth Notch where native Vermonters Tom Gilbert and Jackie McCuin make Frog City Cheese. Coolidge's grandson John once ran the operation and today, thousands of people come and visit the home of "Silent Cal" and the current cheesemakers.

Gilbert and McCuin are producing granular curd cheese, or stirred cheese, as it was known, which was made by the Coolidge family for generations. The cheese comes from raw milk and was typically hand-made in New England farmhouses during the colonial period. It is rarely made today.

What's unique about Frog City Cheese is that this is the third century of cheese making in Plymouth. Early settlers in Plymouth were homesteaders, but eventually the area turned into a farming community when farmers began to have a surplus of milk and a cheese factory was built to handle the excess milk. The creation of the Plymouth Cheese Factory came from local townsmen, including John Coolidge, where they produced one variety of cheese. Food historians today call it an old-fashioned relative of cheddar with a granular, curd texture. It's made from raw Jersey milk and vegetable rennet and has a high degree of tanginess that increases with age.

Orb Weaver - This farm is located in the Champlain Valley. Marjorie Susman and Marian Pollack have been farming the land for 25 years, originally as dairy farmers. In 1995, they abandoned selling fluid milk in favor of expanding the cheese operation. Now they produce 7,000 pounds of cheese yearly from eight  Jersey cows and sell most of it around Middlebury.

One of their favorites is a creamy, butter-yellow cheese with a slight tang, similar to Colby. Orb's Weaver Farm's cave-aged cheese, although made with the same recipe as their waxed wheel cheese, has a nutty flavor and dry texture. Making unwaxed natural-rind cheese requires more work from constant brushing of the rinds to control the growth of mold, to flipping the cheeses to prevent the butterfat from settling on one side.

Photos Courtesy of Orb Weaver

Champlain Valley Creamery, LTD: Carlton Yoder is a small cheesemaker even by Vermont standards. Yoder is probably one of the few artisan cheesemakers in the country who picks up his main ingredient in a Honda minivan with his toddler's car seat strapped in front to nine stainless steel cans. The 20-minute weekly trip he makes to Journey's Hope Farm in Bridport is one of his favorite times of the day. Yoder makes hand-crafted organic cream cheese. Yoder picks up the milk from Journey's Hope and transports it to his small processing facility in Vergennes. Most Vermont artisan cheesemakers use the milk from their animals to make cheese on the farm.

Carlton Yoder, Champlain Valley Creamery

Jasper Hill Farm: Angela and Mateo Kehler of Jasper Hill Farm in Greensboro are working to help build the state's farmstead cheese industry by building a cellar large enough to age cheese for other cheesemakers. Mateo and his brother Andy milk 35 Ayrshires in an aging barn on a dirt road, but their Bayley-Hazen Blue, Constant Bliss, Aspenhurst and Winnemer cheeses are on menus in the best stores in California and sold at some of the country's best cheese shops. Jasper Hill Farm doubled production in 2007 as buyers snapped up all 70,000 pounds of cheese. Mateo believes that Vermont with its lush pastureland, offers an ideal cuisine for milk-producing cows, goats and sheep.

The Kehlers invested $1.2 million in a 30,000 square foot brick-lined cheese cellar, like those found in Europe. (The quality of artisan raw-milk cheeses depends on the quality of the milk, the recipe, the skill of the cheesemaker, and, finally, the careful aging of the cheese for many months in a special environment. The cheeses have to be checked and moved about the cellar on a regular basis.) Many small Vermont farmers want to milk cows and make cheese but need help with both the aging process and the marketing. Mateo hopes to fill the gap by helping other cheesemakers. He said, "Our goal is to create the infrastructure that provides incentives for the production of farmstead cheeses."

Courtesy Jasper Hill Farm

Cabot Cheese: Cabot is by far Vermont's largest cheesemaker. In 2003, Cabot Cooperative Creamery began sending 38-pound wheels of cheddar to Jasper Hill, where it was wrapped in cloth and shelved in the cellar to be aged and flavored by mold for 10 months. One of the first of those wheels won a gold medal at the World Cheese Awards in London. Cabot Clothbound Cheddar occupies up to half the space in the Kehler's new cellars. Kehler shared a "best of show" prize with Cabot from a field of 941 cheeses at the American Society Competition in Portland, Oregon

Thistle Hill Farm:
John and Janine Putnam own and manage Thistle Hill Farm in North Pomfret, Vermont. The milk for their award-winning cheese Tarentaise comes from a small herd of Jersey cows, which produce milk with a high protein and butterfat content.

John and Janine Putnam from Thistle HIll

Like many Vermont farmstead cheesemakers, the Putnams make cheese only when their milkers are feeding on pasture and fresh hay -- from late April through early December. The golden 20-pound cheese rounds are made entirely by hand with raw milk from the herd's organic cows. The Putnams are unusual because they make their own rennet, the ingredient that separates the curds from the whey. The cheeses are brined and then aged in a climate-controlled cave on the farm for five months.

John Putnam says, "Everything to do with our cheese is ours. It's our feed, our cows, our milk, our cheese. The milk travels all of about 50 feet from the barn to the cheese house. We do it all right on the farm."

Cindy Dawley, General Manager of the Crowley Cheese Factory

Vermont Butter and Cheese Company: Alison Hooper and Bob Reese, are making a million-dollar addition to their goat cheese making operation. When they began in 1984, few Americans had tried goat cheese, but now there is a real appetite for this specialty food product. Vermont Butter and Cheese sells fresh goat cheese as well as European-style butter, mascarpone, and creame fraiche from cow's milk. Sales were up 28 percent in January and February of 2006, as compared to 2005.

Hooper and Reese's new cheese, Bonne Bouche, is in heavy demand, though production is barely under way. Bonne Bouche is not a fresh cheese and needs special rooms where the molds can ripen. Whole Foods, the largest organic food store business in the country, carries Bonne Bouche. It was also featured in the upscale Williams-Sonoma catalog.

The biggest challenge Hooper and Reese face is finding enough goat milk from dairies in Vermont, New Hampshire and Quebec. They now buy about 2.5 million pounds of milk a year and are going to need another 7 million pounds in the future.

Shelburne Farms Cheese:

This is not the typical Vermont artisan cheese producer by any stretch of the imagination. Shelburne Farms is the former Vanderbilt estate with the grounds designed by the great landscape architect Frederick Law Olmstead. The farm is now a non-profit working farm focused on education, drawing more than 100,000 people a year and producing tons of raw-milk cheddar cheese from their purebred herd of 125 Brown Swiss.

Mary Lou Strodel of Atlanta, Georgia watches as the cheesemaker, Jamie Yturriondobetia makes farmstead cheddar. The milk comes from the farm's herd of Brown Swiss, which graze on green grass in the meadows close to the milk house. After she stirs the milk, the milk's whey is drained, leaving rich, clumpy curds. The curds are then sliced into slabs and stacked and rotated in an age-old process known as cheddaring. After more cutting, salting and pressing in the morning, the result will be 40-pound blocks of solid cheese.

Raw-milk cheese is allowed under Vermont State law if it goes through a long aging process that kills any harmful bacteria. The minimum period is six months Some of the Shelburne Farm cheeses age for six months. Others age for one year or longer in the Shelburne Farms cellar before it is ready for sale. The longer its ages, the stronger the taste.

From what I learned regarding the history of Shelburne Farms, Derek Webb, the son of Electra Havemeyer Webb, wanted to sell raw milk, but was told by the State of Vermont it would have to be pasteurized. Webb did not want to pasteurize the milk so he decided to make raw-milk cheese. From there it's history.

Shelburne, Vermont

* See more on Shelburne Farms in Resources in the Lifting the Yoke website.
* In his James Beard Award winning book, "Cheese: A Connoisseur's Guide to the World's Best", (Clarkson Potter, 2005), Max McCalman honored 7 Vermont cheeses on his list of the best 200. The following Vermont farms were included: Thistle Hill, Jasper Hill (two cheeses), Grafton Village Cheese Co., Orb Weaver, Vermont Shepherd, and Jersey Blue.
* Vermont's cheesemakers recently received awards in the September 2008 issue of Wine Spectator Magazine as well as a number of ribbons from the American Cheese Society. The new edition of Wine Spectator features 10 Vermont cheeses making their top 100 cheeses in the world -- a large showing for a small state and close to one-third of the 32 American cheeses that made the list. For more information on how to purchase these and other Vermont cheeses, go to www.vtcheese.com
* According to the Vermont Institute for Artisan Cheese (VIAC) at the University of Vermont, the state has 37 artisan cheesemakers, 20 of whom have been established since 2000.
* The Vermont Cheese Book by Ellen Ecker Ogden describes the Vermont Cheese Trail and the many cheesemaking and cheesemakers throughout Vermont. Many of the photos in The Cheese Trail came from The Vermont Cheese Book.

Jamie Yturriondobetia, Cheesemaker,
Photo Courtesy of Shelburne Farms

Photos Courtesy of Shelburne Farms

VERMONT QUALITY DAIRIES: A CHANGE IN DIRECTION

John Cole and his partners came together to make yogurt and snacking cheese products. Cole was tired of milking cows for twenty years with little cash in his pocket. So in 2003, he and a small group of dairy farmers decided to turn some of the milk into yogurt and cheese for a better financial return on their labor. They formed Vermont Quality Dairies (VQD) and bought a defunct cheese plant in Hardwick.

The company made yogurt once or twice a month, but concentrated on its second product: fresh, unaged cheddar cheese in firm bite-sized curds, the kind of cheese French-Canadians eat with fries and gravy in a dish called poutine. The cheese was made weekly, packed in eight-ounce containers and driven to 150 Vermont stores. Cole and his partners found that they couldn't continue unless they made more cheese, supplied more outlets and found a distributor. Unfortunately, VQD went out of business in the fall of 2006 and the Vermont Milk Company (VMC) took over the plant. The Vermont Milk Company is a small dairy processor that's supplied with milk from a couple of local dairy farms.

THE VERMONT MILK COMPANY(VMC): A NEW MODEL

VMC produces yogurt, old fashioned cheddar cheese curds and ice cream under their own label or under contract for other firms. What's unique about the Vermont Milk Company is that the board of directors is made up of farmers. A group of private investors support the operation.

If you read the VMC website, you will see the following quote. "Too many farmers have been forced into the corporate circle, becoming powerless in their markets and enjoying little of the profits... Today, there is a growing trend to return to our sensible roots -- eating locally support our community and offers us fresher foods.

The Vermont Milk Company, founded with the goal of getting dairy farmers more money for their milk and more control over products made from it, VMC had to lay off some of its employees in August 2008. The company struggled in part because of higher fuel and milk prices as well as poor management decisions in developing its new dairy products. They went out of business in the fall of 2008.

Anthony Pollina, one of the founders of VMC and a highly visible political figure, who ran for Governor of Vermont in 2008 said, "It's not easy for farmers to gain control of their milk and rebuild a local dairy industry that has been taken over by a few big corporations..." He went on to say, "It reinforces for me the need to do everything possible to support local businesses and find new ways to help them lower costs and access capital. The bottom line is they need our support because what they are building is a very important model for Vermont."

"We always put our farmers first, knowing that if we do that, everyone wins, including the cows, our partners and customers." -VT Milk Company

AN AGRICULTURAL ENTREPRENEUR AND VISIONARY

Andrew Meyer is helping to define the future of agriculture in the town of Hardwick, Vermont by stretching the boundaries of niche marketing. Meyer's hope is that more farms and food processors will one day dot the hillsides of this Northeast Kingdom community with value-added farm products. Meyer's family owns North Hardwick Dairy, which is run by his brothers.

Hardwick, a town of about 3,000, has long suffered from economic depression and lack of employment. In 2005, a fire devastated the Bemis Block, a large historic building on Main Street. It has since been renovated and is home to Claire's Restaurant and Pub -- described earlier, the Buffalo Mountain Co-op and other businesses.

Meyer's philosophy is that entrepreneurs thrive when using local ingredients to sell value-added products New businesses will follow, for example, from turning the waste from one production line into the raw material for another. Take for instance, one of Meyer's companies, Vermont Natural Coatings, of which he is co-owner. The company is making a commercial clear wood furniture finish from whey protein, a by-product of the cheese making process. Toymaker Mike Rainville of Middlebury at Maple Landmark

Soybeans, USDA

Woodcraft is using batches of the wood finish on baby rattles and helping Meyer to refine the wood finish so it can be used in commercial applications.

With partner Todd Pinkham of Vermont Soy, Meyer is developing a fresh, organic soy milk drink and tofu. Todd established Vermont Soy 13 years ago with his wife in their kitchen where they began making tempeh -- fermented soybean cakes.

This newest venture of producing soymilk will be challenging as Vermont Soy will be competing with Silk brand soy owned by Dean Foods, the largest processor of dairy and soy products in the U.S. "It will taste better than anything you've ever had," declares Meyer, who compares mass-marketed soymilk to Kraft American cheese. He said, " Vermont Soy doesn't need to be the biggest producer in the land; it just needs to be the best."

Vermont Soy milk is different from commercial soy milk products because it has a 21 day shelf life, shorter than the Silk brand. It is the only authentic soy milk in the Northeast. The key is to educate customers to the quality of fresh Vermont soymilk, which is lightly pasteurized, organic and GMO free. According to Sophia Smith, the outreach and marketing coordinator for Vermont Soy, 2008 was the "take-off" year for Vermont Soy.

She told me it has taken a lot of coordination and cooperation with the state of Vermont, with private farm businesses like High Mowing Seeds of Wolcott, helping with the seed cleaning, Pete's Greens Winter CSA in Craftsbury for selling soymilk and Black River Produce for distribution. The mission is to make the highest quality soymilk in the northeast.

Soy production has already begun in Vermont Soy's 3000 square-foot plant at the Hardwick Industrial Park. Some people are concerned that Vermont Soy will be a threat to Vermont's dairy industry. Pinkham responded by saying, "Soy actually fits in nicely with Vermont agriculture. A lot of farms could benefit from using soybeans in crop rotations, and farmers might make money from growing soybeans." Only about a half dozen Vermont farmers grow soybeans for human consumption. Among them is Ken van Hazinga of Shoreham. Some soybeans come from the Champlain Valley of Vermont and a farmer from Quebec. An added advantage is that you can feed the meal left over from processing the soy beans to livestock.

Staff at Vermont Soy Checking Soybean Plants.
Photo Courtesy of Vermont Soy

Both the whey protein and most of the soybeans are now imported from other places like Michigan and Canada, but Meyer hopes that his soy businesses will provide an incentive for more in-state processing of whey protein and for farmers in the Hardwick area to put unused and marginal land into soybeans. The wood finish and soy products are only part of Meyer's larger vision of developing non-traditional products for farmers in Caledonia County. He would like to see the town of Hardwick become an agricultural center. Hardwick is a poor town in a poor part of Vermont, but life is changing. A meeting of farmers was held in the summer of 2006 in Hardwick to discuss soybean production and over 100 farmers attended. There are a number of soybean trials and test plots being tried all over Vermont. Ben Gleason of Bridport, who grows wheat, is taking part in the trials as is Bernard Rainville of Highgate.

The University of Vermont Agricultural Extension Service is participating in these experiments by contacting Vermont farmers interested in growing soybeans and helping to find harvesting and drying equipment. Some varieties were featured at the High Mowing Seeds Field Day in September of 2006. High Mowing is an organic/biodynamic seed company located close to Hardwick in the town of Wolcott.

The key is to find the appropriate soy varieties and be able to replicate them at different farms in Vermont. The goal is to grow about 200 acres, which would come to 37 tons of soybeans. Finding the right varieties is just one part of the formula. The other part is the technical assistance necessary to help farmers grow the organic beans along with the harvesting equipment. One idea floating around is to have a custom harvester (combine) that goes from farm to farm harvesting the beans. Other issues include equipment to clean and store the seeds along with proper storage facilities.

Vermont Soy markets its soy milk and tofu to natural food co-ops and food stores, general stores, and cafeterias at the University of Vermont, Dartmouth, Middlebury and Bennington Colleges, the Putney School and its newest customer, Fletcher Allen Hospital in Burlington, the largest hospital in the state. The artisan tofu is also different than commercial tofu in the that it uses large Japanese kettles. The tofu is organic and GMO free and contains no stabilizers or preservatives.

According to the Soyfoods Association of North America, soy food sales in the U.S. went from $300 million in 1992 to $4 billion in 2004. Bon Appetit ranked artisan tofu among one of the Hot 10 for 2007.

From left: June Van Houten, Highfields Institute; Andrew Meyer, Vermont Soy and Vermont Natural Coatings; Linda Ramsdell, Claire's Restaurant; Tom Stearns, High Mowing Organic Seeds; Andy Kehler, Jasper Hill Farm cheeses; Meg Gardner, Pete's Greens; and Monty Fischer, executive director of the Center for an Agricultural Economy

Photos of the new CEOs of the Northeast Kingdom. Photo Courtesy Jeb Wallace-Brodeur

THE NEW CEOs OF THE NORTHEAST KINGDOM

Andrew Meyers is part of a new group of CEOs engaged in value-added farm products in the Hardwick area. The non-profit group is called the Center for an Agricultural Economy and the board is made up of successful agricultural business owners from Hardwick, Greensboro, Craftsbury, Wolcott and East Johnson.

The aim of the Center is to promote a rural economy that links growers, manufacturers and consumers. The Center recently purchased Atkins Field, a 15.2-acre tract of land in Hardwick along the Lamoille River. It will eventually be the site of a year-round farmers' market, farm and forest land, and an agricultural education center. A community garden along with a greenhouse has been on the site for two years.

Atkins Field is the former historic home to the Woodbury Granite Company, which in the late 1800s and early 1900s was the primary employer in Hardwick. The Center plans to maintain the historic site while establishing a small-scale version of Burlington's Intervale Center which has a number of small organic farms, community gardens, trails and wildlife corridors.

Money for the purchase of Atkins Field came from the Vermont Housing and Conservation Trust, the Vermont Land Trust, along with private donations and loans. Acquisition of the property will protect 4.4 acres of bottomland by the Northern Rivers Land Trust as a valuable agricultural resource. The Vermont Housing Conservation Board and the Vermont Agency of Agriculture will hold a conservation easement on the property. * For more information on the Center for an Agricultural Economy, go to their website.

The CENTER for an AGRICULTURAL ECONOMY

THE SUSTAINABLE OWNERS BUSINESS NETWORK

What happens when a herb company needs help in writing a business plan or a farm family needs financing for the expansion of their cheesemaking operation? About two years ago, a group of farmers and food businesses in the Hardwick area starting meeting informally on a monthly basis to help each other solve problems like the ones mentioned above. The word got around and it wasn't long before the number of growers and producers expanded all the way to the Champlain Valley.

The Sustainable CEOs as they're sometimes called discuss cash-flow problems, accounting questions, and technical issues. Each meeting showcases one member's business, focuses on a topic of the host's choosing and features dinner. Some of the members are part of the Center for an Agricultural Economy. Their purpose is to focus on making their businesses more profitable.

In one case, Tom Stearns of High Mowing Seeds, asked if anyone could lend him money as his business was having cash flow problems during the spring when seeds orders were high and his credit line at the bank was tight. Two members of the group stepped up and lent him money for 45 days.

The 20 companies in the network are relatively small with sales ranging from $250,000 to $2 million. They employ from five to 25 employees each. They companies found that it was better to help each other rather than paying a consultant. They also know and trust one another. Most of them don't have a human resource manager, but are growing to the size where they may need one. If several companies pooled resources, they could share a manager.

Turning compost at Highfields

HIGHFIELDS INSTITUTE - COMPLETING THE CYCLE

I want to describe one of the Network businesses that's making a difference in terms of a sustainable food system. The work they do is not popular or well-known but in some ways its more critical than some other initiatives. I'm referring to the Highfields Institute, an educational group that works with farmers, schools, restaurants and waste districts to convert food and animal wastes into compost for use on farms.

Highfields continued ...

Tom Gilbert of Highfields Institute, estimates that 35 percent of the trash in the landfills in Vermont is made up of food scraps and organic wastes like leaves and grass clippings. Less than 10 percent of those food scraps and organic wastes are composted. Gilbert told me that if all those materials were composted, it would provide the enough nitrogen and other nutrients for growing 19,000 acres of mixed vegetables.

Local Examples: Two small schools in the Hardwick area produce 12 tons of compost each year and remove 600,000 tons of carbon. The food scraps are trucked to Highfields some 5 miles away. Lyndon State College with 1,500 students collects one ton of food scraps a week, which they compost on site. Highfields provides composting education and support.

Highfields consults with farmers on compost management and technical assistance, provides lectures and workshops, sets up food waste collection programs, and serves schools with composting education. They provide composting services to 6 solid waste districts, 60 businesses, 23 schools and 545 farms.

Many organic and conventional farmers in Vermont use compost to feed the soil that produces the plants that provide the food to households, schools, grocery stores and restaurants. It's one large circle. This is why Highfields is such an important slice of the food pie. For more information, go to www.highfieldsinstitute.org.

Photos Courtesy of Highfields Institute

THE RISING TIDE LIFTS ALL BOATS

The farmers and entrepreneurs in Hardwick who make up the CEOs of the Northeast Kingdom are helping others in the area with new food projects. Pete's Greens and High Mowing Seeds helped Theresa Snow start Salvation Farms - a gleaning project that brings fresh surplus vegetables from local farms to food shelves. In 2008, Salvation Farm joined the Vermont Foodbank to start a statewide gleaning system. Salvation Farms was described earlier in Part II. The CEOs are part of the Center for an Agricultural Economy.

Besides helping others, the CEOs of the Northeast Kingdom help each other. I'll explain. The three biggest challenges for value-added food businesses are infrastructure, financing and a sound business plan. And what happens if a business succeeds? Does it continue to grow? Does it diversify? And where do the capital and operating funds come from for the growth? Should the business be sold to a larger entity or does it maintain itself at a sustainable level? The CEOs are discussing these issues with one another. In a couple of cases they have made short-term loans to one of the enterprises.

Another issue that comes up for discussion is affordable food. It is one that I would like to address. Most people I know can afford artisan cheese now and then, however, it's not part of what they put in their grocery bag each week. I don't knock those farmers and processors who are trying to pay the bills. They can't be responsible for the economic well-being of society. They need to make a decent standard of living like everyone else; send their children to college; take a vacation once in a while. They deserve a fair return on their labor and a fair price for their farm products. There's a place in Vermont for all kinds of value-added products. Some are expensive and others are not-so-expensive. I'll leave it at that.

OTHER HARDWICK INITIATIVES

The Vermont Food Venture Center (VFVC) is planning to build a new facility in the Hardwick Industrial Park based on "Green" principles. VFVC was described earlier in Part 3. They are currently located in Fairfax. The new facility will provide space for value-added food businesses to grow when they emerge from the incubator stage. The space would also include a community food kitchen where vegetables could be canned and frozen. The Vermont Milk Company used to be located in the industrial park.

WHERE HAVE ALL THE SLAUGHTERHOUSES GONE?

Over the past decade the media has been full of stories concerning the health and safety of our meat supply. We have seen 10,000 cow feedlots and mountains of manure polluting our streams and rivers. We have seen pictures of animal cruelty. We have witnessed outbreaks of E. coli bacteria in our food supply and mad cow disease. Add to this the use of hormones for increased beef production and the greater use of antibiotics to stave off diseases. Why not throw in the possible introduction of cloned meat in the future to complete the picture.

Because of these troublesome issues and the demand for more local beef, it's critical that we support farmers who want to raise livestock. More farmers would raise meat if there were slaughterhouses nearby; and more farmers would raise meat if there were fewer state and federal regulations regarding on-farm slaughtering. In this last scenario, consumers could purchase meat from their farmer neighbors.

A Slaughterhouse Saga: Allen Cushing reopened Bushway's Slaughterhouse in February of 2007 in Grand Isle. In November, 2009, the slaughterhouse closed when workers were caught on video abusing day-old calves. Here is an earlier story.

Erik Wells' round trip to the Bushway's slaughterhouse with his pasture-raised beef cows was 12 miles. Before Cushing came along, Well's had to travel over 100 miles to Randolph - quite a cost in gas for this South Hero farmer as well as the other dairy farmers in the area.

Allen Cushing had owned Swanton Packing, but it closed in 2004. The Swanton Operation worked on high volume and narrow profit margins, processing about 100 beef cows and 300 calves a week. The problems included high overhead, increased workers' compensation insurance and higher costs for waste.

The slaughterhouse business is seasonal, with most of the demand in the fall when animals are taken for slaughter. Electricity use is high with coolers, freezers and equipment, along with the disposal of waste called rendering. Bushway's Slaughterhouse was a much smaller business. Cushing hoped to add a smoker to the operation and bring on family members as needed. By the summer of 2007 the operation had shut its doors. There are plans to reopen the business with three new investors.

Forty years ago, there were 18 commercial slaughterhouses in the state; now there are six certified slaughterhouses in Benson, Troy, St. Johnsbury, Braintree, Randolph, and Sharon. The beef industry in New England is small. In 2006, there were 1,000 beef operations in Vermont compared to 130,000 operations in the U.S. Still, Vermont accounted for 25 percent of the beef cows in New England -- 10,000 out of 40,000.

The slaughterhouse business is tough. Besides the hard physical work, worker turnover, and poor health benefits, workers' compensation is high because of the dangers of cutting meat and the many regulations. One custom slaughterer who didn't want his name mentioned told me the state of Vermont wanted him to open up a slaughterhouse, but they expected him to have a his and hers bathroom; and a separate area for an office. He showed them where the door was.

The lack of slaughterhouse facilities means farmers are forced to book months in advance and travel long distances. Erik Wells was booking three or four months ahead at a facility in Randolph, over a hundred miles away from the Bushway facility in Grand Isle. Some dairy and beef farmers in Vermont have to truck their animals as far as New York and Pennsylvania for slaughter.

As you can see, the distance between a slaughterhouse and a farmer can make all the difference in the world, especially with high gas prices. In December, 2006 a slaughterhouse fire in Athol, Massachusetts had local farmers in Massachusetts and southern Vermont scrambling to find a way to get their products to market. The tragedy had repercussions for anyone concerned about small-scale farming and eating locally. Judy Sopenski of Not Your Ordinary Farm in Guilford in southern Vermont is now facing much longer drives to take her sheep and hogs to slaughter. She plans to start using Blood Farm in West Groton, the sole remaining USDA slaughterhouse in Massachusetts.

To be sold commercially, animals must be slaughtered in a state or federally-certified facility. To be sold across state lines, only a facility certified by the USDA may be used. All six Vermont USDA certified slaughterhouses are in the central or northern part of the state. A closer alternative for southern Vermont farmers, Fresh Farm's Beef of Rutland, burned down in July 2006 and the owners do not plan to rebuild.

According to the livestock expert at the University of Vermont, demand is high in the fall when animals born in the spring are ready for slaughter. During the remainder of the year there is uneven demand, making it difficult to run a slaughterhouse at a profit. Farmers complain that they book a time with the slaughterhouse but then as the due date approaches, they keep getting pushed back. They say that some animals like lambs need to be slaughtered for Easter, which can't be delayed. Farmers also say that while they invest in high quality meat products, many of the cuts come out wrong.

Another Cushing: There is some hope on the horizon. Carl Cushing purchased Clark's Slaughterhouse in Ferrisburgh in 2007. It's now called Vermont Livestock Slaughter and Processing.

Cushing worked alongside the former owner, Bob Clark, for more than 30 years as a federal meat inspector.- so he knows all about the business from both ends of the cow. Some people think Cushing is a little crazy to be starting-up a slaughter business at age 54. Cushing doesn't believe he has gone off his rocker, as the location of his operation is well positioned -- on the border of Addison and Chittenden counties -- in the heart of farm country. Cushing grew up on a small family farm in Milton, Vermont.

Cushing told me that the high cost running his operation is a heavy burden to take on especially when it's so difficult to get local banks to lend you any money. While the Vermont Agency of Agriculture talks up the idea of local slaughterhouses, they provide little financial and technical support. Add on the numerous federal health regulations and you've got yourself quite a challenge.

Carl Cushing

Vermont Ski Burgers: A partnership between the Vermont Agency of Agriculture, Vermont Ski Areas Association, and Vermont Beef Producers in 2007 brought a Vermont burger to the ski slopes. Over 8,000 burgers were consumed by December. "This fits right into our Buy-Local campaign," said Roger Allbee, Secretary of the Vermont Agency of Agriculture. Under the partnership, the ski resorts pay a premium back to farmers, which help a number of beef producers find a steady market for their animals.

VERMONT SMOKE & CURE

This Vermont business started in 1962 as Roland's. The Farmers Diner bought the business in 1999. In 2005, Chris Bailey of Vermont Smoke & Cure took over the reins and formed a separate company but retained strong ties to the Farmers Diner and the original Roland business. Their mission has been to "Keep Vermont Farmers Smokin" with their two labels: Vermont Smoke & Cure and Farmers Diner. The business promotes its two labels "with a commitment to old-fashioned traditional smoked meats with natural pure ingredients prepared in small batches." Vermont Smoke & Cure brines their bacon and ham with maple syrup from Northfield, using a low salt solution and then slowly smoking the meat with corncobs and maple wood. Previously, the Farmers Diner brand contained at least 50 percent locally produced meats in the sausages and bacon. In 2008, that percentage moved closer to 100 percent. One farmer from St. Albans provides ten pigs a week to the company. Most of the pork for the Vermont Smoke & Cure brand comes from Quebec.

Some new products coming out are smoked turkey from Misty Knoll Farm in New Haven and hot dogs from Vermont and New Hampshire farmers that are processed in Massachusetts. Vermont Smoke and Cure also provides smoked meats to other Vermont businesses such as Shelburne Farms, which has their own label. Pork sold by other Vermont companies, such as Dakin Farm, Harrington's and McKenzie comes from pigs raised in Pennsylvania, the Midwest and the southeastern states. According to R.B. Klinkerberg, chief operating office of Harrington's of Vermont, which sells thousands of hams by mail order, there is virtually no hog production in the State.

Vermont Grown Pigs: Walter Jeffries of Sugar Mountain Farm in West Topsham provides one source of genuine Vermont hams. He said that Vermont lacks the infrastructure to sustain hog farming on a broad commercial scale because it's basically a "cow state." Jeffries said that most Vermont-raised pigs forage outdoors on pasture, while those imported to Vermont have been confined in pens where they are fattened with corn and soybeans. He went on to add, "You are what you eat." His pigs get hay and whey from Vermont Butter & Cheese in Westerville, cheese trimmings from Cabot, and boiled barley from the Stonecutter Brewery in Barre. According to Jeffries, there is no comparison in the taste between his pork and commercial pork.

I know this for a fact because I raised hogs on my farm in Saxton's River. The meat was sweet and light tasting and far more flavorful than what you buy in the supermarket. My pigs were pastured out and fed lots of discarded veggies along with corn grown from my fields.

Breeds also affect taste, according to Christa Alexander of Jericho Settlers' Farm in Jericho. The Tamworth and Bershire pigs she raises are known around town "for the flavor of their meat."

Most pig raisers like Alexander and Jeffries can't compete on price with large, industrial pig operations, but they can be successful in providing a high-quality pork product.

Not all pigs raised in Vermont roam pasture land. At the Duclos & Thompson Farm in Weybridge, some 50 hogs are kept in pens and fed grains. But they're not given hormones or antibiotics and the pork is sold at restaurants, health food stores and food co-ops.

Dakin Farms of Ferrisburg sells a lot of hams in-state and through mail-order. According to Sam Cutting IV, the smoking process is the key to creating the taste of pork. He still uses corn cobs to produce the meat's distinctive taste. Cutting said, "Though they're not Green Mountain oinkers, most of the pigs the company sells come from small scale farms in Pennnsylvania's Amish country.

Another local porker is McKenzie's, which still bills itself as "Vermont's Original Purveyor of Specialty Meats." Founded in 1909, today it operates a distribution center in Burlington. It is now called, McKenzie Country Classics, a division of Massachusetts based Kayem Foods, Inc.

THE MOBILE SLAUGHTER-HOUSE

In 2007, the state proposed buying a couple of mobile processing facilities for chickens and small animals. The mobile processing of beef and other large animals isn't practical.

In 2009, the mobile poultry slaughter unit became available to Vermonters for use on small chicken farms. The unit cost $200,000. It's the first of its kind in the US to process poultry right on the farm.

Processing is a serious issue in Vermont and this mobile unit will help to ensure that agriculture remains viable for farmers of all sizes. The unit is approximately 36 feet long. It is estimated that, with a crew of two, the mobile slaughter unit will be able to process 200 chickens and 50 turkeys per day. In Vermont farmers raise over 51,000 turkeys a year which translate to an economic impact of over 1.8 million dollars.

Anson Tebbetts, former Deputy Secretary of the Vermont Agency of Agriculture said that the mobile slaughterhouse makes it easier and more affordable for farmers to have their poultry USDA inspected.

A M E R I C A N
FLATBREAD®

ALL NATURAL PIZZA BAKED IN A WOOD-FIRED OVEN

THE CHICKEN EVENT

George Schenk, the owner and CEO of American Flatbread wanted to buy his neighbor's chickens but the state of Vermont said no. Hadley Gaylord, the neighbor, grows vegetables, and raises pork, beef and chickens. In the fall of 2006, Hadley's daughter was busted for selling chickens at the Montpelier farmer's market. At the time -- early 2006 -- Vermont allowed only inspected chickens to be sold at restaurants.

George Schenk Being Served Papers
by Local Police.

Hadley Gaylord said, "There isn't a place to slaughter the chickens for sixty miles. It's a lot of time back and forth - if you can get in - and it's money out of my pocket. So I process them on the farm myself and sell what I can from the farm stand ... The rules and regulations that govern animal protein processing were written by and for large producers and make it almost impossible for the small guy to compete."

On June 6, 2006, the Chicken Event was planned at American Flatbread in Waitsfield. The event was to be a public act of civil disobedience in support of local agriculture. George Schenk planned to host the event at his bakery and restaurant, American Flatbread, to raise awareness of the regulatory obstacles small farmers face; and to engage the community in a public conversation. One of the questions being raised was why does the food system make it easy and cheap to buy industrial-processed chicken from a thousand miles away, but, make it virtually impossible to buy chicken from the local farmers down the road?

Two days before the event, the Vermont Secretary of Health said she would serve an injunction prohibiting Schenk from using Gaylord's chickens at American Flatbread. Then the state backed off and said they were willing to sit down and discuss the issue. Three representative came from the Vermont Agency of Agriculture and answered questions to the crowd of 400 people. It was the largest small chicken event ever to take place in the Green Mountains. The protests resulted in hearings that took place in the Vermont legislature in the winter of 2007.

In the spring of 2007, the Vermont legislature passed a bill that allowed Vermont chicken farmers to raise, slaughter and sell up to 1,000 birds to the public, including restaurants and farmers' markets. These chickens would not be inspected by the federal government.

Restaurants would be required to state that they have uninspected chicken on the menu. Farmers would be required to get a signed statement from the restaurant that the meat was not inspected. Currently, 23 other states allow farmers to sell their chickens to restaurants. The three states bordering Vermont are among them.

In summer 2008, five restaurants were serving uninspected chicken from Vermont farms. These eateries are listed on the Vermont Agency of Agriculture website. The largest response has taken place at over 20 farmers' markets in the state where uninspected chicken is a big hit.

Comments on Rabbits, Turkeys and Chickens: Rabbit meat does not require inspection yet many Vermont restaurants serve it. They don't have to label it as uninspected on the menu. Rep. Dexter Randall, a former progressive legislator from Troy, said he has been raising turkeys for 20 years. He can sell directly to the consumer but not to restaurants. Randall argued that small local farms are cleaner than large operations.

Sharon Moffat, acting State Health Commissioner, said she wouldn't eat any uninspected poultry served in a restaurant as it poses increased exposure to bacteria, including salmonella. She said that inspection ensures that birds are killed the right way and are clear of any fecal matter.

Robin McDermott is a leader in the localvore movement in the Mad River Valley. She's had some comments to make about local chicken. McDermott purchased a large fowl from her neighbor, Hadley Gaylord, for a whopping $15. She originally thought it was more of an investment than a purchase. She was also aware that the price of factory-farmed meat is cheap, but you get what you pay for. Just look at the external costs of pollution, poor nutrition, bad health, and lack of taste.

McDermott said, "With only two of us in my family I cut the bird in half and remove the breasts. That is at least one dinner or two if I stir-fry the meat. I remove the legs and thighs and pop them in the freezer for another meal. The rest goes into a pot of soup which will give us another couple of meals. So for the $15 investment, I have gotten 5 meals -- not a bad deal at all! It is much more economical to buy the whole bird than the parts." And, as was pointed out in Eric Schlosser's, *Fast Food Nation,* commercial chicken parts may come from chickens who have been maimed or who are otherwise less than perfect to sell as a whole bird."

Photos Courtesy of
American Flatbread

A LOT OF NASTY THINGS HAPPEN TO USDA AND STATE INSPECTED FOOD.

Personally, I am much more afraid of getting sick from food that comes from the industrial food system than from Gaylord's chickens. I don't buy any meat, especially that fatty chicken from the local supermarket unless it's local.

My friend Elizabeth raises hens for eggs and meat. The local mobile butcher chap drives up to her home on Bliss Pond in his chicken truck to slaughter the birds. Elizabeth cuts up the whole bird and freezes the parts. She figures it costs a little less than purchasing organic chickens but not much less due to the high cost of organic feed. If she had more land, the meat birds could range more freely and the costs of feed would be less. I provide lots of greens and corn from my garden. And just think of all that good compost that's comes from the chicken manure and sawdust.

CONTAMINATION AND FOODBORNE DISEASES:

Just look at the contamination of our food supply in the past couple of years from hamburger meat, peanut butter, spinach, lettuce, peanuts and pistachios.

HERE ARE A COUPLE MORE RECALLS:

• Baby formula had melamine

• Cerignola Olives from Florida -- contamination from a bacterium. . Mineral Water from Armenia -- contamination from arsenic.

• Simply Fresh Cut Fruit Trays -- salmonella poisoning.

• 90 products from chili sauce to corned beef hash to dog food -- contaminated with botulism. Castleberry's Food Co, closed the suspect plant.

• Tomatoes caused salmonella poisoning in the summer of 2008. It was found later that the bacteria came from peppers in Mexico.

The Centers for Disease Control estimate 76 million people suffer from foodborne illnesses each year in the U.S., accounting for 325,000 hospitalizations and 5,000 deaths. The main ones are botulism, campylobacteriosis, E. coli, and salmonellosis.

THE NATIONAL ANIMAL IDENTIFICATION SYSTEM

The most recent challenge to small family farms in the U.S. is the National Animal Identification System. (NAIS) The so-called purpose of this government run program is to protect the health of U.S. livestock and poultry by being able to quickly and effectively trace an animal disease to its source. When an animal outbreak occurs, animal health officials need to know which animals are involved, where they are located and what other animals might be exposed.

While NAIS is voluntary, money received by some states from the USDA will be used to make some parts or all of the program mandatory. There will be a computer based premises identification number along with a computerized animal identification number and an animal tracking system.

Some of the concerns with NAIS include financial, civil rights and religious aspects. The cost of the program will be high and some fear it will drive small farmers out of business due to the cost of having each animal registered. Small farmers and families will have to register and pay a registration fee for every head of livestock or poultry, while corporate farms with large herds and flocks or more than 30,000 chickens will only have to pay the fee equivalent to owning one animal. This will result in hastening the decline of the small family farm.

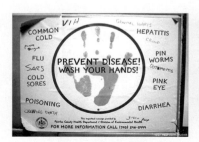
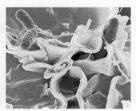

Salmonella bacteria

There are also civil rights concerns as NAIS establishes extensive government control over livestock, which are considered private property. What if I raise 25 chickens on my small farm in rural Vermont? Does the government have the right to make me put a computerized chip on each one of my birds? As you can see, NAIS is very controversial.

In Wisconsin, NAIS has been made mandatory, with the ability to allow exemptions for small farms. Another concern is that the system is not maintained by state government, but instead relies upon the Wisconsin Livestock Identification Consortium (WLIC) to maintain the database of Premises ID registrants.

Side Notes:

Many folks call NAIS a lunatic system that is akin to the Marx Brothers bumbling around Animal Farm. Can you imagine a bunch of chicken trackers running around your chicken yard in the name of homeland security? I'm told this new surveillance program is there to protect me and those around me from a new security threat called terrorist chickens. And then there are terrorist cows, pigs, and llamas.

Advanced under the guise of protecting public health from outbreaks of animal-borne diseases, this program is intended to track every farm animal in American from birth to death. It's one thing if this was meant for large factory farms run by agribusiness, which account for the vast number of disease outbreaks. But why should my twenty odd chickens need microchips? Stay tuned on this one.

Source: Hightower Lowdown, September 2007.

* For more information on NAIS, go to www.familyfarm-defenders.org,
www.themeatrix.com,
You can also check the Rural Vermont and Family Farm Defenders websites for more information.

The problem is that WLIC is made up of large, private agribusiness groups, including Cargill, Genetics/Biotect Corporations and the like.

Finally, fears persist about plans to make NAIS mandatory, which would threaten the religious freedom of those who believe that making a "mark" is sinful, such as the Amish. The Amish also object to the use of electronic devices such as microchips.

On June 25th, over 70 organizations including Family Farm Defenders sent letters to Congress not to connect NAIS to the federal School Lunch Program. The 2009 Agricultural Appropriations Bill would require the School Lunch Program to buy only meat from farms that have registered under NAIS. This proposal would discriminate against small scale producers who have chosen not to participate in NAIS. If passed, this proposal would force many local farm-to-school lunch programs that use grassfed meat into the cafeterias to go back to factory meat suppliers.

J. THE EAT LOCAL/SLOW FOOD/ LOCALVORE MOVEMENT

By now, you've heard the mantra time and again -- "think global- act local." In the best of worlds, I want to know the farmers and how they grow the food I'm buying. That's why farmers' markets are so popular. You meet the farmers and talk to them about how they grow the food or process the jam and pickles or make the loaf of bread. It all has to do with making connections. Food co-ops and natural-food stores do the same when they have local-food displays in which there is a picture of the farmers and the farm. The restaurants served by the Vermont Fresh Network have cards on their tables also show pictures of the farmer and the farm.

Two long-time organic farmers from New York, Mark Dunau and Elizabeth Henderson, put it well when they said, "In this act of creation, the farmer offers the consumer sustenance, taste, and the sense of connection to the land that is so lacking in modern life. In buying from local farmers, consumers allow them to continue this ancient human craft, to raise families, and to survive in the global marketplace."

Coming Home to Eat: In the last few years, new movements to connect consumers to local farmers have sprung up under several different names, including Slow Food, Eat-Local, Beyond Organic and Localvores. The most recent wave of converts are the "Localvores," people who choose to eat as much food as possible that is grown within 100 miles of their homes. They are sprouting up all around Vermont and the country.

Of course, the localvores could learn a lot from the folks who lived two hundred years ago, when Vermont was largely self-sufficient. Rural people depended on growing crops and raising livestock, root cellaring and "putting food by" for the winter. In the late 19th century and earlier, rural families grew and processed their own food and sold some of their cash crops at the local general stores. The localvores may be a new movement but consumers have been connecting to local farmers for thousands of years in villages, towns and cities.

HISTORY OF SELF-SUFFICIENCY IN THE GREEN MOUNTAINS

Let's go back in time. We can learn much from our forbearers and then move on to the present.

Over 75 years ago, in 1923, in the towns of Randolph and Royalton, 98 percent of households kept vegetable gardens, 97 percent had milk cows and poultry, 93 percent grew potatoes, 58 percent raised pigs, and 54 percent had apple trees. Maple syrup provided sweetening, hard cider provided drink, and processed vegetables, berries, and meat were enjoyed year-round. Canning, pickling, and smoking and root cellaring were common practices.

Corn was the other favorite food. It appeared as cornmeal mush, cornbread, "Johnnycakes," or succotash -- corn and beans. Vermonters grew two types of corn. The first type was sweet corn, such as Golden Bantam -- eaten fresh off the cob or stripped from the cob and cooked for succotash. The other was flint corn, which was a harder variety, dried and ground into cornmeal or used for grain to feed livestock.

Two foods central to the New England diet in the early 20th century and back in colonial times were beans and corn. Baked beans were a staple in those days. The beans would be soaked and left to simmer for one night and then baked all day in the wood oven the next day. The favorites were Soldier, Jacob's cattle, yellow beans and Vermont cranberry.

Source: University of Vermont Agricultural Experiment Station

Food Canning Workshop, Photo Courtesy Mad River Localvores, Waitsfield

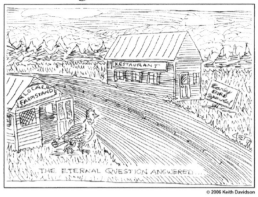

Celebrating Local Food in Vermont

© 2006 Keith Davidson

Other crops, such as potatoes, eggs, dried beans and parsnips were often traded for goods at the local general store. Some older folks still refer to doing their grocery shopping as "trading." In those days, rural families purchased only those foods they couldn't grow on the farm, such as flour, salt, spices, and dried cod. Some farmers did grow wheat, oats, rye and barley.

Life was organized around planting, weeding, berrying, harvesting, threshing, canning, and, of course, milking the family cow for milk, butter and cheese. In the fall, beans were threshed and sorted, apples were cored and then dried or stored, hard cider was made, and flint corn was dried.

During the winter, folks ate all the food they had put by along with salt pork, beef and dried cod. Root crops went into stews along with corned beef for a New England boiled dinner. The next day beets were added and it was called red flannel hash. By the time spring arrived, there was a craving for greens. Parsnips were dug, and dandelion greens, nettles, ramps, and fiddleheads were gathered along with horseradish root.

Source: Nickerson, Ginger. "Revisiting the Traditional." Local Banquet, Summer 2007.
* If one were to go back to the Vermont Agency of Agriculture archives, a treasure of town reports is available on food and farming, including the need to "go local."

THE PRESENT

Gary Nabhan's book, *Coming Home to Eat*, details his efforts to live for one year on food grown or caught within 250 miles of his home in Flagstaff, Arizona. Nabhan stresses the need to support small-scale, sustainable farms, as they protect cultural and biological diversity, food safety and local economies. Eating local also saves the environment from fossil fuels. He said "Organic is great." We don't want to stop that. But if we're getting organic carrots from halfway across the country, we're gaining one thing and losing another."

Nabhan spoke in the late fall of 2003 to 80 Vermonters gathered at Shelburne Farms, a Vanderbilt estate built in the mid-1800s and one of the loveliest spots along Lake Champlain, when looking across to the Adirondack Mountains. He said, "I am reconnecting what I think is the biggest disconnect in America today -- the link between food producers and food consumers." The participants were served Shelburne Farms cheddar cheese, local jams, apples and

Bill McKibben
Author, Environmentalist,
Activist.

honey, and bread baked from Vermont and New York grains, along with apple cider and pine tea, which kept everyone warm and enthusiastic. The event was part of the "slow-food movement," in contrast to our current "fast-food movement.".

Closer To Home: Let me tell you a story of environmentalist Bill McKibben and how he and his family lived almost entirely on food close to home in Ripton, Vermont for seven months during the long winter months and early spring of 2004.

McKibben purchased food from local farmers and stores that sold Vermont products. If you visited him in January, he might have given you a plate of oatmeal cookies made from local butter, honey, maple syrup and eggs, wheat from Ben Gleason's farm down the road, and rolled oats from Quebec (about 75 miles away), along with a mug of hot apple cider from Champlain Orchards in Shoreham. Bill likes beer and he was lucky, as a local brewer, Otter Creek, makes an organic beer with wheat from Gleason's farm.

McKibben acknowledges that some local products cost more like the beer and that it takes time to put food by, to get to the right stores, and to travel to the source of some foods. His family could not always afford the higher cost of local organic chicken and beef, so they did what more than four-fifths of the people in the world do, and that is eat more beans and less meat. He said we should think of meat as an ingredient in a stir-fry rather than an entree.

Side Notes:

Some part-time cynics like me believe it's a bit elitist when the slow-food movement touts dishes such as slow-cured hams, which are just too expensive for many folks. You shouldn't have to make lots of gelt to join a movement or eat local food.

On the other hand, eating more traditional/less processed food is part of a healthy lifestyle. We need to eat nutritious food because we can't afford ill health. It all has to do with balance. The choice is yours according to your values and pocketbook. I buy as much local as possible when I can afford it. 🌿

Home Canning, Courtesy Mad River Localvores, Waitsfield

MORE MCKIBBEN THOUGHTS

• The cost of eating locally during the winter was not necessarily more expensive and it's more environmentally friendly to freeze local broccoli when its available in the summer than to buy it fresh from California during the winter.

• Although organically raised food is in principle a good thing, I prefer locally grown - if I have to choose one or the other. As national corporations have entered the market, organic food often travels long distances.

• Most people don't have time to bake bread or can tomatoes, but there is a price to be paid when we purchase food sent all the way across the country. I figure many Vermonters could get at least 30 percent of their food from Vermont-grown meat, dairy products, eggs, bread, and other products available year-round without changing much about how they eat. Today I add chocolate chips to my oatmeal cookies and eat bananas like the rest of you.

Some of the material for this story came from an article in the July 2005 issue of Gourmet magazine. He is best known for his book The End of Nature.
McKibben has written a number of books, including Deep Economy: The Wealth of Communities and the Durable Future.

* Barbara Kingsolver's new book, Animal, Vegetable and Mineral, traces the story of how her family decided to journey away from the industrial food pipeline to a rural life in which they vowed to buy only food raised in their own neighborhood, grow it themselves, or learn to live without it. Animal, Vegetable and Mineral makes a passionate case for putting the kitchen back at the center of family life.

Slow Food USA©

The Slow Food Movement has been called the "Anti-Fast-Food" movement in the U.S. It is part of an international movement started in 1986 when Italian author Carlo Petrini, incensed by a McDonald's opening near his home in Rome, accused the corporate chain of destroying local foods and traditions. The movement urges people to find time for meals made from scratch, and extols the benefits of regional foods and recipes using all-natural foods grown by local farmers. Patrick Martins, director of Slow Food USA, says, "It's about slowing down, respecting people's natural rhythms and reacquainting people with the ritual of the table."

Slow Foods International: In October of 2004, nearly 5,000 small-scale farmers, food makers, nomadic herders and foragers from 128 countries came together in Turin, Italy for an international conference on Slow Food.

There were Kyrgyz men in felt hats who made a fermented yak drink. Argentine farmers passed around horns of yerba mate, a green tea; and women from a cooperative in the Himalayas shared a sweet-smelling apricot powder.

Slow Food Continued...

"It's just wonderful to be able to connect," said Penny Marshall, an organic farmer from Alberta, Canada, who was looking for heirloom potatoes. She met with South American growers hoping to develop markets. Mohammad Naser Jami from Herat, Afghanistan was looking for raisin producers. He brought 32 varieties from his farm. He said that raisins are a main crop in his country, but the war has damaged international sales.

Many of the delegates had never traveled far from home, much less heard of Slow Food. In the 18 years of its existence, the movement has spread to 80 countries, with 81,000 members. The staff, with the help of many non-profit organizations and universities, researched and recruited farmers from developing nations.

Source: The information on Slow Foods International was taken from: Bowen, Dana. "A Food Festival, Coffee to Caterpillars." New York Times, 27 Oct. 2004.
* For more information on the slow-food movement, go to www. slowfood.com.

* "Come to the Table" was the motto of Slow Food '08 Labor Day weekend when 60,000 people gathered in San Francisco to eat organic food, meet local farmers and listen to panel discussions about the future of sustainable agriculture. The plaza in front of City Hall was turned into a fruit and vegetable garden along with outdoor markets. The crowds were large, the lines were long and almost all the events were sold out.

VOTE for Small Farms & Local Food

Join Slow Food U.S.A.

SLOW FOOD USA supports sustainable farms and producers at farmers markets across the country

For more information visit www.slowfoodusa.org

Eating is an agricultural act
Wendell Berry

SLOW MONEY -- A TANGENT TO SLOW FOOD

There is now a movement afoot called "Slow Money – Slow Food." It began as a protest against McDonald's, but it quickly turned into supporting pro-small-farm initiatives. Similarly, Slow Money seeks to support the creative powers of entrepreneurship and build new commercial relationships between farmers, food consumers and their local communities.

What's behind Slow Money? Slow folks would say that venture capitalists are stuck in a 19th century way of thinking that leads to large-scale, centralized production and power generation. This is the result of the inefficient use of capital that has ended up with cheap food, millions of acres of GMO corn, billions of food miles in transportation costs, dying Main Streets, dead zones such as the Gulf of Mexico, and the obesity epidemic that exists side by side with persistent hunger. Look at two examples of over-specialization: colony collapse in bees and drug-resistant staph in humans. Whenever we try to rearrange natural systems along the lines of a factory or machine, we come out the losers.

Speed is a part of the problem. Take for example, the loss of fertility in the soil. Over half of the topsoil in the midwest has been removed in the last 100 years. The problems we face with respect to soil fertility, biodiversity, food quality and local economics could be solved in part through financial investment in long-term small-scale solutions. In a world of monocultures and special interests, the emergence of for-profit companies combined with public benefits is worthy of support.

THE LOCALVORE MOVEMENT

Besides the "slow fooders," there is another major grassroots movement sweeping the country by the name "localvores." They're dedicated to eating food grown locally, within 100 miles of home. The original localvores started in the San Francisco Bay area with a commitment to eat only foods grown within a 100-mile radius for the month of August in 2005. Groups all over New England took up "the challenge" and planned events in August and September of 2006.

At that time, there were 7 localvore groups in Vermont -- from the Champlain Valley to Montpelier to the Mad River Valley, west to the Upper Valley, east to Rutland and south to Brattleboro. The groups sponsored what they called the "localvore challenge." In 2007, the number increased to ten groups.

Each group in 2006 determined how it wanted to honor the challenge -- how far away the food could be grown and whether they would eat food within that distance for one meal a week, for one week, or for one month. Often the groups started with a potluck of locally grown foods along with a speaker, discussion and local treats. In many cases, the food was organic.

The challenge was to find enough local food that would provide nutritionally balanced, delicious meals. In order to encourage more people to eat local, the localvores in the Mad River Valley invited people to choose "wild cards" such as spices, coffee or chocolate, which weren't local.

Garden Workshop, Mad River Localvores

The idea wasn't to be the "food police," but to challenge people to eat as many locally grown foods as possible. Some localvore groups allowed participants to consume locally produced products even if they didn't contain 100 percent indigenous ingredients, such as Vermont-brewed beers and Vermont-roasted coffees. Sophie Quest, who is 72 and lives in South Burlington, said the hardest thing for her to give up were the Turkish apricots in her oatmeal.

The Champlain Valley Localvores came up with the "Marco Polo" exemption, which permits any spices from the 13th-century, explorer like salt and pepper. The Mad River group invited local restaurants, bed-and-breakfasts and inns to offer at least one localvore meal or menu item during the challenge week. They also asked grocery stores in the valley to stock and label their shelves with Vermont-grown products. The Mad River localvores worked with local elementary schools to serve one meal each day for a week.

Robin McDermott, a spokesperson for the local-vore movement, said there are many hidden costs of not eating locally -- such as the billions of tax dollars spent subsidizing multi-national corporations, the expense of excess packaging that fills up our landfills, and the environmental toll that industrial agriculture takes on our water, air, and soil.

Another thing that the localvore challenge forced people to do was to look at how much money they spend on food. One might here the following comment. "So maybe I spent a little more on the local broccoli for a stir fry with wheatberries, but I didn't spend money on ChexMix, a snack at a gas station, or pre-prepared meals at the supermarket."

One of the positive results of the challenge was that it built awareness of where food comes from and how it is grown, processed and transported. Folks learned that it's not easy to eat local. There aren't cooking oils or oil for salads and it's even hard to find local apple cider vinegar. It was clear that change would come but it would take time and ingenuity. Consumers are beginning to demand products that can be grown and produced close to home. The key is to communicate with farmers and processors before the growing season begins.

One of the localvore challenges was the need to find locally grown grain. I know of only three bakeries -- Red Hen, Trukenbrod and Good Companion -- that make loaves from regional grains. There are only a handful of established grain growers in Vermont, even though the number is increasing every year. Pete Johnson of Pete's Greens commissions two bread makers for his CSA in Greensboro.

Besides wheat, there are other products consumers wish to buy locally. Here is a list of organic food items. All of these are highly sought after and hard to find. They are part of the starter/localvore kit. The cost for the kit was $25.00 in 2007. It should be pointed out that the monies were used for fundraising purposes. It was not the actual cost of the kit.

LOCALVORE STARTER KIT FROM THE MAD RIVER VALLEY

- 1 lb Cornmeal - Butterworks Farm, Westfield
- 1 lb. Whole wheat flour - Gleason Grains, Bridport
- 1 lb. Wheat Berries - Gleason Grains
- 1 lb. Yellow-eye beans - Hazen Bean Company, North Hero
- 1 qt. Cider Vinegar - Honest to Goodness, Vershire
- 1 lb. Popping corn - Brignate's Farm, Colchester
- 1 c. Sunflower oil Butterworks Farm, Westfield
- 1 lb. Rolled oats - Michel Gourdreau's, Compton, Quebec

Dried cranberries from Vermont and sea salt from Maine were added to the kit in 2008.

Finding enough local food is tricky. The farms mentioned above would have to expand their operations to supply the needs of the local consumers. New and current farm initiatives are needed to meet the demand for grains, beans, oil and juices. There are lots of gaps in the larder. It will take time, investment, ingenuity, and a willingness by the farmers to take on "the challenge," as well as support by the citizenry.

Farmers need to be encouraged to grow wheat for flour, canola for oil, soy for soy products, and more value-added products made from Vermont products. Why not a Vermont beef stew made up of beef, potatoes, carrots, turnips, garlic and onions? Of course, families need to do more home processing and meal preparation together. This means a lifestyle change is in order.

Photos Courtesy Mad River Localvores, Waitsfield, Vermont

Early Winter Greens

Digging Carrots in the Fall

Separating Root Crops

Mid Winter

Canning Cabbage

FROM THE SUMMER 2006 LOCALVORE CHALLENGE - MAD RIVER VALLEY

- 155 total participants

- 85 percent felt that one week was just right for the challenge.

- The most used resource was the Mad River Valley website with many recipes.

- Over half ate out at restaurants that used local ingredients.

- Over half would like to see a late fall/winter farmer's market and continued potlucks, films, and workshops.

- 70 percent would like to attend a workshop on home canning, root cellaring, freezing, making cheese, veggie gardening and raising eggs from hens.

- Over half would like a one-week winter challenge.

- Over 1000 consumers in Vermont participated in the localvore challenge in August of 2006. Localvore challenges will continue into the future.

A DISCUSSION ON THE LOCALVORE CHALLENGE:

The localvore challenge is an educational process. It was driven home to many who participated in the challenge just how unavailable certain foods were. You try to make a recipe but you get stymied as you realize what's not locally available.

Bill McKibben said earlier that if you could purchase 30 percent of your food locally, that would be significant. What the localvore movement may help to do in the long run is to educate consumers about the issues, i.e., where food comes from, how far it travels including transportation costs, and the energy needed to grow and produce it.

People's consciousness needs to be raised on what's available and what's not available locally. Consumers need to make more connections with farmers as well as be willing to support more local food initiatives like food processing centers. And they need to share their concerns with their political representatives.

Nicole Carpenter, one of the leaders in the localvore movement in Burlington believes we can't afford not to eat locally. She doesn't agree with those that say that eating locally is for people with money or time on their hands. Carpenter sites the data from Pat McGovern of the Upper-Valley localvore group in the Connecticut River Valley, who recorded all her food consumption during an eat-local week in April of 2007. The total was $50.26. This compares favorably with the food budget for the average American which was estimated to be $68 for a one-person-one-wage-earner family in 2005.

Side Notes:

That last figure seems a little high to me. My food costs are a little lower than what Pat McGovern spends, but then again, I'm rather cheap. I've always been a frugal food shopper, buy whole foods in bulk like oats and other grains and grow a lot of my own vegetables. I also can and freeze vegetables during the growing season, prepare most of my food from scratch and store root crops, onions, potatoes and squash during the cold months. I also don't have a family to support and I have the time to process and prepare food.

Nicolle Carpenter makes some good points. She says that our industrial food system has created soil erosion, aquifer depletion and decreased water quality. She points out that farmers receive 7 cents on the dollar, inputs cost 20 cents and distribution, processing, packaging and transportation come to 73 cents. She addresses the low nutritional value of fast foods and how our health care costs have risen due to the obesity epidemic caused in large part from fast junk food.

Carpenter ends by saying that buying more food from local farmers puts money back into the local economy, keeps more of the land in agricultural production, uses less fossil fuel and keeps fewer pollutants in our waterways along with fewer health care costs. These all make sense. ❧

Some shoppers are going back to Home Economics 101 like the Hamiltons. Jean Hamilton, 25, and her husband Caleb, 27, of Richmond who have found creative ways to afford their commitment to healthy eating. The couple recently put up 20 pints of strawberry jam. Jean Hamilton said she couldn't afford to buy pints of raspberries and blueberries in the grocery store but can afford to take time to pick the fruit from a local berry farmer and freeze it, or make pies and jam.

The Hamiltons bought a share from a local farmer for 60 pounds of beef and pork. They purchase their food in bulk, shop at the local co-op and farmers' market and grow some of their produce. In the winter months, they store squash, potatoes, and onions in a cool place in their home. And finally, they said, "what could be better than making pesto and home-made bread together."

Most families can't do what the Hamilton family did. Many people don't have gardens, time, access or transportation to local farms.

However, they can make some changes like buying in bulk, joining a food-buying club or purchasing produce at the local farmers' market. They can also grow some of their food in a community garden plot. Finally, consumers can learn how to be smart shoppers, such as buying items on sale and staying on the outside rows of the supermarket where there are fewer processed foods.

The Poor: In January 2007, the coordinators of the various localvore groups in Vermont began meeting in Montpelier. One of their concerns was the increasing amount of hunger in Vermont and how eating local healthy food should not only be for the middle class and wealthy but for everyone in the community. Many local foods are sold at premium prices which prohibit poor people from purchasing local products.

THE VERMONT FOOD BANK BUYS WARREN LANDMARK FARM

The Mad River Localvore group has taken up the hunger issue by donating $1,400 to the local food shelf. In 2008, they joined with other groups including the Mad River Valley Planning District, the Friends of the Mad River and the Warren Conservation Trust to purchase the 20-acre Kingbury Farm whose sole purpose will be to provide produce to the Vermont Foodbank. The groups worked closely with the Vermont Land Trust.

The purchase price is $495,000. The plan is for the Vermont Foodbank to buy it for $225,000, but the Land Trust needs to make up the difference. They have applied for a $168,000 grant from the Vermont Housing and Conservation Board, and intend to do private funding for the rest. The sale is scheduled to close in December, but hinges on the financing.

Doug Davis, CEO of the Vermont Foodbank said, "Our intent is to raise 150,000 pounds of fresh produce on an annual basis and make it available to food shelves and pantries around the state."

Vermont Foodbank officials plan to grow vegetables on the land and renovate the aging barn into a four-season facility that can serve as a community gathering place, a winter farmers' market, and an education exhibit that focuses on the link between agriculture and hunger. There are 12 tillable acres at Kingbury Farm.

OTHER ISSUES

Another issue which came up for discussion at the localvore meeting in Montpelier was whether farmers were willing to grow more grains, beans, soybeans, and to make oil from sunflowers as there is demand for these products. Before farmers are willing to buy more harvesting, milling and pressing equipment, they need to know if there is a demand for grains and beans in order to take the financial risk.

The final issue addressed was how to create a central database and interactive website where the consumers can place food orders. The Vermont Fresh Network is partnering with groups such as Food Works to set up an interactive site. Up to now, each localvore group has worked independently. If there were a way to coordinate food orders, distribution and delivery to a number of central locations, the system would begin to work more effectively.

Side Notes:

For years, I've been growing a lot of my own food, canning tomatoes, freezing corn and beans, drying herbs, storing root crops, onions, potatoes and winter squash, baking bread now and then, and saving garden seeds. But I don't think I could get along without bananas, rice, orange juice, and some other foods. After all, I live in the world just like the rest of you.

And it doesn't make sense to drive fifty miles for one item that makes you a 100 percent localvore. We have always relied on others for our sustenance and that's the way it should be. The problem is that today, we rely on foods imported as far away as China.

On May 22 of 2006, a friend and I drove out to the Mad River Valley for a Mad River localvore challenge meeting and potluck. We had fresh apple pie, cider, and cheese, all local. The food was delicious and the meeting was informative, however, I did not take the localvore challenge at the time as I'm not a groupie. You remember what Groucho Marx once said, "I wouldn't join any localvore group that would have me as a member."

On September 25, 2006, the Mad River localvore group sent a letter to Steve Kerr, the former Secretary of the Vermont Agency of Agriculture. They made it clear that the "Buy Local" radio ads and promotional campaigns are small potatoes. They pointed out that the benefits of eating a seasonable, sustainable, and local diet include:

- substantial energy savings
- preservation of the family farm and rural landscape
- greater growth and stability in the Vermont job market in agriculture and food processing
- strengthening a sense of community as food consumers become involved with those who grow and process their foods.
- creating a healthier population

The letter called on the State of Vermont to get more involved in the production of cooking oils (sunflower, pumpkin)

- production of grains like oats and wheat
- development of processing facilities
- research into nuts, beans and seeds like pumpkin seeds
- canning and processing facilities of fruits and vegetables
- creameries for dairy products such as fluid milk
- slaughtering facilities and fairer regulations
- subsidies and financial incentives for new initiatives

A SUSTAINABLE RESEARCH STUDY

The local food movement typically has been about improving the health of the planet. Buying locally means less fuel burned to transport food, which means less pollution. A team of researchers at the University of North Carolina at Chapel Hill is studying the public health impact of moving toward a local, sustainable food system.

They are looking at the environmental benefits of transitioning to sustainable farming practices, determining the nutritional benefits to consumers, and studying the opportunities and barriers to local food systems.

The very nature of eating locally farmed foods means that the food isn't going to come from commercial food companies, so people aren't going to consume much processed food. By focusing on products raised within 100 miles of one's home, consumers will likely eat more fruits and vegetables.

CHECK OUT YOUR LOCALVORE SITE:

The sites are filled with a wealth of information including recipes and sources for local fare and hard-to-find foods from Quebec rolled oats to apple cider vinegar, soybean cooking oils, and locally produced wines and mushrooms. Here are some Localvore sites in Vermont.

Champlain Valley · www.eatlocalvt.org
Upper Valley · www.uvlocalvores.com
Mad River Valley · www.vermontlocalvore.org
* This is my favorite site as it has many links.

In the past two years, the Vermont Agency of Agriculture has joined the bandwagon in promoting local foods. They have a new set of resource links to Vermont-based local food groups. See www.vermontagriculture.com under the Buy Local section.

In the summer of 2008, the Agency began holding workshops on teaching the basics of canning and freezing in the late summer of 2008. The Secretary of Agriculture, Roger Allbee, took up the localvore challenge in August 2008. He said that he tried explaining the movement to his 93 year-old mother last year. She responded by saying, "When I moved from the city of (Brattleboro) to the country (Brookline) in 1938, that's all we ate." Allbee said, "We are seeing a renaissance of the past. People want to know where their food comes from."

Gleaning Project of the Mad River Valley Localvores
Providing Food for the Duxbury Food Shelf

Source: The quotes from Roger Allbee came from an article in the local press. Page, Candace. "Agriculture Secretary Passes the Test." Burlington Free Press 6 Aug. 2008.

* Page has written a series of articles on the localvore challenge in which she participated.

K. THE TOMMY THOMPSON COMMUNITY GARDENS

Up to now, I've described farmers' markets, CSAs, natural food co-ops, local restaurants, diners, country stores, the localvore movement, agritourism and other marketing venues. I haven't mentioned the oldest and largest local food movement in the United States, where an individual or family grows their own food in a community setting. They're called community gardens, and they've helped to feed people and the nation for the last 100 years.

People have been converting vacant lots and open space in cities throughout the U.S. into community gardens for as long as I can remember. The Liberty Gardens of World War I and Victory Gardens of World War II helped to feed the nation, save energy and bring new vigor to urban enclaves. Thirty percent of food came from home gardens during World War II.

John Adams, the first president ever to live in the White House, had a garden to feed his family. Woodrow Wilson had a Liberty Garden and grazed sheep during World War I on the front lawn.

The Roosevelt's had a Victory Garden in World War II, at a time when 40 percent of the nation's produce came from citizen gardeners. There's talk today of having President Obama start a kitchen garden in 2009.

It's estimated that a family of four could feed itself on a 30' by 30' community garden plot through the summer and fall and even save some vegetables for winter. This is especially important for low-income families.

Many cities and towns in Vermont have set aside parcels of land for families and individuals who don't have their own space to grow vegetables, herbs, and flowers. Brattleboro recently set up some new community garden sites, as did the town of Shelburne. Just like the resurgence of farmers' markets in the last ten years, there has been a demand for community gardens. People need space to grow food, and to commune with nature and each other.

My Story: For the past 20 years, I've been a member of the 165 plot Tommy Thompson Community Garden in the Intervale in Burlington, the largest community garden site in Vermont. Each plot is about 30 by 25 feet, which adds up to about three 3 acres of vegetables, flowers, herbs, and, of course, lots of weeds.

I joined the community gardens because of the rich fertility of the bottomland along the Winooski River and because it's a lovely, peaceful place to garden. I also enjoy the human community that grows each year. I'm surrounded by people of all ages, classes, and ethnic backgrounds who garden in their own unique ways.

The Tommy Thompson Community Gardens are just one of eight community garden sites in Burlington. Each site is part of the Burlington Area Community Gardens (BACG), currently administered by Burlington Parks and Recreation.

History: Growing food for the common good began with American Indian gardens as communal plots and produce shared with the community and the new settlers. Later on, there were "poor farms" in most New England communities where individuals and families with few means -- lived and worked.

Before 1900 Philadelphia and other cities had "vacant-lot gardens" to help people grow their own food. During World War I, there were Liberty Gardens or what some called War Gardens or Uncle Sam Gardens. Backyards and public lands were planted with vegetables to feed the nation. Victory gardens came in during World War II. Government officials offered community plots and classes in cultivating and preserving produce, with a goal of 18 million gardens in 1943. This is beginning to happen again in 2009.

Good to the Last Drop.
Photo by Marilyn Maddison

The Vermont Connection: The community gardens in Burlington have been in existence for over 35 years. In 1971, Garden Way CEO Lyman Wood of Charlotte, Vermont and two associates visited a garden site in Boston that had evolved from the Victory Garden era. Called Fenway Community Gardens, it represented three generations and 15 different ethnic groups.

Lyman Wood proposed that the Burlington Parks Department begin such a garden on a smaller scale at Oakledge Park. It wasn't long before other community gardens formed. From this initiative, Gardens-for-All, a non-profit, was formed, and Tommy Thompson acted as the mover and shaker behind the initiative. The for-profit backer of this venture was Garden Way, the producer of Troy Bilt Rototillers, Garden Way Carts and numerous garden publications. Garden Way's philosophy was sustainable living: the idea of growing and preserving food close to home.

In the late 1970's and early 1980's, the Burlington community garden system had more than 20 acres in production on 800 plots in 20 different locations. On a per capita basis, Burlington was considered to be the "Community Garden Capital of the Country."

The garden system is not as large as it once was, but it's still true that no one is turned away because of lack of funds and many gardeners share their vegetables with others or take them to the local food shelf. In many cases, having a garden plot is necessary in order to put food on the table. It's a question of food security. That's why there are garden scholarships for low-income families.

Other Stories: Recent immigrants use techniques and grow varieties native to their countries. The Mai family from Vietnam grow their greens in tightly raised-beds. They introduced me to vegetables completely new to my palate. Five years ago, a woman from the Ukraine, Aida Sarkisova, brought heirloom tomato seeds from her native country and shared them with me and other gardeners. In 2001, ten Bosnian families joined the community gardens. We had a potluck picnic at which we were treated to many ethnic Bosnian dishes. We all stood in a circle and shared with each other our country of origin. My family came from Poland and the Ukraine. I am a first generation American. In 2004, 15 Somali Bantu families joined the gardens.

Sonny the Weed Whacker: There are all kinds of characters at the Tommy Thompson Community Garden. Take "Sonny" for instance. He became homeless years ago and now lives in permanent housing with other people who were homeless. Sonny does odd jobs in the community. You can always find him at Tommy Thompson because this where his heart is at. I call him "the weed whacker" because if people let their gardens get overrun with weeds, I ask Sonny to whack em down and he jumps right in. He also takes care of the weeds around the garden sheds and along the pathways. This gives the gardens a park-like feeling. Sonny can't wait for the garden season to begin so he can grow lots of vegetables, most of which he gives away to those in need. What would we do without him?

K.K.-Wilder, Photo Courtesy Jim Flint

K. K. Wilder, a friend of mine, sits in her wheelchair scooter with her mom at the Winooski Valley Community Garden at the Ethan Allen Homestead in Burlington. Arrangements were made with Vermont concrete manufacturer S.T. Griswold, Inc. to donate two 5 by 7 foot cracked septic tanks for a raised-bed garden. Wilder raises her herbs, flowers, greens, and vegetables in raised beds.

Raised bed gardening. Photo Courtesy of NOFA

The Johnsons, Tommy Thompson Community Garden
Photo by Marilyn Maddison

OTHER COMMUNITY GARDEN MODELS

The community gardening movement now embraces hundreds of gardens in Vermont and thousands more throughout the country. Here are some diverse models:

• In an impoverished neighborhood in Chicago, a three-acre abandoned lot littered with trash was transformed into the "Eden Place Nature Center," a locally run community garden with fruit trees. vegetables, perennials, a small wetland and even a petting zoo for area school children.

• In West Palm Beach, Florida, community gardens were started on the site of a razed drug house and the surrounding land. Since their inception in 2004, the gardens have fed more than 300 local residents with organically grown fruit and vegetables, and the site has become a neighborhood meeting place and playground.

• In a poverty-stricken neighborhood of New Orleans, Earl Antwine set up "God's Vineyard" Community Gardens. About 30 local youths help him raise chickens, ducks, geese, and vegetables. They have set up their own franchise, called Saint Thomas Seven Pepper Hot Sauce, but unfortunately Hurricane Katrina wiped out the pepper crop in 2005.

As you can see, community gardens are as diverse as plants and involve children, seniors, youth, people with disabilities, and others.

In February 2006, 100 gardeners representing 54 communities and 15 nonprofit groups came together in Burlington, Vermont to create the Vermont Community Garden Network. (VCGN) The purpose was to link community gardeners around the state so that they could swap ideas and share resources. VCGN estimates there are at least 50 active community-based garden projects in the state.

Jim Flint, VCGN's coordinator, says, "Community gardening is part of our cultural past. In today's society, we've gotten away from the idea that food can come from close by, that you can grow it yourself, that you can store it for the winter, and that you can share it with your neighbor." As gasoline and other energy costs increase, more people are turning back to the idea of growing their own food.

In 2009, the number of community garden plots in Burlington filled up earlier than usual. There was a long waiting list of folks that wanted to garden. This was directly related to the "Food Crisis." Jim Flint said, "Producing one's own food is suddenly starting to look like a good investment."

THE AMERICAN COMMUNITY GARDENING ASSOCIATION (ACGA)

ACGA estimates that there are around 18,000 community gardens in the U.S. and Canada, and the numbers are growing. The organization was founded in 1979 to help gardening programs share resources, and benefit from each other's experience.

Community gardening brings together neighbors and others of diverse cultures, ethnic groups, and abilities to create community gardens. These efforts serve as a catalyst for neighborhood development, food security, beautification, therapy, and food production.

In the early 1970s, the community gardening movement took root in urban communities. Many of the gardens continue to thrive today in Philadelphia, Boston, New York, Chicago, Denver, Seattle and other cities. Growing out of the energy crisis of the 1970s and the resulting rise in the price of fresh produce, and spurred by the rapid decline of urban neighborhoods, the number of community garden programs in the U.S. has increased significantly. A 1992 ACGA study reported that the rate of new garden starts within existing programs increased 29 percent from 1990.

Over the last 15 years, many community gardening and community greening programs have formed around the country to make green space a reality for large numbers of people.

ACGA board members answer hundreds of requests for information about community gardening and community greening projects each year. They provide resources, conduct educational programs and promote the formation and expansion of national and regional community gardening networks.

FREQUENTLY ASKED QUESTIONS[1]

- How do I start a Community Garden?
- How do I find a Community Garden near me?
- What options are available for making a garden bed accessible to those in a wheelchair?
- How much success have others had with selling produce from a Community Garden?

For more information search for the American Community Gardening Association on the web. The contact person is Betsy Johnson.

The address is:

ACGA
1777 East Broad Street
Columbus, Ohio 43203

(877) 275-2242.

David and Melissa Frishkoff, Two Buddies of Mine,
at the Tommy Thompson Community Garden
Photo by Marilyn Maddison

Kitchen Gardeners International
Promoting the "localest" food of all, globally

Eat the View!

Just imagine the positive messages it would send to the country and the world!

Huh...a veggie garden on the White House lawn?

Made sense before. Makes sense again.

Who will plant the first seed in the White House garden? Will it be the First Lady or the President? See the next page for the answer.

There is a new movement called Kitchen Gardeners International that is attempting to get more people to grow their own home gardens. This reminds me of the following quote in a 1942 gardening book called *Food Gardens for Defense*, by M.G. Kains, former USDA Special Crop Culturist and author of Five Acres and Independence. The quote comes from the introduction by Claude R. Wickard, U.S. Secretary of Agriculture.

"I know there is a tremendous psychological value in having things for people to do in wartime. Gardening is one activity that has great possibilities as a useful outlet for that urge to do something. There's a spiritual uplift in seeing things grow; I think it's probably that as much as anything which makes a man determined to be a farmer. And I'm sure we recognize the health value in getting fresh air, sunshine, and exercise -- as well as vegetables out of the garden. So there are many reasons why the nation needs gardens and a national gardening program."

- Claude R. Wickard, U.S. Secretary of Agriculture

HOME GARDENS

With the financial crisis worsening and food prices staying high, more families are planting home gardens -- some out of necessity. Julie Ruboud, owner of Red Wagon Plants in Hinesburg said her vegetable seedling sales in the spring of 2008 were 80 percent above last year. Tom Stearns, owner of High Mowing Seeds in Wolcott, reported a large increase in seed sales as did Phil Brett, who manages floor sales at Gardener's Supply Co. in Burlington.

If I had to draw a line that describes how and where we shop for food, I would start at one end with supermarkets. The middle tier would include general stores, natural food co-ops and local markets. Toward the other end of the line would be farmers' markets and community gardens, ending with home gardens. A great many things happen when you plant a home garden -- from physical activity -- to eating healthy, fresh food to making home-made compost from the food scraps in your garden.

If I had to draw another line that follows energy consumption and food, it would look similar to the previous line with the home garden being at one end of the line. A home garden reduces energy use with compost, elbow grease and less disturbance of the soil. It's estimated that food production accounts for a fifth of all greenhouse gases. However, if you make compost in your home garden - which feeds and grows the plant - which produces the food - you are saving the planet from excess carbon emissions in the atmosphere as the carbon is held in your healthy garden soil.

Finally, on a spiritual plane, having a home garden is my way of healing the earth and myself in the process. An added bonus is that my neighbors come by for fresh vegetables and the surplus goes to the local foodshelf. Now, that's what I call community.

❧ **Home Gardens**

❧ **Community Gardens**

❧ **Farmers' Markets**

❧ **Local Markets**

❧ **Natural Food Co-ops**

❧ **General Stores**

❧ **Supermarkets**

The first lady, Michelle Obama, planted an organic kitchen garden on March 19, 2009 with school children on the White House lawn. It was the first working garden since Eleanor Roosevelt planted a Victory Garden at the height of World War II.

The president's mother-in-law, Marian Robinson said, "We're just hoping families look at us and say this is something they can do and talk to their kids about and think a little bit critically about the food choices they make."

A Speech by Wendell Berry, October 1, 1974
"Agriculture for a Small Planet"
symposium in Spokane, Washington.

A healthy farm culture can be based only upon familiarity and can grow only among a people soundly established upon the land; it nourishes and safeguards human intelligence of the earth that no amount of technology can satisfactorily replace. The growth of such a culture was once a strong possibility in the farm communities of this country.

We now have only the sad remnants of those communities. If we allow another generation to pass without doing what is necessary to enhance and embolden the possibility now perishing with them, we will lose it altogether. And we will invoke calamity -- we will deserve it.

IV. CONCLUSION

Abraham Lincoln once said, "The greatest fine art of the future will be the making of a comfortable living from a small parcel of land." When Lincoln spoke these words in the 1850s, more than half of Americans were engaged in farming. Vermont farmers could be seen walking their turkeys to market all the way to Boston town.

In the 1930s, twenty percent of Americans were farming and many rural communities were food self-sufficient. You would find canneries, grain mills, slaughterhouses, and creameries spread throughout the countryside. Before World War II, New York City was served by farms in the nearby Hudson Valley and across the river in New Jersey, the Garden State. In those days, many families had home gardens and some raised a small flock of chickens and a pig to boot.

Toward the end of World War II, a food and farming revolution began to take shape. A new industrial farm model replaced the traditional family farm.

The use of chemical fertilizers, pesticides, cheap water, labor and fuel ran the food engine. Progress was made with new technologies in refrigeration, food processing and large farm equipment; plus the coming of interstate highways in the 1950s and massive government farm subsidies. This new industrial model fed the nation and the world. And it still does.

Industrial food was inexpensive up to 2007 because the true costs weren't reflected at the supermarket checkout counter. Until a few years ago, there was little discussion about the damaging effects of factory farming on the environment, including soil depletion and pollution, water shortages and global warming. The social consequences of the industrial food model were the loss of the family farm and erosion of our rural communities. Gone were the days when one in four people farmed the land. Another consequence of industrial agriculture was the introduction of cheap, but unhealthy, processed food into the American diet.

During the Food Crisis of 2008, food costs began to rise at the dinner table. The long food lines of the Great Depression have been replaced with food shelves and pantries. It's estimated that 38 percent of Vermont's population in 2008 had to choose between putting food on the table or heating their homes. (Children eligible for free school lunches stuff food in their pockets on Friday to get them through the weekend.)

Today, national campaigns to end hunger play a major role in raising the consciousness of local citizens to the plight of the hungry. They educate and empower people about good food shopping habits, eating healthy food, growing gardens and preparing home-cooked meals. Of course, if people received a fair wage, we wouldn't need food shelves and pantries. That's a goal as important as providing nutritious meals and groceries to those in need. But that's a tougher challenge.

In the last couple of years, a counter revolution that has simmered for years has gained steam. A farm and food renaissance has begun as people and communities are demanding healthy food grown close to home. This movement is gaining momentum with every mouthful. Its values are sustainable farming, greater food self-sufficiency, community-supported ventures, land stewardship, and food for those in need.

In the winter of 2008, I met a young woman at a University of Vermont marketing conference. Her name is Sophia Light Smith, and she and her parents lived "off the land" at the same time that I did back in the 1970s. Today, she's in charge of marketing and sales for the Vermont Soy Company in Hardwick. Her idealism and commitment to a local food system reminds me of myself in my young "hippie" days when I started the Brattleboro Farmers' Market in the early 70s. There are many young people like Sophia who are making a difference across the country.

When I look to the future, I see a return to diversified farms providing fruits and vegetables, milk, eggs, bread and meat serving their local communities along with local creameries, slaughterhouses, and grain mills. I see farmers and food processors providing more food to prisons, hospitals, and schools. I envision agricultural zones and regional food hubs like the one evolving in Vermont where farmers are linked with manufacturers of value-added food products.

For example, left-over whey from local cheesemakers is being used as a coating and finish on wood products. The Center for an Agricultural Economy in Hardwick is promoting these activities. Their hope is that more farms and food processors will one day dot the hillsides and valleys in this rural region of the Green Mountains.

During World War II, millions of people grew vegetables in "Victory Gardens," as they were necessary to feed the nation. Such gardens are occurring again as the global economic crisis gets out of hand. The new term being used today is "Recession Gardens."

The National Gardening Association estimates the number of home-grown vegetable gardens will increase more than 40 percent between 2007 and 2009. W. Atlee Burpee, the world's largest seed company, project a jump of 25 percent in seed sales this year.

So, why not grow some of your own vegetables in a home or community garden? If you aren't able to grow vegetables, join a CSA or local food group. Shop at a farmers' market, buy local food products and support the farmers in your area.

As consumers we need to become aware of how the global food system operates, who it benefits, who it harms, and how it could be transformed. My wish when I started this writing adventure was to create a primer on farm and food issues. As I peeled away the onion skin, layer upon layer unfolded revealing how food and farming issues are intertwined. To unravel this web is to take control over what you eat. We make choices every time we sit down to a meal. It's kitchen-table democracy in action.

I hope Lifting the Yoke will motivate you towards action. So please, get on with it and plant some seeds in your garden and community.

QUOTES

"To me this not a deprived way of living, it's a rich way of living."
Pete Johnson, Farmer, Pete's Greens, Craftsbury Center

"For me, it wasn't ever about slinging it on a plate, Food is fundamental to our health and well-being.
George Schenk, Restaurant Owner, American Flatbread, Waitsfield

"We opened the school just at the right time. Something was moving. People had enough of overcooked vegetables."
Michael Leborgne, Chef, New England Culinary Institute, Montpelier

"I learned how many people live just above the poverty line and how we're not passing down the traditions and skills of our agrarian culture ..."
Joseph Kiefer, Co-Director, Food Works at Two Rivers Center, Montpelier

"Consumers choosing apple cider over orange juice in February; that's something that thrills me."
Bill Suhr, Apple Grower, Champlain Orchards, Shoreham

Source: Vermont Life, Summer 2008

Joseph Keefer, Food Works

Bill Suhr, Champlain Valley Orchard

FIVE KEYS TO THE KINGDOM

*THE FOLLOWING ARE A LIST OF LOCAL SOLUTIONS DESCRIBED THROUGHOUT LIFTING THE YOKE. SOME OF THEM OVERLAP WITH ONE ANOTHER.

FIRST KEY

Farmer, Processor and Entrepreneur Needs:

. Development of infrastructure necessary to support local farmers and processors of value added products, such as slaughterhouses, grain mills, dairies, and processing plants.

Support for technical training for current farmers and new farmers, food processors, millers and slaughterers and butchers.

Making stronger connections between rural producers and consumers - specifically - changes in state and federal regulations that make it possible for on-farm slaughtering and butchering animals. Consumers should be able to purchase meat directly from their farmer neighbors.

Change in regulations in regards to the selling bottled raw milk to consumers in local markets as long as strict health standards are followed.

Loans, grants and other forms of financial support along with help in business planning for local farmers and processors.

Protection and conservation of farmland and support for next-generation farmers through easements and other transfer methods through the Vermont Land Trust and local land trusts. The state of Vermont must continue to fund the Housing and Conservation Trust for the preservation of Vermont farmland and farms.

Social and economic development of food security programs for people and families in need. Food security means access to safe, affordable food that promotes health and well being.

School food programs must be provided with the necessary funds to supply healthy, nutritious food to students. A lot of this food needs to come from local farmers through farm-to-school programs. Farm and food history, school gardens and food preparation need to be a central part of the school curriculum.

Building of regional food hubs with local markets, winter farmers' markets and year-round enclosed public markets, pick-your-own operations and farmstands.

Development of appropriate technology for farmers, such as combines and other machinery for wheat farmers such as combines for wheat farmers.

Research and data collection into sustainable and organic farming practices as well as food system models by research organizations. The Center for Rural Studies in Morrill Hall at the University of Vermont has been doing farm and food research for over 35 years.

SECOND KEY

Consumers Need To: Learn to develop good shopping habits and to prepare healthy, whole foods as well as to store, can, and freeze foods.

Support the development of local canneries and processing centers, creameries, slaughterhouses and other needed infrastructure such as grain mills.

Demand that consumers have the right to purchase meat products directly from farmers. This would take a change in state and federal regulations regarding on-farm slaughtering and butchering.

Demand that schools as well as other institutions such as hospitals and state governments, provide healthy, local food to its citizens. And demand that schools educate children in the growing, processing and preparation of nutritious food.

Get involved with local farm and food organizations such as the Vermont Grange, and the Vermont Farm Bureau.

Join localvore food groups, post-oil groups, Vermont Earth Institute, Transition Vermont and advocacy groups like Rural Vermont and educational organizations such as the Northeast Organic Farmers Association of Vermont.

Keep abreast of farm and food issues at the local, state and national levels.

Educate political leaders on local/sustainable farm and food issues and demand they take strong stands on those issues.

Support efforts to increase healthy food for soup kitchens and food pantries as well as organizations that provide food for the needy.

Support efforts to empower low income people to grow and process their own food, to be educated as to healthy food choices, good shopping practices and food preparation in the home.

THIRD KEY

Political Needs: Vision, Leadership and Will

I haven't met a governor of late with the political will to take a strong position on local, sustainable farm and food issues. Simply making public service announcements on buying Vermont products won't cut the mustard. It's one thing to tout the benefits of food farming; it's quite another to support a local Vermont brand of milk, a Vermont milk-bottling plan and more slaughterhouses.

This is beginning to change with support for greater purchasing of Vermont farm products in state institutions and prisons. The state and federal government needs to work closely with business leaders, academic institutions and nonprofits to work towards greater food sufficiency.

These entities need to provide food processors and entrepreneurs with loans and grants in developing processing facilities. This is especially true in the case of creameries and slaughterhouses.

FOURTH KEY

Support for Local-Sustainable Farm and Food Solutions include:

Farmers' markets and winter farmers' markets
Area restaurants and diners that serve local food
Country and general stores
Natural-food stores, Natural-food co-ops
Year-round public markets
Community supported agriculture (CSA) farms
Farm stands and pick-your-own operations
Supermarkets that carry local food
Community gardens
Food product research, development centers and enterprise zones
Infrastructures -- canneries, slaughterhouses, mills, dairies
Farms as destinations -- agritourism
Institutions like hospitals, and prisons

Farm-to-school food programs
Senior meal sites
Food shelves and food kitchens
Summer food programs for children

Land Trusts and land reform initiatives
University research on sustainable farming and marketing
Entrepreneurial value-added initiatives including infrastructure and financing needs
Support for farm and food advocacy and educational organizations

FIFTH KEY

Education and Training Needs:

The last key is the training and continuing education of new and current farmers along with farm apprenticeship programs.

ACKNOWLEDGEMENTS

Mud Boots Courtesy
of Wellspring CSA, Marshfield

Autumn,
Photo by Marilyn Maddison.

I could not have completed this adventure without the help of many friends and colleagues. They wore the boots that provided the support I needed these past seven years. Simply put, it took a whole community to bring *Lifting the Yoke* to fruition. Where does one begin to thank them all -- including my dog Autumn for putting up with me.

My friend Pam Cunov helped with administrative support. Elizabeth England of Calais, Vermont painted the front cover. My friend Ash Eames of Wentworth, New Hampshire provided many hours of editing and proof reading as did Wendy Golden Davidson, Julia Lynam, Simon Frishkoff, Monica Marshall, Ken Susskind, and my sister Linda Hartz of St. George, Utah. Jill Mason provided some early editing. Don Jamison helped me come up with the title.

I gathered a lot of information from local farm and food writers Candice Page and Melissa Pasanen of the Burlington Free Press and Suzanne Podhaizer of Seven Days. Many national and Vermont farm and food organizations provided photos and logos for the book. My neighbor Marilyn Maddison took photos of the Tommy Thompson Community Garden and the oxen yoke. Robert Maddison, Marilyn's husband, provided many hours of computer support.

Finally, I worked closely with Marcie Vallette of Johnson, Vermont on the layout and design of the book and Great Big Graphics of Morrisville, Vermont. Again, a warm thank you to everyone.

-- Ron Krupp

* Index - See next page.

* Please check out the LiftingtheYoke.Com website on the inside of the front cover for supplementary information not covered in the book. Plus recent updates on farm and food issues.

INDEX